DEVELOPMENTS IN MATHEMATICAL PSYCHOLOGY

Information, Learning, and Tracking

A Study of the Behavioral Models Project,
Bureau of Applied Social Research,
Columbia University

DEVELOPMENTS IN

Mathematical Psychology

Information, Learning, and Tracking

EDITED BY *R. Duncan Luce,* UNIVERSITY OF PENNSYLVANIA

WITH CONTRIBUTIONS BY
R. Duncan Luce
Robert R. Bush
J. C. R. Licklider

The Free Press of Glencoe, Illinois

LITHOGRAPHED FOR THE PUBLISHER BY
PROMOTION PRINTING & LITHOGRAPHING CORP., N. Y.

Preface

THIS VOLUME, the third issued by the Behavioral Models Project of the Bureau of Applied Social Research, Columbia University, presents surveys of three of the more extensive mathematical developments in psychology. Our intended audience is two groups: those behavioral scientists who, although sympathetic and to some degree facile with mathematical applications, either are not sufficiently conversant with the mathematics involved or are so pressed for time that they have not read many of the relevant papers; and those mathematicians who are not only interested in the formal developments *per se*, but who also want to know how these are related to substantive and empirical problems. These essays attempt to present the central ideas and the way they are presently represented in mathematical terms in each of the three areas, to convey a sense of both the sweep and the limitations of the literature up to 1957, and to give a clear indication where further to read. Put another way, each paper is, first, an introduction to an area of mathematical psychology and, second, a systematized and extensively annotated bibliography.

As is true with the other two volumes issued by the Behavioral Models Project*, we have attempted to hold the formal demands to a minimum, using only those mathematical ideas and notations that we felt were needed to convey the major ideas and results without distortion. This seemed to be the best way to achieve our aim of showing how and why these abstract tools are useful in dealing with certain kinds of empirical materials.

In addition to its more obvious uses for self-study and reference, this book should also be able to play some role in the classroom provided that it is supplemented by good lectures and a selected, more detailed reading of some of the literature. This is not meant to imply that it is a text, for it is not, but rather that it may be possible to put it to use in some of the courses that are currently being developed around mathematical applica-

---

* Luce, R. D. and Howard Raiffa, *Games and Decisions*, John Wiley and Sons, New York, 1957, and Solomon, Herbert, ed., *Mathematical Thinking in the Measurement of Behavior: Small Groups, Utility, Factor Analysis*, The Free Press, Glencoe, Ill., 1960.

tions in the behavioral sciences. A real text for these courses, however, has yet to be written.

One need hardly point out that this volume does not exhaust the important mathematical developments in psychology, let alone in the behavioral sciences. Some of these other topics, namely, utility theory, small group models, and factor analysis, were treated in the second volume (edited by Herbert Solomon) issued by the Behavioral Models Project. Even so, the joint coverage does not begin to be complete. For example, we have no essay on psychophysics, which is, I agree, strange since, outside of economics, it is the behavioral area that has had the longest liaison with mathematics. It is not for want of trying that it has had to be omitted. Another example is psychometric scaling. Here we had more reason to be complacent because there are several volumes in this field.

The final revisions of this book were completed in the summer of 1957. Great delays were experienced in press — and so not only is the work of the last three or four years not covered, but some of the statements made no longer reflect the exact situation in the field. In an area as active as mathematical psychology, changes are rapid. Nonetheless, these three papers should serve as comprehensive introductions to the current research.

It is a pleasure to express my appreciation to various people and organizations who have contributed in important ways to this work:

i. To the Columbia University Faculty Committee for the Behavioral Models Project, composed of Professors T. W. Anderson, C. H. Graham, P. F. Lazarsfeld, E. Nagel, H. Raiffa (chairman), H. Solomon, and W. Vickrey, who organized the Project, set its policies, and guided and assisted me in a variety of ways.

ii. To the Office of Naval Research for its generous financial support of the Project from 1952—1956.

iii. To the Bureau of Applied Social Research whose officers and staff were always cooperative in solving the myriad of problems that seem to be one product of such a venture.

Philadelphia, Penna.   *R. Duncan Luce.*

Contents — An Overview

PART ONE

The Theory of Selective Information and Some of Its Behavioral Applications

By R. DUNCAN LUCE

UNIVERSITY OF PENNSYLVANIA

Contents

SECTION I. THE DISCRETE THEORY

SECTION II. APPLICATIONS TO BEHAVIORAL PROBLEMS

THE DISCRETE THEORY

1. INTRODUCTION(*)(†)

THERE IS a widespread belief – most forcefully articulated by Norbert Wiener [1948] – that we are undergoing a new scientific revolution, one comparable in scope and scientific significance to that of the last century; but where the dominant concepts in the previous development were energy, power, and efficiency, the central notions are now information, communication, and feedback. Many current problems stem from attempts to transmit information and to exercise effective control rather than to achieve an efficient use of energy; little more than chaos would result, for example, were the design of a high-speed computer approached from the energy standpoint. "Information is information, not matter or energy. No materialism which does not admit this can survive at the present day." (Wiener [1948], p. 155).

What then is information? How is it measured? What scientific statements can be made using the term?

Several schools of thought have developed, each formulating and restricting these questions in its own way and offering answers to the resulting and more specific questions. In this essay I shall examine the formulation and the answers of one of these schools and describe some of the impact it has had for certain problems of psychology.(**) But before we turn to this, a certain amount of background material on the history, orientation, and relation of information theory to other theories is appropriate.

(*) Most often the title "information theory" is used without the prefix "selective"; however, some feel that the simpler title is misleading, especially since there exists a theory of structural information and one of semantic information. Indeed, Bar-Hillel [1955] feels the title should be the "theory of signal transmission" for, as he argues, the seductive word "information" has led to considerable confusion; however, it is probably now too late to make such a crucial psychological change.

(†) I wish to express my appreciation to Professors A. H. Hastorf, W. E. Hick, B. Mandelbrot, F. Mosteller, H. Quastler, and H. Raiffa for reading and commenting on the original version of this essay. Many of their suggestions have been incorporated into the present version.

(**) A number of summaries of this theory have been given: Gabor [1953b], Hockett [1953], McMillan [1954], Miller [1953], Osgood [1954], Slepian [1954] and Weaver [1952].

It is clear that if Wiener and others are correct in their views, the intuitive concept "information" must be given at least one precise meaning and maybe more. Considering the variety and vagueness of its meanings in everyday usage, it is *a priori* certain that objections will be raised against any particular formulation, which will surely ignore some of these meanings. This problem — if it be such — has been met many times in science; we need only think of words and concepts such as force, energy, work, etc. It is doubtful that a formal definition ever stands or falls because of such debates; it is rather the power and depth of the resulting theory that determines its ultimate fate.

Within the last two decades two distinct attempts have been made to deal with the notion of information, one in Europe, and one in America; these have been complementary rather than competitive. Both theories seem to have arisen from much the same class of applied problems: communication involving electrical signals. The European school, in which the names of Cherry, Gabor, and MacKay are the most important, has been concerned with the problem of the information contained in a representation of a physical situation. As seems intuitively reasonable, the concepts of size and dimensionality are important here. In America, because of work by Wiener and Shannon, a theory of information transmission has been developed in which the dominant concepts are selection, statistical possibilities, and noise.

In this essay I shall not undertake an examination of the notions of structural and metrical information (the European school). This theory has had, so far as I can determine, almost no effect on behavioral applications. Of interest to the behavioral scientist, however, is the apparently overlooked fact that one basic concept of structural information theory is identical with the central assumption of factor analysis. Both theories are concerned with the number of independent dimensions that are required to represent a certain class of data, and the geometrical model of any particular situation is as a point in an Euclidean *n*-space. If this observation is correct, it is interesting that basically the same concept has been independently arrived at by both physicists and psychologists, and it may be unfortunate that each is unaware of the work of the other.

There are, of course, marked differences of emphasis which reflect the different origins and problems. For example, the European information theorists have examined the basic natural units in which the several dimensions can be scaled. Whether this theory of metrical information, as it is called, is related to any of the scaling work in the behavioral sciences is not immediately obvious and appears not to have been investigated. There is at least a superficial parallel to psychophysical scaling based upon imperfect discrimination. On the other hand, factor analysts have developed an elaborate matrix machinery suited to determining the approximate dimensionality of the Euclidean space representation of certain types of data. A comparable machinery does not appear to exist in structural information theory, though, of course, the close relation of the structural model to matrix theory is apparent.

Our concern, however, is with selective information theory. The central observation of this theory is that for a great many purposes — in particular, in the design of communication equipment — one is never concerned with the particular message that is sent but rather with the class of all messages that might have been sent and with the probability of the occurrence of each. "We are scarcely ever interested in the performance of a communication-engineering machine for a single input. To function adequately it must give a satisfactory performance for a whole class of inputs, and this means a statistically satisfactory performance for the class of inputs which it is statistically expected to receive." (Wiener [1948], p. 55) From this point of view, information is *transmitted* by a selection from certain alternatives. The contention is that selection of an *a priori* rare event conveys more information to the receiver than does the selection of one that is more probable. This use of "information" obviously ignores all questions of meaning. "It is important to emphasize, at the start, that we are not concerned with the meaning or the truth of messages; semantics lies outside the scope of mathematical information theory."(*) (Cherry [1951], p. 383) The failures to adhere to this position, and the consequent difficulties, are discussed in detail by Bar-Hillel [1955]; they have led to considerable confusion and not a little empty debate.

It may be useful to introduce at this point three common-sense observations which will be given precise meanings in the presentation of the theory of selective information — precise to the point where numbers can be attached to them.

1. A person communicating over a noisy telephone line can get less "across" in a given period of time than he can over a perfectly clear line.

(*) Carnap and Bar-Hillel [1952] and Bar-Hillel and Carnap [1953] have presented a theory of semantic information which is based on Carnap's work in inductive logic. Since their approach is different from that of selective information theory, and since, as far as I know, there have been no behavioral applications of it, I have elected not to summarize it here. It may, however, become important, and should therefore not be neglected by the serious student of this area. Also, see Hockett [1952].

2. Not every letter,(*) nor indeed every word, of a message in any natural language is as important as every other one in getting the sense of the message. For example, the missing letter in "q_iet" or the missing word in "many happy _____ of the day" can be filled in, with a high probability of being correct, by anyone knowing English, and therefore in the above context they do not carry much important information.

3. Every person seems to have a limited capacity to assimilate information, and if it is presented to him too rapidly and without adequate repetition, this capacity will be exceeded and communication will break down.

As they stand, it is not immediately obvious that these statements are not concerned with semantics, or, for that matter, that the whole problem of information transmission is not almost wholly semantic. One major contribution of selective information theory is in showing that much of what is implied or suggested in these examples and others like them can be given a precise and useful meaning by a purely statistical treatment.

We shall delve into this more deeply in the following sections; but first, let me discuss briefly some of the origins of the theory and of the developing interest of behavioral scientists in it. (†) Electrical communication engineers gradually had been gaining experience in the handling and transmission of information since the early days of the telegraph, telephone, and radio, and during the 1920's this experience began to be formalized as a theory. One of the most important early papers was by Hartley [1928]; in it the logarithmic measure so characteristic of modern information theory was employed in a simple form and much of the terminology was introduced. The maturation of the theory, however, resulted from the work of two men: Norbert Wiener of MIT and his former student C. E. Shannon of the Bell Telephone Laboratories. Shannon's papers of 1948 (reprinted in book form, Shannon and Weaver [1949]) are now the classic formulation of the theory.

(*) Here, and elsewhere, I shall speak as if the letter is the carrier of information: there will be presented calculations of the number of "bits of information transmitted" per letter, etc. The linguist may quite properly raise objections to this usage, for presumably it is the spoken, not the written, language that determines the information bearing units. Much effort has been expended in recent years to isolate and to understand the natural unit of spoken language — the phoneme — and it is in terms of this unit that we probably should deal. For a survey of this work and an extensive list of references see Osgood [1954]. Yet, for reasons of convenience — both because letters are more familiar to me and to many readers and because many of the existing information theory calculations are in terms of letters (the exceptions being Cherry, Halle, and Jakobson [1953] and Black [1954]) — I shall ignore this basic proposition of modern linguistics. Of course, this is not intended as a scientific position on the matter.

(†) A much more complete history of both the American and European schools has been given by Cherry [1951, 1953].

The more mathematically inclined reader will find McMillan's later [1953] presentation of the central theorems more satisfactory. Also, see the formulations of Feinstein [1954] and Watanabe [1954].

The implications of the theory and of several related concepts — of which feedback(*) is one of the most important — were quickly recognized to extend beyond improved electrical communication. Shannon and Wiener realized this, and the latter in his book *Cybernetics* both outlined the extent of the new discipline and offered a generic title for its somewhat nebulous components. From 1941 on, these concepts and theories have been examined and debated in a series of conferences and seminars.(†) For the most part, these meetings have been held in the East, many of them in Cambridge, and as a consequence the impact of information theory, which has been so strong along the Eastern seaboard, has been less marked in the West.

Many of the empirical sciences dealing with human behavior — psychology, linguistics, physiology, biology, psychophysics, social psychology, neurology, medicine, anthropology — have had representatives at these seminars; indeed, scientists from these fields have organized and dominated many of the meetings. From them emerged a small group of analytically inclined behavioral scientists who believe that information theory is, or can be, a useful tool in handling some problems in various disciplines. I shall try to indicate some of the uses, and the usefulness, of the theory in Part II of this essay.

Our material is organized into two parts. In the first, I shall try to present a synopsis, which draws heavily upon one's everyday experience with communication systems, of the discrete theory of selective information. The presentation is most deeply influenced by Shannon's. I was strongly

(*) "Feedback" has become such a familiar term that it is probably not necessary to define it, especially since it will not be a central notion in this survey. Still, a few suggestive words may do no harm. Many systems are designed, or behave as if they were designed, to respond to a certain class of inputs in such a manner as to achieve a particular goal. For example, an ideal amplifier attempts to reproduce the exact form of the input while changing the amplitude scale. A device designed to do this will, because of variability of its components, etc., fail to respond perfectly, and the problem arises how to improve the performance. One way is this: build into the system certain appropriate adjustable parameters, whose values are determined at any particular time so as to reduce the discrepancy between the desired output and the actual output. This is effected by feeding back a fraction of the output signal and comparing it with the input to determine the discrepancy. Under certain conditions, the resulting system will be stable and large errors will not occur. In a more general context, feedback is taken to mean any messages a system receives informing it as to what *its* response has been, and usually this information is used to modify its behavior to reach a specified goal.

(†) In his introduction to *Cybernetics*, Wiener presents a detailed history of the early meetings.

tempted to depart from his organization completely and to formulate the theory along the lines of a multivariate statistical analysis, following McGill's work, for it is this aspect of information theory that seems most pertinent in behavioral science applications. However, such a course would have reduced the number of familiar signposts available, left much of the language of the theory unmotivated, and rendered some of the applications close to incomprehensible. With some regret, I have elected the well trodden path. In the second part I shall be concerned entirely with applications of the theory to problems in psychology. Again, two modes of organization are possible: either by the conventional categories used in psychology or by the structure of the theory. While the latter more strongly appeals to me, it tends not to seem appropriate to most psychologists — the substantive rather than the methodological boundaries are held sacred — so again I have conformed. I hope one day to see a monograph on the use of information theory in psychology which follows the two courses not used here.

An appendix giving a short summary of Shannon's theory of continuous communication systems concludes the essay. While this theory is of great importance in electrical applications, it has so far been of minor significance for traditional problems of the behavioral sciences. However, it is interwoven into certain new work; see Licklider [1960].

2. GENERAL CONCEPTS

Communication Systems. Information transmission always occurs within a certain physical framework which may be termed a communication system. Basically such a system consists of three central parts: a *source* of messages, a *channel* over which the messages flow, and a *destination* for the messages. The source, which very often is a human being, generates messages (and so information, see below) by making a series of decisions among certain alternatives. It is the sequence of such decisions that we call a message in a discrete system. These messages are then sent over the channel, which is nothing more than an appropriate medium which establishes a connection having certain physical characteristics between the source and the destination. Mechanically, this picture is incomplete, since the decisions made by the source must be put into a form which is suitable for transmission over the channel, and the signals coming from the channel must be transformed at the destination into stimuli acceptable to it. Thus, between the source and the channel a *transmitter* is introduced to "match" the channel to the source, and between the channel and the destination a *receiver* is introduced to "match" the channel to the destination. In other words, the transmitter encodes the message for the channel and the receiver decodes it. A schematic diagram of the system is shown in Fig. 1.

FIG. 1.

It is entirely possible to have transmitters which so encode messages that it is not possible to design a receiver which can completely recover the original message. For example, if one has a transmitter which encodes all affirmative statements such as "O.K.," "yes," "all right," etc. into the same signal, then no device can be built which will translate that signal back into the particular word chosen by the source. A transmitter having this property is called *singular ;* otherwise it is called *non-singular*. (These terms arise if one thinks of the transmitter as a many-many transformation or as a one-to-one transformation.) When the transmitter is non-singular it is possible to design a receiver which will completely recover the original message. In other words, there exists a receiver which is the inverse of the transmitter. Throughout our discussion we shall assume that the transmitter is non-singular and that the receiver is its inverse. In effect, this means that we can ignore them in our discussion and suppose that the source and destination are both matched to the channel.

Our abstract communication system seems fairly complete except that it does not allow for the possibility that more than one source may be using the same channel at the same time. Certainly this can happen. It occurs when, by mistake, one telephone line carries two conversations at once (crosstalk). It also happens in telephone or radio communication when there is static in addition to the desired message. In all such cases the messages from sources other than the one under consideration — which will simply be called *the* source — cause interference with messages from the source. Such interference may be minor and have no effect on the intelligibility of the message, as for example in the usual low-level telephone static, or it may be most destructive, as when another conversation is cut in. Another example which one might tend to put into the same category of interferences is the 60-cycle hum which is common to so many cheap radios. If the hum level is high enough it certainly can lower the intelligibility of speech. However, there is an important difference between the problem of interference from hum and from that due to static or to other conversations. The former is completely predictable and it is possible from a short sample to determine its exact frequency, phase, and amplitude. Thus, if there is hum, one can build into the transmitter or into the receiver a network to subtract it from the resulting signal, leaving only the message. Static, hiss, and crosstalk cannot be predicted in detail from any amount of past evidence about them. Therefore, once they enter the channel, they cannot be characterized in full and subtracted from the signal, but rather they must be accepted and compensated for in other ways.

Thus in our abstraction we must conceive a second source (which in fact may be several lumped together) also feeding signals into the channel. It has the property that (for the problem under consideration) neither *the* source nor the destination can predict in detail the messages that will emanate from it. The source or the destination may have or may obtain statistical data about the nature of this second source. For example, in an electrical communication system the average power of the second signal may be measured. Such a source is known as a *noise source* and the signal it generates will be called *noise*. Clearly, these are often relative terms and what in one context is noise may be the message in another. This, then, completes our model of a communication system, and it is shown schematically in Fig. 2.

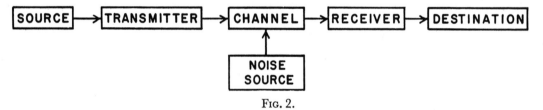

FIG. 2.

When there is a noise source in a system it is conventional to speak of the channel as being noisy, but it is well to keep in mind that this is merely an abbreviated, and slightly misleading, way of speaking. The noise signal is not an invariant of the channel, as are its physical characteristics. It is clear that one can change the amount of noise in a system while keeping the physical characteristics of the channel, the source, and the destination the same. In any given problem under consideration, the noise level will presumably remain constant and so it can be thought of as a property of the channel, but as we shall see it is a property which must be handled very differently, in the theory, from the physical characteristics of the channel.

Noiseless Systems. In one sense, no communication system is ever noiseless; there is always some noise signal. For example, in any electrical system there must always be signals resulting from the random agitation of molecules — thermal noise. This can be a serious problem in a high-gain amplifier, but it is not in a telegraph. The point, of course, is that noise is not, in and of itself, bad, but only when it causes a significant interference in the messages sent by the source. The only pertinent feature of noise is whether it ever causes the destination to infer that a different message was sent from the one actually sent. Thus, if the noise level is low compared with the signal level, so low that it does not *significantly* alter the message as it passes along the channel, then it may be completely disregarded and the system can be treated as if there were no noise present.

Since it is assumed that by definition the effect of noise is unpredictable in advance (except statistically), all we shall be able to state about the effect of noise on messages — and all we need to state — is the probability that it changes one signal into another. If the signals sent (in a given situation) are always received correctly, then we say the system (or the channel) is *noiseless*. It must always be kept in mind that if we change the level at which the transmitter operates, or the level of the noise signal, we may change a noiseless system into a noisy one. Being noiseless is a property of the whole system and not of the channel alone!

In principle, it is not necessary to deal separately with the theory of the noiseless and noisy cases, for the former is but a special case of the latter. The presentation, however, is simpler if we bring in the complications one at a time, so we shall examine the noiseless case first (Chapter 3) and then the noisy one (Chapter 4).

The Bit — a Unit of Information Transmitted. To carry out the program mentioned in the Introduction, namely, to make precise and measurable some features of the transmission of information, it is necessary to introduce a unit in terms of which amounts of information transmitted may be measured. The central observation which is needed before one can arrive at an appropriate unit is that a message conveys information in the sense of reducing uncertainty only by its relation to all the other messages that might have been received. Suppose a person is asked whether he smokes. If we have no prior information other than population statistics on smoking, then all we know is the probability that he, as a random selection from the population, will answer "yes" or "no." When he selects one of these alternatives and transmits it, some information has been conveyed. But if it is known *a priori* that he does smoke, e.g., from previous conversations or from seeing him smoke, then with probability 1 the answer will be "yes" and the receipt of "yes" from him cannot convey any (new) information. In effect, our prior knowledge reduced the set of possible messages to a single element, and so far as we are concerned there was no choice to be made. Thus, no information could be transmitted.

The minimum condition, therefore, under which information can be transmitted is that of a choice between two alternatives. The maximum uncertainty in such a choice exists when the two alternatives are equally probable. Hence the maximum information is conveyed by a choice between two alternatives when they are equally likely. We take such a choice to be one unit of information. That is, whenever a choice is made between two *a priori* equally likely alternatives (no matter what they are) we shall say that one unit of information has been transmitted by the choice. According to Shannon, Tukey proposed that the unit be called a *bit* — a shortened form of binary digit — and that term is commonly used. Goldman [1953] prefers the term "binit" in order to avoid such expressions as "a bit of information" which, unfortunately, has quite another everyday meaning, but I shall conform to common usage. All statements about information transmission, therefore, will be given in this unit; we shall speak of so many "bits in a message," or the "bits transmitted per second," or the "bits per English letter," etc.

With this as the definition of the unit, the next problem is to say just how many such units are transmitted when a selection is made from an arbitrary finite set with an arbitrary *a priori* probability distribution over it; and just how many units are transmitted when several selections are made. Certainly, one wants to require at least this: if two independent choices are made between *a priori* equally likely alternatives, then a total of two bits of information are transmitted. More generally, we shall impose the condition that whenever two statistically independent selections occur, the total information transmitted is the sum of the amounts transmitted by each of the selections, i.e., the measure of information transmitted shall be *additive*.

As an example of how the additivity condition and the bit may be used, consider a set of elements (think of them as letters of an alphabet or phonemes in a phonemic system) in which each element is equally likely to be selected. (This, of course, does not hold for any natural language.) Further, suppose that the number n of elements is of the form 2^N, where N is an integer. Question: when an element is chosen from this set, how many bits of information are conveyed? The answer is N bits per selection. We can easily show that there are no more than N bits. Let any element be selected and divide the set of elements into half, each half being composed of 2^{N-1} elements. The element selected is in one half or the other, and the information transmitted as to which half it is in is a decision between two equally likely alternatives (since each element has the same probability of being chosen). So, that conveys one bit of information. Take that set and divide it in half, each half now consisting of 2^{N-2} elements. Again, the decision as to which of the two sets contains the selected element is between two *a priori* equally likely alternatives, and so another bit of information is transmitted in isolating it. Continuing the process until the element is isolated clearly requires N steps, and, assuming additivity, N bits of information are transmitted. The fact that all the elements were assumed to be equally likely should suggest that no scheme can be devised to isolate the element in fewer than N binary decisions. This can be proved to be the case. I shall not prove it, for the conclusion that there are N bits per selection in this situation will follow from much stronger and deeper results to be presented later.

The English alphabet consists of 26 letters which with punctuation marks comes to about $32 = 2^5$ symbols. Were we to suppose them to be chosen independently and with equal probabilities (both patently false assumptions) then each letter of a message would yield five bits of information. Clearly, this is not an accurate estimate of the bits per letter in English prose. However, it does stand as an upper bound to this number. Later (Chapter 7) more precise estimates will be given which show that it is actually somewhere between 1 and 2 bits per letter.

Continuing with the example, observe that when $n = 2^N$, then $N = \log_2 n$ by definition of the logarithm, and so we may say that in this situation there are $\log_2 n$ bits of information per element. We will find that our subsequent discussion of information transmission results in logarithmic measures slightly more complicated than this.

3. THE DISCRETE NOISELESS SYSTEM

IN THIS CHAPTER I shall discuss what is known as the discrete noiseless communication system. The definition of a noiseless system was given in the last section, and it may be summarized by saying that in such a system there is never any confusion at the destination as to which signal (of a known class of signals) was emitted by the source. This, of course, does not mean that the signal received is necessarily physically identical to the signal sent, but only that no confusion can arise as to what signal was sent.

The word 'discrete' refers to the nature of the information source. It describes a source which generates messages by temporally ordered sequences of selections from a finite set of possible choices. Thus, the discrete case includes a vast amount of familiar communication, such as the selections made from a phonemic system to generate words and sentences. But the theory of this section does not include sources, such as a musical instrument, which *can* select from a continuum of continuous functions; that theory is outlined in the appendix.

Channel Capacity. In any communication system the transmitter is so chosen as to match the source to the channel. Signals emanating from the transmitter, which are assumed to be in one-to-one correspondence with the selections made by the source, are propagated along the channel. As far as this communication process is concerned, the relevant effect of the physical characteristics of the channel is to determine how many different signals can be transmitted over it in a given space of time. Roughly, this is what we mean by the capacity of the channel. Formally, let $N(T)$ denote the number of different signals which satisfy the following three properties:

i. each signal can be emitted by the transmitter as a result of selections by the source,

ii. each signal is admissible on the channel, i.e., each signal is compatible with the physical characteristics of the channel,

iii. each signal is of duration T time units.

From the discussion in the last section, it is suggested (though by no means proved) that if each of these $N(T)$ signals were equally likely then there would be $\log_2 N(T)$ bits per signal of duration T time units, or

$$C(T) = \frac{\log_2 N(T)}{T}$$

bits per signal per unit time. Now, extending the discussion of the two-alternative case, it is plausible to suppose that the maximum information is transmitted when each signal is equally likely. Since we have taken $N(T)$ to be the largest number of different signals which may be transmitted over the channel in T time units, it is therefore reasonable to suppose that $C(T)$ is approximately the maximum number of bits of information per signal transmittible over the channel in one time unit. Since there can be only one signal on the channel at a time, $C(T)$ is approximately the maximum number of bits that can be handled by the channel in one unit of time. The approximation will tend to be better the larger we take T, so we are led to define the capacity C of the channel to be:

$$C = \lim_{T \to \infty} C(T) = \lim_{T \to \infty} \frac{\log_2 \mathcal{N}(T)}{T}.$$

For any practical application of this concept the trick is to determine $\mathcal{N}(T)$ from the physical characteristics of the channel or from any theorems we may derive which involve C. In the following subsection an example of the first procedure is given, and in a later subsection a theorem is given which has been used to find approximations to C empirically.

A Special Case of Channel Capacity.(*) For the moment let us restrict ourselves to a special class of transmitter-channel combinations which, possibly, is best illustrated by the familiar dot-dash telegraphy code. Suppose that at any instant there either is or is not a signal on the wire connecting the transmitter to the receiver. A dot will be represented by one time unit of signal and one time unit of no signal, and a dash by three units of signal followed by one unit of no signal. Between letters three units and between words six units of no signal are allowed. Problem: compute the channel capacity.

For this system, let us define two different states which we shall call a_1 and a_2. The system is in state a_1 following either a letter or a word space, and it is in state a_2 following either a dot or a dash. Since a word or letter space can never follow either a word or letter space, we know that the next signal after the system is in state a_1 must be a dot or a dash, so state a_1 must be followed by state a_2; however, when the system is in state a_2 it can be followed by any of the four possibilities and so by either state a_1 or a_2. This is illustrated schematically in Fig. 3.

We are now in a position to generalize this in a natural manner to a system having m possible states $a_1, a_2, \ldots, a_m$ and n possible signals $S_1, S_2, \ldots, S_n$. When the system is in state a_i only a certain subset of the signals may arise; let S_s denote a typical one. We suppose that a_i and the admissible S_s together determine what the next state will be. Let us denote it by a_j. For all such possible triples (i, s, j), let $b_{ij}^{(s)}$ denote the time duration of the sth symbol. Obviously certain of the combinations cannot arise, e.g., in the telegraphy case the triple $(a_1, \text{word space}, a_2)$ is not admissible (see Fig. 3).

(*) This subsection is not essential to the rest of the paper, and, as it is a little more difficult, some readers may choose to omit it.

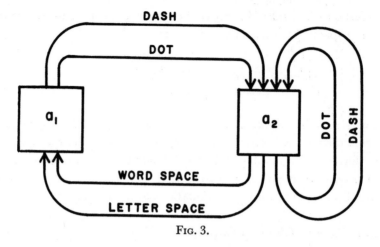

Fɪɢ. 3.

On the other hand, $(a_1$, dash, $a_2)$ is admissible and its b value is four time units.

The channel capacity of this system can be shown (Shannon, [1948]) to be given by

$$C = \log_2 W_o,$$

where W_o is the largest real root of the determinantal equation

$$\left| \sum_s{}' \mathrm{W}^{-b_{ij}^{(s)}} - \delta_{ij} \right| = 0,$$

where

$$\delta_{ij} = \begin{cases} 1 & \text{if } i=j \\ 0 & \text{if } i \neq j. \end{cases}$$

In the telegraphy case, the graph of Fig. 3 can be put in the following matrix form:

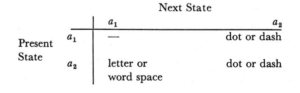

		Next State	
		a_1	a_2
Present State	a_1	—	dot or dash
	a_2	letter or word space	dot or dash

From this we see that the determinantal equation reads

$$\begin{vmatrix} -1 & W^{-2} + W^{-4} \\ W^{-3} + W^{-6} & W^{-2} + W^{-4} - 1 \end{vmatrix} = 0$$

$$= \frac{1}{W^{10}} [W^{10} - W^8 - W^6 - W^5 - W^3 - W^2 - 1].$$

Solving for W_o and computing $\log_2 W_o$ one finds that $C = 0.539$ bits per unit time.

   More will be said about channel capacity before we are done, but first it is necessary to discuss the source and to develop a suitable measure for the average information generated by any discrete source.

The Discrete Source. As I have said, it is assumed there is a source that makes selections (with replacement) from a finite set of elements and that messages are generated by temporally ordered selections from this set. The general situation is typified by the way we form written sentences by ordered selections of letters, blanks, and punctuation marks.

   A moment's reflection about English will suggest two important statistical facts about many sources:

   i. There is no reason to suppose that the probability that one symbol will be selected is the same as that for another symbol: the letter "z" is much less frequently used in English than is "e".

   ii. In general, the choice of one symbol in the middle of a message will not be independent of the preceding choices: although "e" has a high *a priori* probability of being chosen, the probability is markedly reduced if the letters "automobi" have already been received and it is markedly increased if the letters "automobil" have been received.

   Although most human sources produce an interdependence between symbol selections – often called intersymbol influences – there are some cases of independence, such as the transmission of random numbers or of an unconnected set of telephone numbers. In the next subsection we shall analyze the case of independent selections and later the more complicated case where there are dependencies.

   To deal with these problems of symbols selected with different frequencies and of the interdependence of symbol selection, we shall obviously want to introduce probability distributions over the set of symbols. For this to make sense, we shall have to assume that the source is homogeneous in time, so that its statistical character – measured by any statistical parameter we choose – is the same at one time as at any other time. Such a source is said to be *stationary* and the time series (of symbol selections) is called a stationary time series. This assumption is essential to the theory; it is one which seems plausible for many sources and not for others. For example, it does not hold for an individual who is learning. In most cases, however, it is quite difficult to assure oneself that a source is stationary. The problem is very closely related to the difficulty in deciding whether a particular finite set of numbers can be considered a typical sample from a random sequence generated by some probability law. The condition does serve, however, to prevent us from considering as one source the *New York Times* from time O to time T and *Izvestia* from time T to time T', for the statistical structure of messages in these two time intervals will certainly be different – indeed, some of the symbols will differ.

Assuming a stationary source S, we may now introduce a little necessary notation. We let $p(i)$ denote the probability that symbol i in S will be selected and $p(i,j)$ the probability that symbols i and j in S will be selected in the order i and then j. In general, $p(i,j) \neq p(j,i)$ (consider, for example, q and u in English). In general, if $i_1, i_2, \ldots, i_k$ is an ordered sequence of symbols, $p(i_1, i_2, \ldots, i_k)$ denotes the probability of its occurrence.

The selection of symbols is said to be *independent* if for every k and every possible sequence $i_1, i_2, \ldots, i_k$

$$p(i_1, i_2, \ldots, i_k) = p(i_1) p(i_2) \ldots p(i_k).$$

Before turning to the analysis of the case of independent selections, let me indicate how messages look when generated according to various assumed statistical dependencies. I shall present the output generated from a source which takes into account some (but not all) of the statistical structure of English. First, suppose that selections are independent but with the simple frequencies of English text. Using these frequencies and a table of random numbers, Shannon [1948] generated

OCRO HLI RGWR NMIELWIS EU LL NBNESEBYA TH EEI ALHENHTTPA OOBTTVA NAH BRL

If, however, one includes some intersymbol influences, one may, for example, generate a message in which each selection depends on the two preceding ones. Using such data for English, Shannon generated

IN NO IST LAT WHEY CRATICT FROURE BIRS GROCID PONDENOME OF DEMONSTURES OF THE REPTAGIN IS REGOACTIONA OF CRE

Neither message is English, but the second is "more" English than the first. The greater ease a typist finds in copying the second passage as against the first reflects the difference.

A Measure of Information Transmitted for Independent Selections. Let us assume for the present that messages are generated by independent selections from a discrete source. Statistically, then, the source is completely characterized by the probability distribution

$$P = [p(1), p(2), \ldots, p(n)]$$

of symbol selection over the n symbols of the source S. The problem is to assign a number to the source, i.e., to the probability distribution P, which is deemed a suitable measure of the *average* amount of information transmitted when a symbol is selected from S. There are at least four ways to get to an answer (fortunately the same answer), and since each reveals something of the structure of the problem and since the resulting statistic is of such great importance, I shall present all four.

What we want is a function which assigns a number to each probability distribution; we may denote it by

$$H = H[p(1), p(2), \ldots, p(n)].$$

The first procedure, which is heuristic and easily remembered, rests on accepting the earlier argument that, when there are $n = 2^N$ equally likely alternatives, a suitable measure of the amount of information is $N = \log_2 n$. Let us extend this definition to n equally likely alternatives where n is now any integer, i.e., we shall say there are $\log_2 n$ bits per selection from among n equally likely selections. Now, if we consider any event of probability $p = 1/n$, then we may treat this event as one among n equally likely alternatives and so the information involved in its selection is

$$\log_2 n = \log_2 \frac{1}{p} = -\log_2 p.$$

Finally, consider an event of probability p (not necessarily the reciprocal of an integer): it is plausible to extend the above definitions further and to say that $-\log_2 p$ bits of information are transmitted by the occurrence of this event of probability p. Thus, for the given source S, the selection of symbol i, which occurs with probability $p(i)$, transmits $-\log_2 p(i)$ bits of information. We see that this has the very reasonable property that an occurrence of a very rare event transmits a great deal of information and an event with probability near 1 transmits almost no information. On the average, however, the amount of information transmitted is the expected value of a single selection from the source, i.e.,

$$H = -\sum_{i=1}^{n} p(i) \log_2 p(i) \qquad \text{bits/selection.}$$

The above expression is without a doubt the best known aspect of information theory, and there are reasons to believe that this formula has blinded some to the content of the theory. It is, of course, nothing more nor less than a statistical parameter defined for all distributions — one which is in some ways similar to the variance. It obtains meaning and value in only two ways: first, as it is given a meaning in a theory, and second, as it becomes a conventionally accepted way of summarizing certain phenomena.

Shannon called H the entropy of the source (or more properly of the distribution characterizing the source) because the same expression (with the opposite sign) arises in statistical mechanics and is called entropy there. There has been considerable controversy as to whether this is only a formal similarity, or whether physical entropy and information are two closely related phenomena. This is a point requiring careful and sophisticated discussion and a rather deeper knowledge of physics than I want to assume here. Certain authors have been displeased with the term "entropy" and they have used terms such as the "amount of information" or simply the "information", the "specifity", and the "uncertainty" of this source. It is hard to say which term is the most common and which is the least objectionable — these two surely not being the same. Certainly, neither "amount of information" nor "information" are acceptable, since they lead much too easily to misinterpretations. Most often I shall use either "amount of information transmitted" or "entropy", the former without intending any semantic overtones and the latter without a commitment as to the identity of this statistic with physical entropy. On occasions when "uncertainty" seems the more suggestive term, I shall use it too with the tacit understanding that it really means "average uncertainty."

The second procedure to arrive at H, which many feel to be both the simplest and most elegant, amounts to a rigorous formulation of the first one.(*) The technique is to state four conditions which intuitively seem to be met by the concept of "the information transmitted when a symbol i is selected, given that the *a priori* probability of its selection was $p(i)$." From these conditions we shall derive the entropy expression; they are:

1. *Independence of irrelevant alternatives.*(†) The amount of information transmitted by a selection of i shall be a real number which depends only upon $p(i)$ and not upon the probability distribution over the other symbols. Thus, we may denote the amount of information transmitted by the selection of i by $f[p(i)]$.

2. *Continuity.* $f[p(i)]$ shall be a continuous function of $p(i)$, since one feels that a very small change in $p(i)$ should result in only a small change in the amount of information transmitted.

3. *Additivity.* If two independent selections i and j with probabilities $p(i)$ and $p(j)$ are effected, then the amount of information transmitted in the joint selection (i,j), which has probability $p(i)p(j)$ of occurring, shall be the simple sum of amount of information transmitted by each of the selections, i.e.,

$$f[p(i)p(j)] = f[p(i)] + f[p(j)].$$

4. *Scale.* In our discussion of the bit, we said that a selection with probability $1/2$ shall convey one bit, so we assume

$$f(1/2) = 1.$$

Now, observe that if n is an integer, then repeated application of the third assumption yields

$$f(p^n) = nf(p).$$

Let $q^n = p$, then from the last equation,

$$f(p^{\frac{1}{n}}) = f(q) = \frac{1}{n}f(q^n) = \frac{1}{n}f(p).$$

Thus, if m and n are integers, these two results combine to show that

$$f(p^{\frac{m}{n}}) = \frac{m}{n}f(p).$$

(*) This formalization was pointed out to me by Howard Raiffa.
(†) This term is not traditional in information theory, but it is in the closely related decision theories where it has been widely assumed and debated. There is every evidence from there that this condition, whatever it is called, must be considered much less innocent than it appears to be at first glance.

Let x be any number. We can choose integers m and n such that m/n is arbitrarily close to x, so by the continuity assumption

$$f(p^x) = xf(p).$$

Now, choose $x = -\log_2 p$, so $(\frac{1}{2})^x = p$, then

$$f(p) = f[(\tfrac{1}{2})^x] = xf(\tfrac{1}{2}) = -\log_2 p.$$

Thus, we have the form of the expression for the amount of information transmitted by the selection of any symbol with an *a priori* probability p of being selected.

The expected value of the amount of information transmitted by a source with probability distribution $p(i)$ is therefore

$$-\sum_{i=1}^{n} p(i) \log_2 p(i).$$

A third method to obtain the above expression, which is due to Shannon [1948], is similar to the last one except that it deals with the whole distribution at once. The procedure is to state five *a priori* conditions which many feel must be met by any measure of the average amount of information transmitted per selection from the source.

1. The average amount of information transmitted shall be a real-valued function of the n arguments $p(1), p(2), \ldots, p(n)$; it will be denoted by $H[p(1), p(2), \ldots, p(n)]$.

Next, it seems reasonable, as in the second method, to suppose that if the distribution is changed very slightly, then H should also change only slightly, so we require that

2. H shall be a continuous function in each of its n arguments.

Further, suppose we consider all sources for which the symbols are equally likely, i.e., $p(i) = 1/n$. As n is increased there is more information transmitted by the selection of one symbol since more messages of a given length are possible, so we require

3. When $p(i) = 1/n$ for all i, then H is a monotonically increasing function of n.

Next, we wish to require that if the calculation of the amount of information in a source is divided into a series of subcalculations, then the mode of subdivision shall not alter its value. More exactly, suppose S' is a subset of S (which by relabeling we may always take to be the elements $1, 2, \ldots, s$). The set S' can, of course, be treated as a single element s' with probability of occurrence

$$p(s') = p(1) + p(2) + \ldots + p(s).$$

If the form for H is known, we can compute its value for S, for the set with elements $s', s + 1, \ldots, n$, and for the set S' alone.(*) Our condition asserts that the first number shall be equal to the weighted sum of the last two, i.e.,

4. $H[p(1), p(2), \ldots, p(n)] = H[p(s'), p(s+1), \ldots, p(n)]$

$$+ p(s') H\left[\frac{p(1)}{p(s')}, \frac{p(2)}{p(s')}, \ldots, \frac{p(s)}{p(s')}\right].$$

Finally, we impose the definition of the unit:

5. $H(\frac{1}{2}, \frac{1}{2}) = 1$.

From these five conditions, each of which seems to be plausible, Shannon has shown, in a manner similar to that employed in the second method, that H must be of the form

$$-\sum_{i=1}^{n} p(i) \log_2 p(i).$$

Before we discuss any of the properties of H and relate it to the other quantity — channel capacity — which we have defined, let us arrive at the expression for H from a fourth point of view. The following argument is given by Fano [1949], and it is similar to one presented by Shannon [1948]. A plausible way to compare sources is to define a recoding of any source which takes into account the probability distribution of the source and which results in one of a set of standard normal forms of sources. If we can assign a number to each of these normal forms in an intuitively acceptable way, then we have indirectly assigned a number to each source. Of course, the

(*) The analogue of the "independence of irrelevant alternatives" is implicitly assumed at this point when we suppose that choices from S' are governed by the probabilities $p(1)/p(s'), \ldots, p(s)/p(s')$. Actually, this is an extremely powerful, if seemingly plausible, assumption which is the common thread of many theories of choice behavior, as I have shown elsewhere (Luce, [1959]).

only sources to which we have associated any numbers so far are the binary equally likely ones, so it is more than reasonable that we should attempt a recoding into binary equally likely selections.

This may be done in the following manner. Form all possible messages of length r, i.e., messages consisting of r symbols, and call this set R. Since the selections are independent, the probability of each message is simply the product of the probabilities of the individual selections which make it up, hence we know the probability of each message. Thus, we have a probability distribution over R. Divide R into a subset R_1 and its complement $\overline{R}_1$ with respect to R in such a manner that the sum of the probabilities of messages in R_1 is as near $1/2$ as possible. To each message in R_1 assign the digit 1 and to each in $\overline{R}_1$ the digit 0. Now, divide R_1 into a subset R_2 and its complement $\overline{R}_2$ with respect to R_1 (not R). Again the choice of R_2 is such that the probability of messages in R_2 is as nearly equal as possible to those in $\overline{R}_2$. To those messages in R_2 assign a second digit 1, so now 11 is assigned to each message in R_2. To those in $\overline{R}_2$ assign as the second digit 0, so 10 is assigned to each message of $\overline{R}_2$. Carry out a similar process in $\overline{R}_1$ leading to the numbers 01 and 00. Continue this "probability halving" until the classes contain single messages. In this manner each message will have assigned to it a sequence of binary digits, the length of the sequence being in large part determined by the probability that the message will occur — the more probable messages having fewer digits than the less probable ones.

An example may make the process clearer:

Message	Probability of occurrence	first digit	second digit	third digit	fourth digit
A	0.50	1	–	–	–
B	0.13	0	1	1	–
C	0.12	0	1	0	–
D	0.12	0	0	1	–
E	0.06	0	0	0	1
F	0.07	0	0	0	0

The first division is between {A} and {B, C, D, E, F,}. No further division of A is possible. The other set is divided into {B, C} and {D, E, F}. These in turn are divided as {B} and {C} and as {D} and {E, F}. The final division is of {E, F} into {E} and {F}.

Such a coding as this is efficient in the sense that the fewest number of binary digits are assigned to the most probable messages and the largest number to the least probable ones. Now, one can ask how many binary digits are required on the average per symbol when messages of length r

are considered. That is, for each message we multiply the number of digits required by the probability that the message occurs, sum these products over all messages, and divide the sum by the total number of symbols r in a message. Call this number H_r. In the above example $H_r = 2.13/r$ bits per symbol. The $\lim_{r \to \infty} H_r$ is a number assigned to each discrete source which both has a plausible meaning and will serve to compare different sources. Fortunately, it can be shown that

$$H = \lim_{r \to \infty} H_r = -\sum_{i=1}^{n} p(i) \log_2 p(i).$$

Thus by four (really only three) routes we have come to the same statistic as the appropriate one to describe the average nature of the source. We can defend it in two further ways; first, by stating some of its properties and showing that they are reasonable for a measure of information transmitted, and second, by using it to make theoretical statements about the transmission of information.

Properties of H. A number of theorems about H may be proved (Shannon, [1948]); as we shall need them later, and as they help to give a feel for H, I shall state them.

i. $H \geq 0$, and $H = 0$ if and only if all $p(i)$ except one equal zero. In other words, the entropy of a distribution is always non-negative, and it is zero if and only if the selection of one symbol is certain. Intuitively, no information is conveyed when the selection is certain, and accordingly $H = 0$.

ii. Any averaging of the probabilities in the source increases the value of H. From this, or in other ways, it can be shown that H assumes its maximum value, which is $\log_2 n$, when and only when each of the symbols is equally likely, i.e., when each has probability $p(i) = 1/n$ of being selected.

These two properties of H have led many authors to speak of H as the uncertainty of the source: H assumes its maximum when the selections are maximally "uncertain" and its minimum when absolute certainty obtains. Without disputing the point they have made, it must be mentioned that this use of the word "uncertainty" is at variance with its use in (statistical) decision theory. There, if an *a priori* probability distribution is known, one speaks of decision making under *risk*, and uncertainty is reserved for those cases where the distribution is not completely known. Thus, if the two vocabularies were to be consistent, H should be described as an average measure of risk, not of uncertainty.

iii. Let any long message of N symbols be selected and suppose that it has probability p of occurring, then $-(\log_2 p)/N$ is an estimator of $H(*)$. This last result is, of course, important in estimating H in practical situations, since all that can be observed generally is one message of some long duration. It must be pointed out that when this result is given in precise mathematical language, it asserts that $-(\log_2 p)/N$ almost certainly approaches H as N approaches infinity, i. e., the estimation scheme is consistent.

Non-independent Selections. So far our discussion of the source has been restricted to the independent case, which, as was pointed out, does not include most sources. But our efforts will not be lost, for fortunately we can readily carry over the results for independent sources to the non-independent case.

Consider the selection of one symbol from the set $S = \{1, 2, \ldots, n\}$ followed by a second selection from the same set (possibly the next one in forming a message, but we do not need to restrict ourselves to that case). More formally, let x and y be random variables with range S. The joint distribution of x and y is assumed to be known and we shall, for convenience, denote the probability that $x = i$ and $y = j$ by $p(i,j)$. In general, of course, $p(i,j) \neq p(i)p(j)$ since the selections need not be independent. The distribution $p(i,j)$ is now defined over the product space(†) of S with itself, $S \times S$, which is of course a set and so is included among the arbitrary sources we have considered earlier. The definition of entropy can be applied without alteration to the distribution $p(i,j)$, and hence we have as the entropy of the joint distribution of x, y,

$$H(x,y) = -\sum_{i,j}' p(i,j) \log_2 p(i,j).$$

Similarly, the definition can be applied to the distribution of the random variable x alone and to that of y alone, and so we have

(*) The plausibility of this can be seen as follows: In a message of length N, the expected number of times that the symbol i will occur is $p(i)N$. Thus, the expectation of the message itself is

$$p' = p(1)^{p(1)N} p(2)^{p(2)N} \ldots . p(n)^{p(n)N}.$$

Observe,

$$-\frac{\log_2 p'}{N} = -\sum p(i) \log_2 p(i) = H.$$

(†) The product space of two sets R and S, $R \times S$, is the set of all ordered pairs (r,s), where r is an element from R and s an element from S.

$$H(x) = -\sum_{i,j}' p(i,j) \log_2 \sum_j' p(i,j)$$

$$= -\sum_i' p(i) \log_2 p(i)$$

and

$$H(y) = -\sum_{i,j}' p(i,j) \log_2 \sum_i' p(i,j)$$

$$= -\sum_j' p(j) \log_2 p(j),$$

where

$$p(i) = \sum_j' p(i,j) \text{ and } p(j) = \sum_i' p(i,j).$$

From these definitions Shannon [1948] noted the following theorem:(*)

$$H(x,y) \leq H(x) + H(y).$$

This result simply states that the entropy (or average uncertainty or amount of information transmitted) of the joint distribution has the intuitively

(*) A simple proof, which was pointed out to me by Lee Abramson, is this: From elementary properties of the logarithm,

$$-[H(x) + H(y) - H(x,y)] = \sum_{i,j} p(i,j) \log_2 \frac{p(i)p(j)}{p(i,j)}$$

$$= \sum_{i,j} p(i,j) \log_2 a_{ij},$$

where $a_{ij} = \dfrac{p(i)p(j)}{p(i,j)}$. Since $\sum_{i,j} p(i)p(j) = \sum_i p(i) \sum_j p(j) = 1$,

$$0 = \log_2 1 = \log_2 \left\{ \sum_{i,j} p(i,j) \left[\frac{p(i)p(j)}{p(i,j)} \right] \right\}$$

$$= \log_2 \left\{ \sum_{i,j} p(i,j) a_{ij} \right\}$$

Since $\sum_{i,j} p(i,j) = 1$ and the logarithm is convex,

$$\sum_{i,j} p(i,j) \log_2 a_{ij} \leq \log_2 \left\{ \sum_{i,j} p(i,j) a_{ij} \right\} ,$$

so $H(x) + H(y) - H(x,y) \geq 0.$

necessary property that it is no larger than the sum of the entropies for the two distributions considered separately. In addition it is easily seen that

$$H(x,y) = H(x) + H(y)$$

if the events x and y are independent. Thus, whenever there is any inter-symbol influence in the selections, less information is transmitted per symbol than if they had been independent.

If we introduce the conditional probabilities relating the distribution of y to that of x, further relationships of interest can be established. Let $p(j|i)$ denote the conditional probability that $y = j$ given that $x = i$, i. e.,

$$p(j|i) = \frac{p(i,j)}{\sum_j p(i,j)} \quad .$$

The conditional entropy of the random variable y given that $x = i$ is defined to be

$$H(y|x = i) = -\sum_j p(j|i) \log_2 p(j|i).$$

Hence the expected *conditional entropy* of the random variable y given x is

$$H_x(y) = -\sum_i p(i) \sum_j p(j|i) \log_2 p(j|i)$$

$$= -\sum_{i,j} p(i,j) \log_2 p(j|i).$$

$H_x(y)$ measures the average uncertainty in the selection represented by y after the selection denoted by x is known.

Shannon has shown that(*)

$$H(x,y) = H(x) + H_x(y),$$

which, in words, states that the average uncertainty of the joint distribution is equal to the average uncertainty of the distribution of x added to the

(*) This result is readily proved:

$$H(x) + H_x(y) = -\sum_{i,j} p(i,j) \log_2 \sum_j p(i,j) - \sum_{i,j} p(i,j) \log_2 p(j|i)$$

$$= -\sum_{i,j} p(i,j) \log_2 [\sum_j p(i,j)] p(j|i)$$

$$= -\sum_{i,j} p(i,j) \log_2 p(i,j)$$

$$= H(x,y).$$

average uncertainty of the distribution of y when the value of x is known. From this and the preceding result, the following corollary is readily seen to hold:

$$H(y) \geq H_x(y),$$

i. e., the average uncertainty of the distribution of y is never increased by a knowledge of x. The two are equal if and only if the two random variables are independent.

One final concept: the ratio of the entropy of a source to the maximum entropy possible with the same set of symbols is a measure of the information transmitting efficiency of the source — Shannon called it the *relative entropy*. It is generally less than one, either because there is a non-uniform distribution over the symbols or because of the non-independence of symbol selection or, most commonly, because of both. One minus this quantity indicates the percentage of symbols which, though sent, carry no information, i. e., which are redundant. Thus we define the *redundancy* of a source to be

$$1 - \frac{H}{\max H} = 1 - \frac{H}{\log_2 n} \quad .$$

Several estimation procedures indicate that the redundancy of written English is at least 50 per cent and very likely nearer 75 per cent (see Chapter 7). The reason for such high redundancy will become apparent later.

In discussing the applicability of information theory to certain problems in psychology, Miller and Frick [1949] suggested that redundancy be called the *index of behavioral stereotypy*. The motive for this term of course is that redundancy is a quantity which is 1 when the behavior is completely stereotypic and 0 when each of the several alternatives arises with equal probability. For the most part, however, the shorter term is used.

The Fundamental Theorem of a Noiseless System. The following fundamental result, due to Shannon [1948], shows in effect that the above definitions of channel capacity and of source entropy or average uncertainty are suitable formalizations of our intuitions about the limitations on information transmission.

Theorem: *Let the entropy of a source be* H *bits per symbol and the capacity of a noiseless channel be* C *bits per second. For any positive number* ε *no matter how small, there exists a coding of the source, i. e., there exists a transmitter, such that it is* *possible to transmit at an average rate of* $(C/H) - \epsilon$ *symbols per second. It is not possible to devise a code so as to transmit at an average rate of more than* C/H *symbols per second.*

Three points should be made about this theorem. First, it must be kept in mind that the definition of the entropy of a source rests only upon the statistical structure of the source, and it does not in any way depend upon the properties of the channel. The capacity of the channel depends only upon channel properties and not at all upon the statistical structure of the source. The theorem asserts that these definitions have, however, been so chosen that the ratio C/H is the least upper bound of the transmission rate.

Second, the code which the theorem asserts to exist is, of course, influenced by how small we take ϵ. If ϵ is near C/H then nearly any code will do, but as ϵ approaches 0 fewer and fewer codes will produce a rate of $(C/H) - \epsilon$. But the theorem asserts that there will always be at least one. A major unsolved problem of information theory is to devise a theorem which describes such a code in detail for given values of C, H, and ϵ; the above theorem only asserts that such a code exists.

Third, such optimal use of the channel as described in the theorem is not effected without paying some price. The price is delay. If one is to code a message optimally when there are intersymbol influences, then it is necessary to wait before transmission to see how that influence can be utilized in the coding, thus effecting a delay in the transmission. Similarly, at the receiver, the translation into the language of the destination must be delayed in exactly the same way, for a single received symbol will have meaning only by its relation to a number of others. In practical engineering work a compromise is reached between long delays (and hence expensive storage equipment) and nearly optimal use of the channel.

The theorem may be recast in a slightly different form, which may help clarify it and which will be useful when we study the noisy system. Let R denote the average rate at which symbols are transmitted over the channel when a given code is used. The theorem then asserts that $C/H \geq R$ and that there exist codes such that the corresponding R is arbitrarily close to C/H. If we rewrite this as $C \geq HR$ and then maximize both sides with respect to all possible codes we have

$$C = \max_{\text{codes}} C = \max_{\text{codes}} (HR).$$

It is conventional, though misleading, simply to replace HR in the above expression by H. Previously, the entropy of a source was measured in "bits per symbol," but in this reformulation we measure the entropy of the source (and transmitter combination) in "bits per symbol" times "symbols per second," i. e., in "bits per second" transmitted. The theorem then asserts that the channel capacity is equal to the maximum number of bits per second which can be transmitted by the source-transmitter combination over the channel. In this form, and in a corresponding form for noisy systems, the fundamental theorem has been used in behavioral applications.

4. THE DISCRETE NOISY SYSTEM

As in the preceding chapter, I shall suppose that the source is discrete, but I shall now drop the condition of a noiseless system.

Equivocation and Channel Capacity. The significant effect of noise in a system, as was pointed out in Chapter 2, is to cause the destination sometimes to be mistaken as to which symbol was transmitted. Any other properties the noise may have are irrelevant in this theory of information transmission. Thus, if we assume that both the signal and the noise time series are stationary, and that the noise affects successive selections independently, then the noise is completely characterized by the matrix of conditional probabilities $p(j|i)$ which state the probability that symbol j is received when i was sent. Formally, this situation is identical to the case of non-independent selections: in that case we interpreted j as a selection following i; here we shall interpret j as the selection received at the destination when i was actually selected at the source.

The quantities $H(x)$, $H(y)$, $H(x,y)$ and $H_x(y)$ are defined as before. $H(x)$ is the entropy of the source distribution, $H(y)$ the entropy of the destination distribution, $H(x,y)$ the entropy of the joint distribution of x and y, $H_y(x)$ measures the average ambiguity in the signal sent given the received signal, while $H_x(y)$ measures the average ambiguity of the received signal given the signal which was sent. When we are considering noise, $H_y(x)$ is called *equivocation*.

If a system is noiseless, then $H_x(y) = 0 = H_y(x)$ and so $H(x) = H(y)$.

Let us suppose that all the entropies are calculated in bits/sec, rather than bits/symbol, then the effective *average rate of transmission*, R, (in bits/sec) is the average rate of information sent, $H(x)$, minus that which was lost as a result of the noise, $H_y(x)$:

$$R = H(x) - H_y(x).$$

This can easily be shown to be equal to two other expressions, the first of which states that the rate of transmission is the difference between what was received and what was received incorrectly. In symbols,

$$R = H(y) - H_x(y)$$
$$= H(x) + H(y) - H(x,y).$$

The notion of rate of transmission for the noisy case is analogous to that introduced for the noiseless case in the last statement of the fundamental theorem of the noiseless case. It suggests that one way to define channel capacity in the noisy case is as follows:

$$C = \max_{\text{codes}} [H(x) - H_y(x)].$$

By the theorem of the last section, this definition reduces to that of channel capacity of a noiseless system since in that case $H_y(x) = 0$. Note, it does not reduce directly to the *definition* of channel capacity as given early in Chapter 3; however, later a theorem will be presented which shows that there is an analogous, though more complicated, definition for the noisy case.

Theorems. Consider the communication system diagrammed in Fig. 4. We assume that there is an observer who is able to perceive without error both the selections made by the source and the corresponding signals received at the destination. Let us suppose that the equivocation due to noise is $H_y(x)$. If there is a noiseless correction channel from the observer

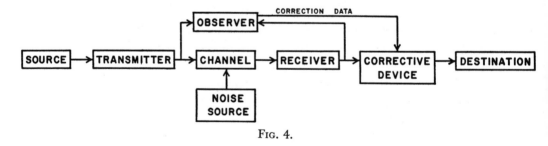

FIG. 4.

to the destination with capacity $H_y(x)$ bits/sec, it can be shown (Shannon, [1948]) that it is possible to encode correction data in such a manner as to correct all but an arbitrarily small fraction of the errors due to the noise. This is impossible if the channel capacity of the correction channel is less than $H_y(x)$. This theorem is of theoretical interest — it shows that $H_y(x)$

does in fact summarize the average effect of the noise. But it is certainly not a practical scheme to combat noise.

The following result, which is due to Feinstein [1954] and which is somewhat sharper than the original result of Shannon [1948], is a fundamental theorem for the noisy case.

Theorem. *Let the entropy of a source be* H *bits per second and the capacity of the channel* C *bits per second. Let* ϵ *be any number larger than* 0. *If* H $<$ C, *then there is a number* N (ϵ, H) *such that among all messages of length* N $\geq$ N (ϵ, H) *we can find a subset* $\{u_i\}$ *having at least* 2^{NH} *members with the properties that*

1. *we may associate a set* B_i *of messages of length* N *to each* u_i *in such a way that if* u_i *is sent the probability that a member of* B_i *is received is greater than* $1 - \epsilon$, *and*

2. *the sets* B_i *are non-overlapping.*

If H $>$ C, *this cannot be done.*

Let us examine the various components of this result. As in all such theorems, ϵ is to be thought of as a very small number which represents the permitted error tolerance. We are then required to consider long messages, the length depending upon both the value of H and how small we take ϵ. Of these n^N possible messages we consider a subset $\{u_i\}$. This subset includes most of the possible messages, e. g., if the selections are equiprobable, then it includes all of them since $n^N = 2^{N\log_2 n} = 2^{NH}$. The theorem asserts that to each of these messages we can associate a subset B_i of messages such that if, whenever a member of B_i is received, we infer that u_i was sent, then we know that the probability of being wrong is less than ϵ. This last statement is not justified by 1 alone, for if the sets B_i were to overlap there would not always be a unique inference. So part of the assertion is that they do not overlap. In this way, the effect of the noise can be combatted as effectively as we choose whenever $H < C$. The more effective we require the coding process to be, the larger we are forced to take N. This means that the price of combatting noise is delay, which in practice means extensive storage equipment.

Note that the theorem also asserts that it is never possible to do this if $H > C$.

Shannon's original theorem, which is weaker than Feinstein's result, can be stated in the following way:

Theorem: *Let the entropy of a source be* H *bits per second and the capacity of the channel* C *bits per second. If* H $\leq$ C, *then there exists a coding scheme such that the output of the source can be transmitted over the channel with an arbitrarily small frequency of errors. If* H $>$ C, *it is possible to reduce the equivocation to as near* H—C *as one chooses, but it is not possible to reduce it below* H—C.

McMillan's comments on this result seem to be worth repeating:

"Engineering experience has been that the presence in the channel of pertubation, noise, in the engineer's language, always degrades the exactitude of transmission. [The theorem] above leads us to expect that this need not always be the case, that perfect transmission can sometimes be achieved in spite of noise. This practical conclusion runs so counter to naive experience that it has been publicly challenged on occasion. What is overlooked by the challengers is, of course, that 'perfect transmission' is here defined quantitatively in terms of the capabilities of the channel or medium, perfection can be possible only when transmission proceeds at a slow enough rate. When it is pointed out that merely by repeating each message sufficiently often one can achieve virtually perfect transmission at a very slow rate, the challenger usually withdraws. In doing so, however, he is again misled, for in most cases the device of repeating messages for accuracy does not by any means exploit the actual capacity of the channel.

"Historically, engineers have always faced the problem of *bulk* in their messages, that is, the problem of transmitting rapidly or efficiently in order to make a given facility as useful as possible. The problem of noise has also plagued them, and in many contexts it was realized that some kind of exchange was possible, for example, noise could be eliminated by slower or less 'efficient' transmission. Shannon's theorem has given a general and precise statement of the asymptotic manner in which this exchange takes place." (1953, p. 207).

He goes on to point out the similarity in the exchange between bulk and noise and the rather general exchange between sample size and power in statistical tests.

Although the simple repetition of a message is not usually an efficient way to employ the channel capacity to eliminate errors, some form of redundant transmission is required. In general it will be far more complicated than repetition, but, as with repetition, a delay in the reception of a message must result. The essential point of the theorem is that the delay need not be such as to reduce the rate of transmission to zero. The proof of the theorem is not constructive and so there is no indication what code to use to utilize fully the channel capacity. Shannon and Weaver write, "Probably this is no accident but is related to the difficulty of giving an explicit construction for a good approximation to a random sequence." ([1948], p. 43) Much recent (engineering) work in information theory has been devoted to finding near optimal codes for certain important special cases.

Shannon's fundamental theorem of the noisy case may be recast in a form that shows the relation of the present definition of channel capacity to that given for the noiseless case. Let q be a number such that $0 < q < 1$. Consider all possible signals of duration T time units which might be transmitted over the channel and let R denote a typical subset of these signals. Under the assumption that each signal of R is equally probable and taking into account the statistics of the noise, let a receiver be designed to choose as the cause of the signal it receives the one in R which most likely is distorted into the one received. It is clear that in general errors will be made; let $p(R)$ denote the probability that an incorrect interpretation will be made when the subset is R. Consider now all those subsets R such that $p(R) \leq q$. Among these sets there is one which contains the most signals, let that number be denoted by $N(T, q)$. Shannon [1948] then showed that

$$C = \lim_{T \to \infty} \frac{\log_2 N(T, q)}{T},$$

which is clearly analogous to the original definition of channel capacity for the noiseless case. It is remarkable that this result is independent of the value of q. Presumably, however, the rate of convergence of the limit is not independent of q, and so in any application of the theorem one should attempt to exploit the freedom in choosing q.

Channel Capacity of a Noisy System: Independent Selections. Shannon [1948] and Fano [1950] have shown that if one assumes that the selections at the source are independent, then the capacity of the channel is given by the transcendental equation

$$\sum_j 2^{-\sum_i h(j|i)[C - \sum_j p(j|i)\log_2 p(j|i)]} = 1,$$

where $h(j|i)$ is a typical element of the inverse of the noise matrix, i. e.,

$$\sum_j h(j|i)p(j|k) = \begin{array}{l} 1 \text{ if } i = k \\ 0 \text{ if } i \neq k \end{array}.$$

It is difficult, if not impossible, to see the dependence of channel capacity on the noise matrix from this equation, but, of course, in any given case one can solve for C numerically. However, if we can assume that the noise has the same disturbing effect on each symbol of the source, i. e.,

$$H_x(y) = -\sum_i{}' p(i) \sum_j{}' p(j|i) \log_2 p(j|i)$$

is independent of $p(i)$, then it can be shown (Fano [1950]) that

$$C = \log_2 n - H_x(y).$$

In the special case of a binary source (two elements) and noise such that the probability of an erroneous transmission is a, then the capacity is given by

$$C = 1 + a \log_2 a + (1-a) \log_2 (1-a).$$

It is easy to make interesting calculations using this last expression. For example, if the chance of an error is 1 per cent, then the channel capacity is reduced to approximately 90 per cent of its value in the absence of noise. This marked non-linearity must be kept in mind whenever thinking about the effects of noise.

5. SOME ASPECTS OF DISCRETE THEORY RELATED TO APPLICATIONS

As WE SHALL SEE in some detail in Section II, many of the applications of information theory in psychology are to problems not classically described as communication. Indeed, they are communication problems only in the sense that any experiment, or any decision, can be treated as a transmission of information. Put another way, in the attempt to analyze communication systems, a mathematical formalism has been produced to deal with the average character of certain inference problems, and this mathematics can be completely divorced from its realization as a communication system. At the same time, there are other realizations of the same mathematical system in psychology. Because of its origins, however, the information terminology is associated with the mathematics and so with its applications. Some of this vocabulary may seem peculiar in some applications, but it is probably not as misleading as it may seem initially. In this section, I propose to discuss (but divorced from the communication model) a part of the formalism that has been particularly important in psychological applications. The topics to be considered are: a relation between the rate of information transmission and statistical inference, a generalization of the notion of transmission rate, and the statistical sampling and significance problems.

Inverse Probabilities, Bayes Theorem, Contingency Tables. The structure of very many problems in psychology and the other behavioral sciences can be reduced to the existence of two classes of possible occurrences, usually called stimuli and responses, such that an occurrence in the response class is in some degree dependent upon what stimulus occurred. It is not easy to characterize in a useful and simple way the relation between these two classes of occurrences. It is, of course, possible to present the whole matrix of joint probabilities $p(i,j)$, i. e., to give the entire contingency table, but this hardly can be called simple. Various measures of contingency have been proposed and used, but objections have been raised to each of these. Still another possibility — one that has found favor among some psychologists — is the entropy measure. The expression most often used is

$$R = H(x) + H(y) - H(x,y),$$

which, when the entropies are measured in bits/sec, is called the rate of information transmission (Chapter 4). As often as not, time does not enter into psychological applications in a natural manner, and it is more appropriate to treat the stimuli and the responses as static and to measure entropies in bits. In that case the following notation is employed:

$$\begin{aligned} T(x;y) &= H(x) + H(y) - H(x,y) \\ &= H(x) - H_y(x) \\ &= H(y) - H_x(y), \end{aligned}$$

and the quantity $T(x;y)$ is simply called the *information transmitted* from the stimulus to the response. It is a quantity which is 0 when the random variables x and y are statistically independent and it is a maximum when they are in one-to-one correspondence, i. e., when a knowledge of the value of x uniquely determines the value of y and conversely. In other words, T is a measure of the contingency between x and y.

Note that in this interpretation of the formalism the role of the human being has changed: Previously, we had thought of the source and the destination as people and the channel as a physical entity. In most psychological applications, the stimuli correspond to the source and the responses to the destination; the subject is treated as a noisy channel causing less than perfect correspondence between the stimuli and the responses.

One can also think of the relation between the two random variables x and y as a problem of inferring as well as possible the value of x from a knowledge of the value of y. This is, of course, the problem of inverse probabilities which has had a long history in statistical theory, and Bayes theorem is one of the most famous results. We may think of it in the following form: There are n possible underlying states of nature, $i = 1,2,...,n$, which are known *a priori* to have probabilities $p(i)$ of occurring. We suppose an experiment is performed with possible outcomes $j = 1,2,...,m$, the actual outcome depending somewhat upon which state obtains. Let x be a random variable with range the states of nature and distributed according to $p(i)$ and y a random variable with range the experimental outcomes. Further, let us assume as known the conditional probabilities, $p(j|i)$, that $y = j$ when $x = i$. The problem then is to estimate the probability $x = i$ when the outcome of the experiment is known, i. e., when $y = j$ is given.

Cherry [1953] describes the analogy to the noisy communication system as "... an observer receives the distorted output signals (the posterior data...) from which he attempts to reconstruct the input signals (the hypotheses), knowing only the language statistics (the prior data)." (p. 39).

It is well known that Bayes theorem reads,

$$p(i|j) = \frac{p(j|i)p(i)}{\sum_i p(j|i)p(i)} \ .$$

If one takes logarithms on both sides of this equation, multiplies the result by $p(i,j)$, and then sums on both i and j, the result is simply

$$H(x) - H_y(x) = H(y) - H_x(y),$$

i. e., the information transmitted from x to y.

Deeper connections between conventional statistics and the information statistic have been explored by Kullback and Leibler [1951] and Kullback [1952].

Modern statistical inference, stemming largely from Wald [1947] (also see Blackwell and Girshick [1954], and Savage [1954]), takes a somewhat different tack. One of the central notions is that there must be given an evaluation of incorrect decisions, i.e., a loss function must be selected, and the problem is then to reach inferences which are optimal relative to that function. Our point of view has been tacitly to minimize information loss. However, other possible loss functions could be examined. Van Meter and Middleton [1954] have presented a theory along these lines which rests upon statistical decision theory and is therefore beyond the scope of this survey.

Multivariate Theory. An alternative way of viewing information theory — one which seems especially useful in many psychological applications — draws a close parallel between an information analysis of stimulus-response patterns and analysis of variance. It is a more general, and so a weaker, analysis than analysis of variance since it does not presuppose any metric information about the stimulus or the response sets.

Suppose we are analyzing a stimulus-response situation by information theoretical techniques, then the basic equation we have developed,

$$H(y) = H_x(y) + T(x;y),$$

decomposes an average measure of the response pattern into two parts: $T(x;y)$, which is determined by the stimulus, and $H_x(y)$, which is unexplained "random" variation — random in the sense that it is uncorrelated with the stimulus x. It may very well happen that a considerable portion of the residue $H_x(y)$ can be explained in a systematic manner, though not by the experimental stimuli that have so far been considered. For example, consider an experiment in which subjects are required to classify liminal tones into one of n categories. It may very well happen that the subject's response is determined only in small part by the tone presented, but that in large part it is predictable from a knowledge of his previous response, even if we do not know the stimulus. In such a case, it may be not only appropriate but essential to consider as the stimulus the pair of random variables (u,v), where u has the possible tones as its range and v the possible previous responses of the subject. In other words, in some cases we may be able to understand the phenomenon adequately only if we treat as the stimulus a random variable with a range which is the product space of two, or more, simpler sets. McGill [1953, 1954, 1955 a, 1955 b] has examined this problem in some detail and he has appropriately generalized the transmission concepts so as to produce a multivariate theory where, of course, Shannon's theory is the bivariate case. I shall recount this development briefly.

First of all, we may replace x by the symbol (u,v), which is equivalent to x when the range of x is the product space of the ranges of the random variables u and v, in the equation for information transmission. This yields

$$T(u,v;y) = H(u,v) + H(y) - H(u,v,y).$$

(I have systematically omitted the extra parentheses about u,v for greater clarity). It is clear that in our discussion there has not been any formal notion of direction of transmission between source and receiver, and so they may be interchanged. Formally,

$$T(u,v;y) = T(y;u,v).$$

Next, we want to introduce a measure which gives the separate dependence of y upon u and upon v. To do this, it seems appropriate to define a measure of the conditional information transmitted from the stimulus u to the response y when the stimulus v is held constant, say at the value j. With v fixed, this is simply the transmission expression we have obtained previously, namely,

$$T_j(u;y) = H_j(u) + H_j(y) - H_j(u;y).$$

Now, since we deal only with averages, we shall need

$$T_v(u;y) = \sum_j p(j)\, T_j(u;y)$$

$$= \sum_j p(j)\, H_j(u) + \sum_j p(j)\, H_j(y) - \sum_j p(j)\, H_j(u,y).$$

Expand each of the three terms on the right, e. g., the first gives:

$$\sum_j p(j)\, H_j(u) = \sum_j p(j) \sum_i p(i|j)\, \log_2 p(i|j)$$

$$= \sum_j \sum_i p(j) p(i|j)\, \log_2 p(i|j)$$

$$= \sum_j \sum_i p(i,j)\, \log_2 \frac{p(i,j)}{p(j)}$$

$$= H(u,v) - H(v).$$

The other terms are similar, and combining them we obtain

$$T_v(u;y) = H(u,v) + H(v,y) - H(v) - H(u,v,y).$$

In like manner,

$$T_u(v;y) = H(u,v) + H(u,y) - H(u) - H(u,v,y),$$
$$T_y(u;v) = H(u,y) + H(v,y) - H(y) - H(u,v,y).$$

Clearly, v will have an effect on the average transmission from u to y if and only if $T_v(u;y) \neq T(u;y)$, and the magnitude of this effect is measured by

$$A(uvy) = T_v(u;y) - T(u;y).$$

Similar quantities can be defined to measure the effect of u on the transmission from v to y and of y on the transmission from u to v. There is not, however, any need to introduce a new symbol for each of these since they can all easily be shown to be equal, i. e.,

$$A(uvy) = T_u(v;y) - T(v;y)$$
$$= T_y(u;v) - T(u;v).$$

"In view of this symmetry, we may call $A(uvy)$ the *u.v.y* interaction information. We see that $A(uvy)$ is the gain (or loss) in sample information transmitted between any two of the variables, due to additional knowledge of the third variables." [McGill, 1954, p. 101]. We shall return to the exact meaning of this term below.

With these concepts, it is now possible to express the three-dimensional average information transmitted in terms of the two-dimensional ones and the interaction information. We show that

$$T(u,v;y) = T(u;y) + T(v;y) + A(uvy)$$
$$= T_v(u;y) + T_u(v;y) - A(uvy).$$

Substituting one of the expressions for A,

$$T(u;y) + T(v;y) + A(uvy) = T_v(u;y) + T(v;y).$$

Now substitute the H expressions for the two right hand terms,

$$T_v(u;y) + T(v;y) = H(u,v) + H(v,y) - H(v) - H(u,v,y)$$
$$+ H(v) + H(y) - H(v,y)$$
$$= H(u,v) + H(y) - H(u,v,y),$$

but this was previously shown to be equal to $T(u,v;y)$. The second expression follows immediately from the definition of A.

We may write this three-dimensional information transmission in another way which parallels the familiar equation $H(y) = H_x(y) + T(x;y)$, namely,

$$H(y) = H_{uv}(y) + T(u,v;y)$$
$$= H_{uv}(y) + T(u;y) + T(v;y) + A(uvy).$$

The term $H_{uv}(y)$ is the residual or unexplained variability in the response y after the information about y given by u and by v and the interaction information of the three variables has been removed.

An initially unexpected feature of McGill's analysis was the possibility that the interaction term may be negative. As Miller ([1954 a], p. 411) put it, "In other words, a knowledge of the input [v] may decrease the amount of information that [y] has about [u] — communication from [u] to [y] would actually be better if no data about [v] were collected at all!" Are we then forced to think of the transmission of negative information? No, for as McGill [1955 a] has pointed out the interaction term A is composed of two effects: the interaction of the three variables plus the correlation of u and v. If the correlation is high, then there is a good chance that A will be negative. Thus, he argues, if sense is to be made of the interaction term, we must choose u and v to be independent in the experimental design. It is not obvious, however, that the organism being studied will necessarily elect to respond only to statistically independent variables. We can easily confine our analysis to such cases, but we may at the same time limit the possibility of describing the behavior simply.

One of the most important and desirable properties of the information statistic — entropy — is its additive character. This was apparent in the two-dimensional case and is even more forcibly illustrated in the three-dimensional theory. Each of the contributions — that from u, from v, from the interaction, and from the unexplained variability — is simply added to obtain the information in the response pattern. Thus, information analysis of a stimulus-response situation seems to parallel analysis of variance. McGill [1953, 1955 a] and Garner and McGill [1956] have shown that there is in fact a striking formal parallel between information analysis, analysis of variance, and correlational analysis. To be sure, there are differences: "... information transmission is made to order for contingency tables. Measures of transmitted information are zero when variables are independent in the contingency-sense (as opposed to the restriction to linear independence in analysis of variance). In addition, the analysis is designed for frequency data in discrete categories, while methods based on analysis of variance are not." (McGill [1954], p. 107). Nevertheless, "It would seem that information theory effectively corresponds to a nonparametric analysis of variance." (Miller [1954a], p. 411).

There is no reason why the above analysis cannot be extended to more dimensions than three, and McGill [1954] has carried this out in some detail. There is little reason to reproduce it here. It should be mentioned, however, that as with sequential dependencies in the source, the amount of data needed and the number of calculations required mount sharply as the number of dimensions is increased.

Statistical Tests and Estimations of Entropy. In addition to constructing models, the behavioral scientist, unlike many physical scientists, must confront the difficult statistical problem of testing and using his model when the only data available are from comparatively small samples. His use of information theory is no exception to this rule, so we turn now to that incompletely resolved problem.

Let us suppose that a distribution $p(i)$ governs the selections of the n alternatives $1,2,\ldots,n$, and let us suppose that a sample of N independent observations of selections yields $N(i)$ cases of alternative i. The true entropy is, of course,

$$H = -\sum_{i=1}^{n} p(i) \log_2 p(i),$$

while

$$\hat{H} = -\sum_{i=1}^{n} \frac{N(i)}{N} \log_2 \frac{N(i)}{N}$$

is the estimator of the entropy obtained by replacing each $p(i)$ by its maximum likelihood estimator $N(i)/N$. Miller and Madow [1954] have shown that if the $p(i)$ are not all equal, $\sqrt{N}(H-\hat{H})$ has a normal limiting distribution with mean 0 and variance

$$\sigma^2 = \sum_{i=1}^{n} p(i) [\log_2 p(i) + H]^2.$$

If, however, $p(i) = 1/n$ for every i, then $(2N/\log_2 e)(H-\hat{H})$ has a chi-square limiting distribution with $n-1$ degrees of freedom.

They point out (also see Miller [1955]) that if small samples are used to estimate the entropy there is a bias which can be corrected for by the following theorem:

$$H = E(\hat{H}) + (\log_2 e)\left[\frac{n-1}{2N} - \frac{1}{12N^2} + \frac{1}{12N^2}\sum_{i=1}^{n}\frac{1}{p(i)}\right] + 0\left(\frac{1}{N^3}\right),$$

where $E(\hat{H})$ is the expected value of H and $0(1/N^3)$ denotes terms of the order of $1/N^3$ or smaller. They also establish a similar expression for the variance of $\hat{H}$, but as it is fairly complex I shall not reproduce it here.

For the case of equally likely alternatives, Rogers and Green [1955] have developed an exact expression for the expected value of $\hat{H}$, namely,

$$E(\hat{H}) = \log_2 n - \sum_{i=2}^{N}\binom{N-1}{i-1}\frac{\sum_{j=0}^{i-2}(-1)^j\binom{i-1}{i-j-1}\log_2(i-j)}{n^{i-1}}.$$

The Miller and Madow approximation in the same case reduces to

$$E(\hat{H}) = \log_2 n - \frac{(\log_2 e)\,[n^2 + 6N(n-i) - 1]}{12N^2},$$

which, of course, is much simpler. Rogers and Green point out that for $N \geq n$ the two give nearly the same results, but that for $N < n$, "... the Miller-Madow formula ... becomes increasingly less accurate and (their formula) becomes more easily computable." (Rogers and Green [1955], p. 103). They also present a similar expression for the variance which I shall not reproduce here. Tables are given of the mean and variance in the equally likely case for small values of N and n (they use the symbol K for what I have called n).

Miller [1955] has also treated the problem of transmitted information, i. e., of contingency tables having r stimulus alternatives and s response alternatives. Let the three probability distributions be denoted by $p(i)$, $p(j)$, and $p(i,j)$, and let the observed sample frequencies from a sample of size N be denoted by $N(i)$, $N(j)$, and $N(i,j)$. The transmitted information, T, is of course given by

$$T = -\sum_{i=1}^{r} p(i) \log_2 p(i) - \sum_{j=1}^{s} p(j) \log_2 p(j)$$

$$+ \sum_{i=1}^{r} \sum_{j=1}^{s} p(i,j) \log_2 p(i,j).$$

Let $\hat{T}$ be the estimator which is obtained by replacing each $p(i)$ by its maximum likelihood estimator $N(i)/N$. Define:

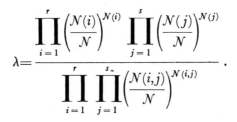

$$\lambda = \frac{\displaystyle\prod_{i=1}^{r}\left(\frac{N(i)}{N}\right)^{N(i)} \prod_{j=1}^{s}\left(\frac{N(j)}{N}\right)^{N(j)}}{\displaystyle\prod_{i=1}^{r}\prod_{j=1}^{s}\left(\frac{N(i,j)}{N}\right)^{N(i,j)}}.$$

It is known from Wilks' [1935] likelihood-ratio test of independence that $-2 \log_e \lambda$ has the chi-square distribution with $(r-1)(s-1)$ degrees of freedom. It is not difficult to show that

$$1.3863\, N\hat{T} = -2 \log_e \lambda,$$

hence $1.3863\, N\hat{T}$ has a chi-square distribution with $(r-1)(s-1)$ degrees of freedom under the null hypothesis $T = 0$, i. e., when the stimuli and the responses are independent.

In the same paper, Miller showed that

$$T = E(\hat{T}) - \frac{\log_2 e}{2N}(r-1)(s-1) + 0\left(\frac{1}{N^2}\right),$$

and so it is possible to correct for small sample bias. He suggests that N should be at least $5rs$ in order to make estimates of the information transmitted.

McGill [1954] has extended some of the above results to the multivariate case. First, he observes that:

$$\text{if}\begin{cases} y \text{ is independent of } (u,v) \\ y \text{ is independent of } v \\ y \text{ is independent of } v \text{ when } u \text{ is held constant} \end{cases} \text{then} \begin{cases} T(u,v;y) = 0 \\ T(v;y) = 0 \\ T_u(v;y) = 0 \end{cases}$$

The last two conditions each imply

$$T_v(u;y) = T(u;y),$$

or, in words, v is not involved in the transmission between u and y when either of the two conditions holds.

There are, of course, analogous statements for the symbols u, v, and y.

To test the hypothesis that any of the T's are zero, McGill uses Miller's result relating independence with the likelihood-ratio test. One obtains

$$\text{if} \begin{cases} T(u,v;y) = 0 \\ T(u;y) = 0 \\ T(v;y) = 0 \\ T_y(u;v) = 0 \end{cases} \text{then} \begin{array}{l} 1.3863N \end{array} \begin{cases} \hat{T}(u,v;y) \\ \hat{T}(u;y) \\ \hat{T}(v;y) \\ \hat{T}(u;v) \end{cases} \begin{array}{l} \text{has approximately} \\ \text{a chi-square} \\ \text{distribution} \\ \text{with} \end{array}$$

$$\begin{cases} (UVY-1)-(U-1)-(V-1)-(Y-1) \\ (U-1)(Y-1) \\ (V-1)(Y-1) \\ Y(U-1)(V-1) \end{cases} \begin{array}{l} \text{degrees of} \\ \text{freedom} \end{array}$$

where U, V, and Y are the number of elements in the ranges of u, v, and y respectively, and N is the size of the sample.

He shows that if the null hypothesis

$$p(i,j,m) = p(i)p(j)p(m)$$

is true, then $T(u;y)$, $T(v;y)$ and $T_y(u;v)$ are asymptotically independent; thus, as an approximation, the corresponding $\hat{T}$'s can be tested simultaneously for significance under the null hypothesis.

McGill presents an interesting example which shows very graphically that "... we cannot decide whether an amount of transmitted information is big or small without knowing its degrees of freedom." ([1954], p. 114).

APPLICATIONS TO BEHAVIORAL PROBLEMS

6. INTRODUCTION

THE APPLICATIONS of information theory, and its indirect influences in substantive areas, are not easily summarized and evaluated. Besides the unambiguous applications which can be cited, information theory has subtly influenced the thinking of many behavioral scientists. Not only has it affected their analysis of certain kinds of data, but also their choice of experimental problems. Such influences cannot be succinctly described or tabulated.

One is, therefore, practically forced to confine his attention to the published papers where information theory has been explicitly employed. But in most of the behavioral areas these articles have been sporadic, and they hardly present a clear pattern.(*) Thus, I am more or less forced to confine my attention to the two behavioral sciences in which these publications have been especially numerous and the patterns are fairly clear: psychophysics and psychology.(†)

The importance of information theory in psychology was realized in the late forties, only a year or two after Shannon's now classic paper was published. This recognition was both symbolized and accelerated by a paper published in 1949 by Miller and Frick. They observed that "...[a] psychologist's experiments usually generate a sequence of symbols: right and wrong, conditioned and unconditioned, left and right, slow and fast, adient and abient, etc." (p. 314). Moreover, very many experiments are of the stimulus-response type where the stimuli form one sequence and the responses another. Generally, the procedures used to analyze such data ignore the sequential relations among the responses (usually, though not

(*) Biology is to some degree an exception. Much of the application to biological problems has stemmed from the interest of Quastler, who has gathered together a good deal of the work in one volume (1953).

(†) Much of the material we shall discuss here has been summarized by Miller [1954 a, 1956] in somewhat less detail. Hick [1954] has also discussed the impact of information theory in psychology, and other surveys of applications can be found in Patton [1954] and Bricker [1955].

always, sequential effects in the stimuli are experimentally eliminated by randomizing procedures). Ignoring the sequential information, they pointed out, is tantamount to assuming the independence of successive responses. They did not imply that psychologists felt that this was a reasonable assumption, but only that many standard statistical techniques are not really suited to analyze such data. An exception, of course, is the use of contingency tables to study temporally ordered pairs of responses (digrams) and the use of contingency measures to characterize the degree of association between the arguments of the table. Miller and Frick then outlined certain aspects of information theory and proposed that the information measure be employed in such situations. As Klemmer and Frick pointed out in a later paper, "The [information] measure may be applied without logical difficulty to any situation in which one is willing to identify the members of the stimulus and response classes and make some statements about their probability distributions. Whether or not the measure is useful in the analysis of human behavior remains to be proven. Early results from its application are, however, encouraging..." ([1953], p. 15).

There are difficulties, for as Miller and Frick pointed out, at least these two serious *a priori* limitations exist on the applicability of information theory:

1. Sequential responses which are generated while learning is occurring do not form a suitable sample from which to estimate the probabilities that are needed: the assumptions of learning and of a stationary response time series are incompatible.

2. The difficulty of obtaining adequate samples to estimate probabilities increases sharply with an increase in the length of dependencies in the response sequence. In fact, it is completely out of hand beyond three step dependencies.

Related computational difficulties also arise with large amounts of sequential data. Basically, however, this problem is less serious than the sampling one, since computation machines are available that are ideally suited to repetitive calculations. In addition, special equipment, such as that described by Newman [1951 a], can be constructed to carry out information-type analysis. In practice, however, most computations will be done by hand, so tables of $\log_2 p$ and $p \log_2 p$ are useful to have. Several have been published: Newman [1951 a], Dolanský and Dolanský [1952], and Klemmer [1955].

For the five years immediately after the publication of the Miller-Frick paper there was a steady increase in the number of psychological papers employing information theory. In 1955 it seemed to reach a plateau provided we count the separate contributions in Quastler's *Information Theory in Psychology*. (Actually, not all should be counted, since some summarize already published studies, so the trend may have turned down somewhere in 1954 or 1955.) But even if it reached its peak in 1954, it will certainly not vanish completely in the near future; hence, any summary I attempt here is bound to be out-of-date before it can be very widely read. However, there is some pattern to the publications and a summary may serve a function, so long as it is remembered that it only covers a cross-section of an incomplete trend. Excepting the applications of information theory to psychological testing,(*) I believe this summary is fairly complete through 1954. I have not tried exhaustively to survey the contributions in 1955 and the first half of 1956 (when the final revisions were completed); however, since much of the 1955 material appears in Quastler's book, a quick and adequate view of the most recent work is readily available.

Four features of the applications seem worth noting here:

1. Few of the applications are to problems traditionally classed as communication; this was predicted by Miller and Frick.

2. The applications do not generally use the fundamental theorem relating channel capacity, the statistical structure of the source, and the transmission rate. I know of only two limited attempts to characterize directly the channel capacity of a human being — other than by observing the actual rates of transmission that can be experimentally achieved.

3. The theory has not really generated new problems to be studied in psychology. Rather it has caused re-examination and reformulation of old problems. In some cases (see Chapter 10) it has permitted several apparently disparate effects to be included within a single theoretical framework. The fact that old problems are being treated does not, unfortunately, mean that new data are not needed. A published experiment rarely fulfills the exact conditions another worker would like. More important, the isolation of sequential dependencies requires a new analysis of the raw data, and it is very rare indeed to find extensive publications of raw data.

4. Like a new mistress, information theory seemed at first elusive and full of promise. She was justification for both intensity and irresponsibility:

(*) See Cronback [1952, 1953], Glaser and Schwarz [1954], Hick [1951], Lord [1954], and Willis [1954].

a thing of perfection requiring little more than some experimentation to bear fruit. With the passing years, a more "mature" if less exciting relationship has developed. A reading of Licklider's [1954] transcription of a conference on information theory conveys this to some extent, and Cronbach [1955] has systematically presented some sobering views on the use of information theory in psychology. Although I shall try to summarize some of his points, I would suggest that his paper be read by anyone interested in applications to psychology.

Cronbach points out that many psychologists have accepted information theory, particularly the information measures, without adequate scrutiny of its underpinnings and relevance to the particular problem under consideration. Entropy is by no means the only measure one can use to summarize the relationship between two variables. And since it effects a very serious compression of the data, it is well to check that one is throwing away what one intends to and keeping what one wants. This amounts to saying that a logical rationale must be given for its use. Let me cite three general types of examples where the information model may not be as appropriate as some other models. First, some stimulus dimensions possess natural metrics, and if the subjects are thought to react, however crudely, to these metrics, then probably the entropy measure should not be used, since it completely ignores all metric information. Second, the information model for noisy systems is concerned with limiting behavior — with infinitely long messages and delays. Subjects invariably deal with finite messages and introduce comparatively short delays. It does not immediately follow that the model gives bad approximations for such cases, but it does suggest that caution is needed. Third, the model supposes that the destination is aware of and uses a good deal of the available statistical information about the source and the noise. In many actual and experimental situations, subjects have only the crudest knowledge of these probabilities, and even when they do know them, there is no *a priori* certainty that they will use this information. For a detailed discussion of these points, see Hake [1955a]. The model for statistical decision making under uncertainty (used in the statistical, not information theory, sense) may often be more appropriate than the information theory model.

With regard to using information theory for error analysis, Cronbach makes at least two points which are important. Information measures are completely insensitive to constant errors, they are only concerned with variable ones! Thus, if a subject continually interchanges responses to a pair of stimuli, information theory will treat this as error free behavior —

as indeed it is in one sense. Yet, for many purposes it is these constant errors that are of greatest interest. Second, information theory is concerned only with the existence of an error; it does not assign any value to it. When there is a metric involved, one often measures the seriousness of the error in terms of that metric — say, as the square of the distance. But even when no metric is available, different errors can be judged as having differential importance. For such problems, a notion of utility has to be introduced and the techniques of statistical decision theory, rather than information theory, seem appropriate (see Van Meter and Middleton, [1954]).

Before turning to the empirical studies themselves, a few words on how this material might have been organized. The theory introduces methods for dealing with three central concepts, and the applications could have been categorized according to which facet of the theory they employ:

1. Sequential dependencies. This would include all the applications which use information theory to deal with sequential data, as proposed by Miller and Frick. Chapters 7 and 13 are illustrative of this approach.

2. Noise. The applications, such as those of Chapters 10 and 11, which use the formalism of noisy communication to cope with problems where stimulus and response are not perfectly correlated, e. g., where there are errors of some type, would fall into this category.

3. Capacity and transmission. Those studies which employ the central theorems of information theory concerning rates of transmission and capacity would be placed in this category. Examples are Chapter 9, and, to some extent, Chapter 10.

7. THE ENTROPY OF PRINTED AND SPOKEN LANGUAGE (*)

N-**Grams of Printed English**. A problem that has intrigued a number of authors, including Shannon, is the estimation of the entropy of printed English (or any other language, for that matter), i. e., the estimation of the average number of bits per letter in a written passage. Put another way, the problem is to characterize the average sequential dependencies in the written language. If we assume, as may be approximately true, that the English in one book or article is the typical output of a stationary source — the author — then in principle all we need do is calculate $p(j|i_1, i_2, \ldots i_N)$

(*) See Miller [1954 b] for a general discussion of the role of information theory in the study of speech.

or all letters j and for all N-tuples of letters and blanks which might precede
. From this we could then compute

$$F_N = - \sum_i \sum_j{}' p(b_i, j) \log_2 p(j \mid b_i),$$

where b_i denotes a typical block of $N-1$ successive letters preceding j.
Were these F_N known, then we could estimate the entropy of the sample to
any desired accuracy using the fact that

$$H = \lim_{N \to \infty} F_N.$$

The difficulty becomes apparent when we realize that a 27 letter alphabet
yields 27^N possible N-grams. Of course, many of these are impossible in
English, but even were we to assume that, say, only one per cent were
possible, there would still be 1,968 cases to be examined with $N = 3$, and
53,144 for $N = 4$.

Nonetheless, F_N can be computed for very small values of N, and Shannon
[1951] reports that

$$F_1 = 4.14 \text{ bits/letter}$$
$$F_2 = 3.56 \text{ bits/letter}$$
$$F_3 = 3.3 \quad \text{bits/letter.}$$

His calculations are based on the letter, digram, and trigram frequencies
which were prepared for coding work (Pratt [1942]). Not only is it practically impossible to carry this approach much further, but Shannon suggests
that F_3, and all higher F's, may be liable to some error since many of the
N-grams in the sample will bridge across two words. It is clear that other
approximate techniques are necessary.

Three proposals have been made. The first employs, in one way or
another, the built-in knowledge of English statistics in English-speaking
people. The second attempts, by an assumption, to by-pass the sampling
difficulties of the direct procedure discussed above. The last utilizes the
known empirical distributions of English words, though ignoring the statistical dependencies among words, to determine an upper bound on the
entropy. We shall discuss the proposals in this order; however, first let us
examine an analogous N-gram calculation for spoken language.

N-Grams of Spoken Language. As I indicated earlier, there is every
*j*reason to suspect the entropy of spoken language, in bits per sound, is a

more basic statistical description of language than the entropy of the corresponding written language. The former studies have lagged behind the latter — probably because they are more difficult. There are two published papers that I know of: Cherry, Halle, and Jakobson [1953] and Black [1954]. In the former a long sample of Russian prose was analyzed into 42 phonemes and the following entropy estimates were obtained:

$$F_1 = 4.78 \text{ bits/sound},$$
$$F_2 = 4.23 \text{ bits/sound},$$
$$F_3 = 3.05 \text{ bits/sound}.$$

Black estimated F_1 and F_2 for English from a sample of one and two syllable words; however the sample possessed certain peculiarities making it not statistically representative of English in general. Black felt the fact that it contained only root forms, present tenses, etc. was a serious draw back.

Were the 41 phonemes in the sample independent and equiprobable, the information transmitted per sound would be 5.35 bits. From the actual simple and digram frequencies, Black obtained:

$$F_1 = 4.15 - 5.04 \text{ bits/sound},$$
$$F_2 = 3.75 - 4.21 \text{ bits/sound}.$$

The range arises from the fact that he calculated separate estimates for each class of words having the same number of syllables and the same number of sounds per word. He noted the following trend: the sounds of the shorter words transmit more information than those of the longer ones.

For exactly the same reasons as with printed language, it is unlikely that this approach can be extended beyond trigrams, so we turn to the other attacks that have been made on printed English.

Estimates Based on Partial Deletion of Messages. In his original report, Shannon (Shannon and Weaver [1949], pp. 25–26) states that "The redundancy of ordinary English, not considering statistical structure over greater distances than about eight letters, is roughly 50 per cent." (The definition of redundancy was given in Chapter 3). In a later paper [1951] he cites his original estimate as about 2.3 bits/letter. He arrived at this figure using two techniques. First, he developed approximations to English using the published frequencies, digram, and trigram frequencies of letters and the frequencies and digram frequencies of words to generate approximations to English. The redundancies in each case were calculated; in the last two cases some extrapolation was required, since the tables were not complete. Second, he selected some unexceptional passages of English from which he randomly deleted a certain percentage of the letters. His subjects(*) then attempted to reconstruct the original passage from the mangled one, and he found that the letters could be restored with high accuracy when 50 per cent were deleted, from which he concluded that the redundancy must be at least 50 per cent.

Chapanis [1954] carried out roughly the same study, but his was an extensive and careful experiment using 91 subjects and 13 passages of 300 units (letters, space, and punctuation marks) each. Deletions were made, with no indication where they occurred, in both random and regular fashion, with 10, 20, 25, 33.3, 50, and 66.7 percent removed. His results are interesting, especially since they differ somewhat from Shannon's. At best one would conclude from these data that one-quarter of a passage can be deleted with a fair degree of recovery, but with a 50 percent rate of deletion the percentage of items restored is only about 20 percent, and of these only about one tenth are correct. Even when only 10 percent of the passage is deleted, only 80 percent of that supplied by the subjects is correct. Both the passages and the subjects showed considerable variability. Some passages were comparatively easy for most subjects to supply the missing letters and marks, others, particularly those judged easiest to read by conventional criteria, were uniformly more difficult to complete. The performance of the subjects was highly correlated with verbal and mental ability as measured by standard tests.

With respect to the disagreement between these results and those Shannon mentioned, Chapanis writes: "Dr. Shannon and I now agree that S's can probably reconstruct from about 80% to 100% of deleted text under the following special conditions: (a) The amount deleted is 50%; (b) The deletions are made by taking out every other space, letter, or punctuation mark (other kinds of 50%, regular deletion patterns are more difficult to reconstruct); (c) The S is told, or can easily discover, the deletion pattern; (d) The S has a high amount of verbal intelligence.

"The results of the present study are valid under these conditions: (a) The S is provided with no supplementary information about the amount or kind of deletion; (b) The total context of the situation is such that S cannot or does not discover the deletion patterns." ([1954], p. 508).

(*) Mostly he and his wife according to Chapanis [1954, p. 496].

The obvious variant in which the deletions, either random or regular, are indicated by dashes appears not to have been run.

In any case, these results are certainly no more than a lower bound on the redundancy of a language, and probably not a very good one at that. For although the redundancy may be 50% or higher according to other estimates, the removal of 50% of the letters gives the subject a good deal of freedom to reconstruct the message. Once he is on the wrong track, say in the first two or three missing letters, then everything else is almost bound to be in error up to the point where a continuous sequence of three or four letters is not deleted.

Shannon's Upper and Lower Bounds. In his 1951 paper, Shannon carries his estimation procedures further by developing both upper and lower bounds for the entropy, and these data indicate that the redundancy may be nearer 75 per cent than 50 per cent. He selected 100 samples of English text, each consisting of 15 letters. A subject was required to guess at the first letter of a passage until he obtained it correctly. Knowing it, he guessed at the second until it was obtained. In general, knowing $N-1$ letters he guessed at the Nth until he was correct. The data may be presented as a table having 15 columns and 27 rows (26 letters and a blank). The entry in column N and row S is the number of times subjects guessed the correct letter on the Sth guess given that they knew the $N-1$ preceding letters. A small portion of the table is reproduced:

		N					
		1	2	5	10	15	100
S	1	18.2	29.2	51	67	60	80
	2	10.7	14.8	13	10	18	7
	3	8.6	10.0	8	4	5	–

The column marked 100 was obtained by presenting the subject with 99 letters from a 100 letter passage. The data for columns 1 and 2 were prepared from published word and digram frequencies which are based on far larger samples.

To use these data, Shannon introduced the notion of an ideal predictor who, knowing $p(b_i, j)$, i. e., the probability of all N-grams, would select letters j in order of decreasing probability for the given b_i. Thus each letter of a message can be replaced by a number between 1 and 27 which tells how many guesses will be needed before the correct letter is obtained. For an ideal predictor this sequence of numbers will contain the same information as the message, since one can be constructed from the other, but it has the added feature that there will be limited statistical dependencies among the numbers, since the difficulty of one will not generally determine that of the next. Hence, computing the entropy of the number sequence is not difficult, and it can be used to estimate the entropy of the language.

The frequency of the number k in the reduced text will, of course, be given by

$$q\,{}^{N}_{k} = \sum{}' p\,(b_i, j)$$

where the sum is taken over all $(N-1)$-grams b_i and over those j's such that it results in the kth largest probability for the given b_i.

Shannon then shows that the Nth order entropy, F_N, is bounded by

$$\sum_{k=1}^{27} k\,(q\,{}^{N}_{k} - q\,{}^{N}_{k+1})\,\log_2 k \leq F_N \leq \sum_{k=1}^{27} q\,{}^{N}_{k}\,\log_2 q\,{}^{N}_{k}\,.$$

Using the data described above, and smoothing them, Shannon calculated upper and lower bounds for $N = 1, 2, \ldots, 15, 100$.
Some of the values are:

Upper and Lower Bounds on F_N

N	1	2	5	10	15	100
upper bound	4.03	3.42	2.7	2.1	2.1	1.3
lower bound	3.19	2.50	1.7	1.0	1.2	0.6

When both sets of points are plotted for $N = 1, 2, \ldots 15$, there still remains some sampling error, but smooth curves can be faired through the points reasonably well.

It should be noted that there is a considerable drop in both bounds between $N = 15$ (at which point the curves are nearly flat) and $N = 100$. Whether or not this is meaningful is difficult to say, but, as we shall see, none of the other estimates suggests that the entropy is as low as 1.3 bits/letter; however, it must be kept in mind that all of these will be upper bounds, and how much too large they are is not known.

The Coefficient of Constraint. Newman and Gerstman [1952] approached the problem in another way which does not depend upon "built-in" knowledge of English statistics, but which does employ an as yet unproved assumption. They define

$$H(1) = -\sum_i p(i)\log_2 p(i)$$

and

$$H(1,N) = -\sum_i \sum_j p(i,j)\log_2 p(i,j),$$

where i and j are letters in a passage which are separated by $N-1$ others. That is, $H(1,N)$ measures the average statistical dependence of a choice j upon the choice i which was made N letters earlier. As N becomes large it is clear that this dependence decreases. A measure of its magnitude is

$$H_1(N) = H(1,N) - H(1).$$

They then define the quantity

$$D(N) = 1 - \frac{H_1(N)}{H(1)},$$

which is called the *coefficient of constraint*. It is a quantity that is 1 when the Nth selection is uniquely determined by the first, and 0 when the Nth is independent of the first. Since only pairs of letters are involved in these quantities, it is comparatively easy to determine them for a given sample of language.

Using a 10,000 word sample from the Bible, they obtained the following data:

	2	3	4	5	6	10
$D(N)$	.223	.103	.064	.039	.027	.012

and a letter frequency entropy of 4.08, which is only slightly different from the 4.14 obtained by Shannon. A plot of these data on log-log paper is approximately linear with a slope of -2.0, or, in other words, $D(N) = 1/N^2$, approximately.

The problem now is whether F_N can be estimated from data for $D(N)$. The answer is "yes," provided it is true that

$$F_N \le [1 - D(N)]F_{N-1}.$$

This relation is certainly true when $N = 2$. Indeed, the equality holds then. It is also true for any N such that the symbols are independent, for then $D(N) = 0$ and $F_N = F_{N-1}$. They point out, however, that no proof of the assumption has been found, and they add without further elaboration the cryptic comment "...and there are limiting cases in which it is proved not to apply." ([1952], p. 120). In any case, if it is assumed, one has

$$F_N \leq F_1 \prod_{i=2}^{N} [1 - D(i)]$$

$$= H(1) \prod_{i=2}^{N} (i-1) \prod_{i=2}^{N} (i+1) \prod_{i=2}^{N} \frac{1}{i^2}$$

$$= H(1) \frac{(N+1)}{2N} ,$$

where the empirically grounded assumption that $D(i) = 1/i^2$ has been used. In the limit $H = \lim_{N \to \infty} F_N = H(1)/2$, which gives an upper bound, if the two assumptions are correct, of 2.04 bits/letter. In addition, for $N = 1, 2, \ldots, 15$ they computed $H(1)(N+1)/2N$ and compared these points with those obtained by Shannon as an upper bound. This curve seems to fit the points as well as Shannon's faired curve.

Distribution of Words to Estimate Letter Entropy. The third, and last, major approach to setting bounds on the letter entropy rests on a computation of word entropies which is based on known frequencies of word use in the language. This entropy, when divided by the average word length, affords an estimate of the letter entropy which is only an upper bound, since the technique, based as it is only on word frequencies, completely ignores the redundancy due to inter-word influences.

Long before information theory, people had determined the frequency of usage of various words, and it was Zipf [1949] who emphasized(*) that if we rank words $1, 2, \ldots r, \ldots$ in order of decreasing frequency, then the frequency of use of a word is simply proportional to the inverse of its rank. That is, the probability p_r that a randomly selected word is of rank r is given, approximately, by

$$p_r = k/r,$$

where k is a proportionality factor *independent* of r. There is a certain ambiguity as to just how many ranks there are and certainly if we consider all

(*) This empirical observation was most systematically explored by Zipf, but it had been noted in certain cases by earlier authors [see Zipf, 1949].

possible English words the approximate law fails for very high ranks. The value of k is chosen so that the empirical relationship, known as Zipf's "law," holds for the lower ranks, and the size N of the vocabulary is given by the condition

$$\sum_{r=1}^{N} p_r = k \sum_{r=1}^{N} \frac{1}{r} = 1.$$

Newman and Gerstman [1952], Miller [1951 b], and Shannon [1951] have all carried out this computation, but as Newman and Gerstman have pointed out, there are certain discrepancies in the results. Shannon obtained $N = 8,727$, while Miller, presumably using a definite integral to approximate the series, got 22,000, and Newman and Gerstman obtained 12,370 by taking into account the discontinuity of the first 100 ranks and approximating the rest of the series by an integral.

Using this distribution, it is then possible to calculate the entropy of the independent word selections according to the distribution, i. e.,

$$H = -\sum_{r=1}^{N} \frac{k}{r} \log_2 \frac{k}{r}.$$

Shannon obtained 11.82, Miller 10.6, and Newman and Gerstman 9.7 bits/ word. These give estimates of 2.62, 2.36, and 2.16 bits/letter if we take 4.5 letters to be the average word length. There appears to be a further disagreement, as was pointed out by Newman and Gerstman ([1952], p. 124). Considering the different values of N obtained, the Shannon and the Newman and Gerstman results should both be either larger or smaller than the Miller result; they are not.

Another approach to the problem from the point of view of words is due to Bell [1953]. He supposes that the space between words is sent infallibly and then he observes that the length of a word carries some information. "As the simplest example, consider the fact that there are only two words of one letter in normal use: the personal pronoun 'I' and the indefinite article 'a'. Hence only two out of the 26 single-letter 'words' which are mathematically available from the alphabet are admitted to the English language, and it follows that when a word of one letter is received in English the choice is only 1 out of 2 instead of 1 out of 26. An alternative expression of this is that the 'internal information' implicit in the fact that the 1-letter word is in the English language equivalent to a selection of 1 out of 13 alternatives; and the communication of a selection of 1 out of 13 would be regarded as a communication of 3.7 'bits' of information ($\log_2 13 = 3.7$), so that the average internal information of 1-letter words in the English language may be stated as 3.7 bits per letter." ([1953], p. 384). For longer words such a detailed analysis is impossible, so Bell formed statistical samples from the dictionary. From this he calculated the internal information in bits/letter and obtained:

Number of Letters	1	2	3	4	5	6	7	8
Internal Information.........	3.7	2.2	1.53	1.93	2.36	2.66	2.98	3.21

This curve was smoothly extrapolated for words longer than 8 letters. Using Dewey's word list [1923] to obtain relative frequencies of words of various lengths he calculated the weighted average of the internal information and obtained 2.1 bits/letter.

The Role of Redundancy. Whatever the correct value of the letter entropy is, it is clear that it is not much over 2 bits/letter and not much less than 1. So the redundancy is somewhere between 50 and 75 per cent. In other words, under ideal conditions we could transmit the same information either by using a considerably smaller alphabet and keeping the length of books and articles the same, or by keeping the same number of symbols in the alphabet and reducing sentences and books to from one quarter to one half their present length. That our language is not fully efficient in this statistical sense presumably results from our need to communicate rapidly and accurately under adverse conditions, i. e., where there is noise: in the presence of other voices, in the wind, at sea, etc. It is clear from the little example given in Chapter 4 that even a small amount of noise can result in a serious drop in the information transmitted — in that case a one per cent chance of error resulted in a ten per cent drop in the entropy transmitted. It thus appears reasonable that if a language is designed to cope with even a slight amount of noise, then it must be quite redundant. Of course, when the noise level is so high that the natural redundancy of the language cannot combat it, other methods are used: Words and even whole sentences are repeated. And in such places as noisy factories the vocabulary between two people may be reduced to a few words — e. g., to "stop" and "go."

An example of a purposeful increase in redundancy is found in the very formal language used for air traffic control at an airport. Frick and Sumby [1952] have presented a summary of their findings for this language, but without much of the data. They used the technique, introduced by Shannon [1951], of having subjects predict the next letter of a message. Using trained personnel as subjects they found that the uncertainty of control tower language is about 28 per cent that of random sequences of letters and spaces. And this, they point out, is a serious overestimation, since in practice the operator almost always knows the pilot's situation and therefore certain messages are excluded. To estimate these situational constraints, they described hypothetical situations to 100 Air Force pilots and asked them to predict the control tower message. Forming equivalence classes of "meaning units" and taking into account the imposed grammar of the language, they found that the uncertainty was no more than 20 per cent of what it would have been had the units been equally likely and randomly selected. The overall effect, they estimate, is a redundancy of about 96 per cent. This is not an implausible result when one considers the high noise level in both the tower and the plane, and the especially low margin of allowable error.

A similar study of tower-pilot communications at the Langley Air Force base has been presented by Felton, Fritz, and Grier [1951]. (Also see Fritz and Grier [1955].) As in the Frick and Sumby work, they divided messages into information elements, "...a word or a group of words representing a type of information, such as runway assignment, elapsed time, etc." ([1951], p. 5). They divided the analysis of redundancy into three levels. First, they simply took into account the frequencies of the various information elements. Second, they determined the predictability within a message. Third, they determined the predictability between messages from the observed conditional probabilities between messages. At the second level, they determined the probability of each message and determined the entropy of whole messages. This divided by the average number of elements per message was taken to be the entropy of each element. A justification of this procedure was given. The data were separated into messages originated in the air and at the tower, and the estimated redundancy using each of the three levels was:

Level	Redundancy		
	1	2	3
Air	.35	.72	.81
Tower	.26	.75	.78

The authors estimate that if contextual constraints are taken into account, as they were in the Frick and Sumby paper, then the redundancy would be about 93 per cent, which compares closely with the 96 per cent mentioned above.

8. DISTRIBUTION OF WORDS IN A LANGUAGE

IN THE LAST chapter, I referred to the empirically grounded observation (Zipf's "law") that if the words of a natural language are ranked from the most to the least common, then the frequency of the rth word is approximately inversely proportional to r. Zipf found that more linguistic data could be fit by the more general equation

$$p_r = P\,r^{-B}\,,$$

where p_r is the frequency of the rth word and P and B are constants, B being in the neighborhood of 1 for all languages and larger than 1 for most. "Although this relation appears with regularity in linguistic data, no one has claimed more than a vague appreciation of its cause or significance. No one, that is, until Mandelbrot." (Miller [1954], p. 413) Mandelbrot's theory and its applications are presented in a series of five publications [1953 a, 1953 b, 1954 a, 1954 b, 1954 c], and Miller [1954 a] has given a very helpful summary of some of it.

Mandelbrot introduces two basic assumptions which distinguish his theory sharply from Shannon's. First, he supposes that a language — like all known ones — is built of discrete units called words, i. e., the communication is broken into units which are separated by a space. Second, he assumes that the transmitter in the communication system encodes and the receiver decodes word by word. Even though one could accept these as plausible assumptions that are valid for known languages, he defends each by a logical argument based upon the assumption that language must be designed to combat noise. In one paper [1954 a] he shows that the discrete character is needed, and in another [1954 c] he shows how the space and the word by word encoding limit the effects of noise to the word within which the error arises. The redundancy within the word is used to combat this noise.

"Although it may seem trivial, the introduction of the space between words is the crux of Mandelbrot's contribution and the main feature that leads him to results different from Shannon's. In Shannon's problem, the entire message is remembered and then coded in the most efficient form for transmission. In Mandelbrot's problem, the message is remembered only one word at a time, so that every time the space occurs the transmitter makes the most efficient coding he can of that word and then begins anew on the next word. Obviously, a transmitter of the kind Shannon studied will be more efficient, but one of the kind that Mandelbrot is studying will be more practical." (Miller [1954 a], p. 414).

Let us assume that the words are ordered by decreasing frequency of occurrence; denote them by W_1, W_2,..., W_R. Let the corresponding frequencies of occurrence be p_1, p_2,..., p_R. Suppose that to each word there is a cost C_r for using it — we do not specify what we mean by cost except that it can be summarized by a real number. It might be the number of bits required to transmit it, or the delay, etc. The first problem Mandelbrot attacked — he calls it the "direct problem" — is to find what the costs C_r should be so as to result in the least costly transmission of messages assuming word-by-word coding and the known frequencies p_r. This condition yields, as a first approximation,

$$C_r = [\log_M r],$$

where $[x]$ denotes the smallest integer greater than or equal to x. A better approximation is

$$C_r = [\log_M (r+m) + \log_M d],$$

where M, m, and d are constants independent of r. Observe that the cost depends upon the ranking, but not upon the details of the probability distribution.

Next, we turn to what Mandelbrot has called the "inverse problem." For this problem he assumed the words are given and their costs are fixed, and the task is to determine the frequency distribution p_r such that some economy criterion is met. He has given several criteria which all lead to essentially the same result.

1. Let us suppose that the average cost per word,

$$C = \sum_{r=1}^{R} p_r C_r$$

is fixed in advance, and we look for the best frequency distribution to transport information in Shannon's sense. That is, we maximize $H = -\Sigma p_r \log p_r$ subject to the above constraint. (This problem is formally identical to Boltzman's problem in statistical mechanics: to find the maximum entropy for a given average energy.) The following conditions are necessary and sufficient to solve the problem:

$$p_r = P' M^{-BC_r}$$

$$B > 0$$

$$\sum{}' p_r = 1$$

$$\sum{}' p_r C_r = C.$$

The third condition determines P' and the fourth B, provided that $C < \log R$. Note that the cost C_0 of the space does not enter here.

  2. A second condition, which is a trivial modification of the first, is to hold H fixed and choose the distribution so as to minimize the average cost C. The only resulting difference is that B is determined by the value of H, provided $H < \log R$. Again the value of C_0 is irrelevant.

  3. A more interesting variant occurs when you allow R and C to be free and minimize the average cost per unit of information: i. e., minimize

$$\frac{\sum p_r C_r + C_0}{-\sum p_r \log p_r}$$

subject to the constraint $\Sigma p_r = 1$. As before, Mandelbrot has shown that

$$p_r = P' \, M^{-BC_r} \, ,$$

but now B is determined by the value of C_0, and so both the value of C and of H are fixed by the choice of C_0.

  Finally, we turn to what Mandelbrot has called the "secrecy problem." He supposes that words are composed of letters $L_1, L_2, \ldots, L_G$, where G is much smaller than R. Let the letters be labeled in order of decreasing frequency, denote the frequency distribution by q_i, and write the cost of the ith letter as c_i. The cost of a word is assumed to be given by the sum of the costs of its component letters.

  "The best possible of all weighed vocabularies from the point of view of the secrecy encoder is the one in which the most economical code is also unbreakable. The code must then be a random sequence of elements, space included, and the enemy must either go to word relationships, that is go beyond our approximation, or try all keys, the number of which is astronomical." ([1954 b], p. 131.) His requirement is that an unbreakable random sequence of letters transport information for the smallest possible cost per unit of information. This is similar to condition 3 of the inverse problem, differing however in that there is no element corresponding to the word space. Formally, the condition is that

$$\frac{\sum q_i c_i}{-\sum q_i \log q_i}$$

should be a minimum subject to the condition that $\Sigma q_i = 1$. From this requirement it can be shown that the word distribution must be

$$p_r = P' M^{-BC_r}$$

as before, but with the added conditions that $B > 1$ and $R = \infty$. The latter condition follows from the requirement of a random sequence of letters to sustain secrecy. I shall discuss the condition $B > 1$ a little later.

Let me summarize: To attain the least costly transmission when words are ranked in order of decreasing frequency, then

$$C_r = [\log_M (r + m) + \log_M d].$$

To attain 1) the maximum information transport with the average cost per word fixed, or 2) the minimum average cost per word with the information transported held fixed, or 3) the minimum average cost per unit of information, then the distribution of the words should be

$$p_r = P' M^{-BC_r}.$$

If we combine these two conditions, taking into account the fact that statistical fluctuations in data will smooth over the steps of the former equation, we obtain

$$p_r = P(r + m)^{-B},$$

which Mandelbrot has called the "canonical curve." Observe that if $m = 0$, this is the generalized Zipf law.

As Mandelbrot points out, the fit of Zipf's law with $B = 1$ to most language data is good only in the central range and is in error for the most frequent and the least frequent words. By choosing values of B and m different from 1 and 0 he has been able to achieve far better fits.

The condition $B > 1$ which results from the secrecy criterion has been found to be met by most natural languages. Zipf called those with $B > 1$ "open vocabularies" and those with $B < 1$ "closed vocabularies." Most languages with closed vocabularies are in some way peculiar or special.

Clearly, Mandelbrot's theory, like Shannon's, is normative, but it is much more closely related to a specific empirical field than is Shannon's. Thus the question must be raised as to exactly what Mandelbrot has shown and what it means for linguistics. "He says that if one wants to communicate efficiently word-by-word, then one must obey Zipf's law. There is a strong temptation to reverse the implication and to argue that because we obey Zipf's law we must therefore be communicating word-by-word with maximal efficiency." (Miller [1954 a], p. 415). Of course, Miller goes on to point out that much other evidence exists — such as the redundancy data discussed in the last section — to suggest that this reversed implication is false. It remains to be shown whether marked deviations in certain directions from perfect efficiency result in only slight deviations from the canonical curve.

It should be pointed out in connection with Mandelbrot's work that a totally different statistical explanation for Zipf's law has been offered by Simon [1955]. His model is not at all concerned with the transmission of information, but is rather of a more traditional statistical type. It has the advantage of suggesting the statistical process whereby the many phenomena other than word distributions are caused to satisfy Zipf's law. For example, Zipf noted that the distribution of cities by population and of incomes by size also satisfy roughly the same relationship. But many doubt that Simon's process accounts for word distributions. Nonetheless, using words in a book as the prototype, let $f(r,k)$ denote the number of different words each of which has occurred exactly r times in the first k words of the book. Simon then makes the following two assumptions concerning the selection of the $(k+1)^{st}$ word.

1. The probability that the $(k+1)^{st}$ word is one which has already appeared exactly r times is proportional to the total number of occurrences of all the words which have appeared exactly r times, i. e., it is proportional to $rf(r,k)$.

2. The probability that the $(k+1)^{st}$ word is a new word, i. e., one which has not already occurred in the first k words, is a constant a.

"If this process correctly describes the selection of words, then the words in a book cannot be regarded as a random sample drawn from a population with a prior distribution." (Simon [1955], p. 427).

From these assumptions, he shows that for a large sample, the probability p_r of words of rank r is given by $AB(r,\rho+1)$, where A and ρ are constants, and $B(r,\rho+1)$ is the Beta function of r and $\rho+1$, i. e.,

$$B(r,\rho+1) = \int_0^1 \lambda^{r-1}(1-\lambda)^\rho \, d\lambda = \frac{\Gamma(r)\Gamma(\rho+1)}{\Gamma(r+\rho+1)},$$

where Γ is the Gamma function. This, he shows, is very similar to Zipf's empirical law and it gives good fits for much of the data.

He explores modifications of this model which lead to essentially the same results and which appear to be more reasonable assumptions for the generation of word frequencies, but to examine this in detail would take us too far afield.

In closing this section, let me quote from Simon (p. 435) concerning the two alternative explanations of word frequencies:

"A very different and very ingenious explanation of the observed word-frequency data has been advanced recently by Dr. Benoit Mandelbrot [1953]. His derivation rests on the assumption that the frequencies are determined so as to maximize the number of bits of information, in the sense of Shannon, transmitted per symbol. There are several reasons why I prefer an explanation that employs averaging rather than maximizing assumptions. First, an assumption that word usage satisfies some criterion of efficiency appears to be much stronger than the probability assumptions required here. Secondly, numerous doubts, which I share, have been expressed as to the relevance of Shannon's information measure for the measurement of semantic information."

9. THE CAPACITY OF THE HUMAN
BEING AND RATES OF INFORMATION TRANSFER

IN RECENT YEARS it has proved necessary to construct a variety of complex information systems in order to deal with certain military and industrial problems. These systems typically receive a tremendous amount of raw information from diverse sources that must be filtered, recoded, and correlated into what may be called a model of some situation of interest. The model must be sufficiently simple so that a person can grasp it completely, and sufficiently accurate so that it can lead him to useful decisions. For example, an air defense system receives raw information from radars, spotters, airline schedules, weather reports, fighter readiness reports, etc. All of this must be reduced to a simplified model of the enemy attack, the defense facilities, and the defensive response, so that a commanding officer can continuously know the situation with only a few seconds' delay. The officer must make and modify his defensive decisions on the basis of such a model. It is clear that much of this processing — especially where speed and accuracy are needed — can and should be reduced to machine operations, but, with our present technology, there are certain steps which are far more simply and effectively carried out by a person than by a machine. For example, one of the first steps in an air defense system, and one which is not easily duplicated by a machine, is the isolation and transfer of pertinent information from a radar scope face. From all the random noise and background reflections on the scope an operator must single out those "blips" which represent aircraft. This he must introduce into the rest of the system, say, as a coded telephone message. The question arises as to how much information he can process per second over a sustained period.

It is clear that for any specific problem of this type, an answer can be obtained by direct experiments on the trained personnel using the equipment. On the other hand, one wonders whether it is necessary to study each new situation separately, or whether the pertinent variable is the amount of information in bits/sec which will be presented to the operator as compared with the maximum amount he can handle.

That is, can we treat a human being as a channel and so determine a channel capacity for him? If this were possible, it would certainly simplify the design problem, for it is generally not too difficult to determine the rate of the information flow in the machine components of a system. The question of whether it is useful to treat men as channels in certain situations remains at best an open problem, and there are some, equipped with strong arguments, who believe that it is an illusory hope. The most direct printed attack has been offered by Hake [1955 b]. The gist of his argument is that the information measure is impartial to many aspects of the stimulus set, e. g., to metric relations among the elements, to whether culturally assigned names exist for the individual stimuli, etc., and yet all sorts of experimental evidence suggest that subjects respond to these characteristics of stimuli. "It appears evident to me that a measure of information transmitted is meaningless unless accompanied with an operational definition of the experimental context. The possibility exists that we may discover invariant limits to information measures of performance within a single type of operation which I have described and across several stimulus-response systems. It appears unreasonable to describe such limits as the 'channel capacity,' however, when with a little thought and analysis the limit can be ascribed to some reasonable and known physiological limitation." ([1955 b], p. 253).

This debate, however, is not really my question here; I shall only recount some of the studies which have been executed to determine the human channel capacity under the dubious assumption that a person can in fact be usefully considered as a channel.

Considering the theory presented in Section I, two procedures to estimate the capacity seem possible. First, estimate the channel capacity from whatever physical, physiological, and psychological facts that are known to be relevant to the type of transmission being employed. Second, by varying certain variables and employing diverse coding schemes, find the maximum amount of information that a person can be caused to handle. This, by the fundamental theorem of information theory, affords a lower bound on the capacity. Roughly speaking, the first procedure has resulted in upper bounds of the order of 10,000 bits/sec, while the second yields a lower bound somewhere in the range of 10 to 100 bits/sec. The consensus is that the lower bound more nearly represents the human capacity, but no really strong argument exists to support this view except that no one has yet devised a way to achieve a higher rate. Presumably, however, they are the more nearly correct and the upper bounds are so large because they ignore so many limitations of the "channel." We shall now examine these estimates in a little more detail.

Upper Bounds. Possibly part of the difficulty in obtaining a satisfactory estimate by the first procedure is the present lack of an adequate model for what happens functionally within a person when he is processing information. Thus, independent measurements on most of the "channel" — which is surely not homogeneous in its properties — cannot be had. As a result, the estimates which have been made are in a sense only concerned with the peripheral aspects of the channel. I will shortly cite another reason which has been offered to explain the difference between the upper and lower bounds.

Licklider and Miller [1951] have pointed out that an estimate of the capacity with respect to auditory signals can be obtained from a result of the theory of information for continuous systems (see the appendix). It is known that if the bandwidth of the channel is W cycles/sec, and if the noise and the signal are simply additive with a power ratio of P/N, then the capacity in bits/sec is given by

$$C = W \log_2 \left(1 + \frac{P}{N} \right).$$

For auditory signals, a bandwidth of 5,000 cycles/sec is conservative and a signal-to-noise ratio of 30 db, or a power ratio of about 1,000, is not unusual, in which case the capacity must be about 50,000 bits/sec. In actual attempts to transmit selective information by auditory means, a rate as high as 50 bits/sec is unusual. In other words, the efficiency of the auditory system must be considered to be about 0.1 per cent. Licklider and Miller, and Peterson [1952], offer the explanation that most of the information transmitted by an auditory signal is personal (and highly redundant) information about the originator — who he is, his way of speaking, his mood, and some of his linguistic history. While this may well be the case, it is interesting that no one has yet devised a way to use this apparently available capacity for the transmission of *preassigned* selective information.

A far more detailed, but rather questionable, estimate of auditory capacity has been made by Jacobson [1950, 1951 a] using various data about hearing, such as the total number of monaurally distinguishable tones. He concludes from his analysis, which ignores all sorts of possible interactions, that one ear should be able to handle about 8,000 bits/sec, and admitting very loud sounds, 10,000 bits/sec. It is known that there are approximately 29,000 ganglion cells from the ear, hence the average rate of information transfer over a nerve fiber is about 0.3 bits/sec. However, he points out that "It is very unlikely that there is any binary or similar coding in the cochlear nerves. It is consequently not particularly meaningful to state that the average informational capacity of a single cochlear fiber is about 0.3 bits/sec." ([1951 a], pp. 470–471).

Jacobson [1951 b] has also carried out a similar calculation for the eye, taking into account facts known about discriminability, etc., but ignoring the effects of color and of the interactions among the several dimensions he has considered. He obtained an estimate of 4.3×10^6 bits/sec for each eye. From this one can conclude the maximum average rate over each neural fiber must be 5 bits/sec. The inclusion of color would, of course, raise this estimate.

So far as I have determined, these are the only estimates of channel capacity which are based on measurements independent of the actual rate of information flow. We turn now to estimates of how rapidly information of a particular type can be, or rather, has been, caused to pass through a person.

Lower Bounds: Maximum Observed Rates of Information Transfer.
Let us first consider the transmission of language encoded information.

Miller [1951 b] points out that if we consider the average measured length of vowels and consonants — about 12.5 sounds/sec — and if we were to suppose that they are equi-probable and independently selected, then speech would convey information at a rate of 67 bits/sec. If, however, we take into account their relative frequencies (Dewey, [1923]), then the rate is reduced to about 60 bits/sec. Further, if we take into account the fact that vowels and consonants tend to alternate in English (for more exact information on this for English and other languages, see Newmann, [1951]), the estimate is only 46 bits/sec. Finally, on the basis of Zipf's law, Miller estimated that there are 10.6 bits/word (Chapter 7). Since a speaker can sustain a maximum of about 3 words/sec, the transmission rate using speech can be no more than 32 bits/sec. "The maximum efficiency within the restriction imposed by the phonetic structure of English words, therefore, is about 50 per cent." (Miller [1951 b], p. 798). In practice, however, an ordinary speaking vocabulary is not nearly as large as that assumed when Zipf's law is employed, nor can a person usefully employ a speaking rate of 3 words/sec. An assumption of an equi-probable distribution over a vocabulary of 5,000 words which are spoken at a rate of 1.5 words/sec yields an information rate of 18 bits/sec.

In addition, as Quastler and Wulff [1955] point out, the various rate estimates using Zipf's law ignore constraints among words. They cite evidence which suggests that guessing a missing word within context may be correct as much as 30 per cent of the time. This reduces the information transmission rate to about 7 or 8 bits/word, and if we assume that 15 per cent of the words are incorrectly received, the estimate must be reduced to 6 or 7 bits/word. Using Miller's speaking rate of 1.5 words/sec, it appears that from 10 to 20 bits/sec is a good average rate of transmission, and that with rapid speech the rate may get as high as 25 bits/sec.

Quastler and Wulff report data on several other methods of information transfer, and in summary they find that 25 bits/sec seems to be the maximum rate. In all cases, a motor response was required of the subject, but they verified that mechanical limitations were not determining an apparent rate by showing that higher rates could be achieved if memorized materials were used. One experiment they discussed was based on typing, but it was known *a priori* that this would not lead to the fastest possible rates, since text can be read aloud faster than a typist can take it down. For this experiment, random sequences of letters were drawn from alphabets of 4, 8, 16, and 32 symbols. Seven experienced typists were paced by a metronome at 2, 3, 4, and 6 beats/sec. In general, the errors that occurred were the transposition of letters, and so it is a question as to whether these should be treated as one or two errors. Depending upon our decision, the following upper and lower bounds on information transmitted (Chapter 5) are obtained.

Information Transmitted in bits/sec

Alphabet size	4	8	16	32
Upper Bound	6.7	10.5	13.2	16.7
Lower Bound	3.8	7.4	11.8	13.4

It was found, as would be expected, that with the higher metronome speeds and with the larger alphabets, the greater percentage of errors occurred. For 8 and 16 symbol alphabets a speed of 3.2 ± 0.2 keys/sec represented the highest effective speed, and beyond that their precision so decreased as to keep the transmission rate about constant, and beyond 4.5 keys/sec the quality of their output decreased very rapidly. With 4 symbols the effective speed was 3.6 keys/sec, and with 32 it was 2.9 keys/sec. When the subjects were not driven by a metronome, but were instructed to type as rapidly as possible, it was found that the rate of transmission was down about 9 per cent.

A second experiment drew upon the sight-reading ability of three young pianists. They were presented with random music (notes selected using random numbers) and they were paced by a metronome which was gradually increased in tempo over trials. Tape recordings were made and each of the subjects scored each of the tapes for errors. The agreement was fair, but both a low count (errors detected by each subject) and a high count (those detected by at least one) were determined. The information transmitted was computed from the error count and from assumptions about the error pattern. Again, several different "alphabets" were employed: 3, 4, 5, 9, 15, 25, 37 and 65 keys.

The data show that the highest speed for which the error rate remained low decreases from 7 keys/sec for an alphabet of 3 or 4 keys to 4.4 keys/sec for the 37 key alphabet. This decreased speed, coupled with an increase in error rate, keeps the information transmission rate at about 22 bits/sec over a fairly wide range of speed and alphabet size. However, for very small alphabets and for very large ones, the rate of transmission is less than for alphabets of 15, 25, and 37 keys. The interpretation given is that channel capacity is the controlling factor for the middle sized alphabets, that the sheer range limits performance in the largest ones, and motor limitations determine the performance when the alphabets are very small.

Individual differences became apparent when the subjects attempted to exceed their limits. One subject kept the error rate low by failing to keep up with the metronome, another kept the pace but allowed the error rate to become large, and the third held the pace for periods and then he would lose the beat. But in all cases, the information transmitted was held roughly constant.

Quastler and Wulff have studied a third set of materials for determining capacity: mental arithmetic problems. They point out that if certain plausible assumptions are made about the information involved in calculations, and if the published time data on so-called "lightning calculators" (people who are noted for rapid mental calculations) are used, one obtains an estimate of 22 to 24 bits/sec for the transmission rate. The feat of such people appears, therefore, not to be a high rate of information transmission, but rather a tremendous storage of information for short periods of time. In addition, Quastler and Wulff conducted some simple experiments on mental addition of columns of figures. On the average they found — again by making some plausible, but debatable, assumptions — a rate of 6 to 12 bits/sec, but one exceptional subject sustained a rate of 23 bits/sec.

From these data, and others not published, it appears that it is difficult to cause a subject, employing familiar operations, to exceed — let me be generous — 50 bits/sec, even though present estimates of ear and eye capacity exceed this several hundred times. It seems an open problem to bring these two estimates closer together, either by devising a method to employ much more of the apparent capacity to transmit selective information, or by a more detailed analysis of the human being as a channel to show that 50 or 100 bits/sec is truly his limit. Jacobson's comments on this disparity are of interest. "Thus it is evident that the brain can digest generally less than 1 per cent of the information our ears will pass. It must be appreciated that the ear is a channel vastly wider than its apprehensible output. It is the ability of the brain to *scan* for those portions of the auditory signal which are of interest which makes the wide capacity of the ear maximally useful." ([1951 a], p. 471).

It will be recalled that in the Quastler and Wulff piano experiment, the subjects appeared to be limited by motor factors rather than by "mental channel capacity" when the range of keys was small. Even so, one can raise this question: is there some sort of exchange between speed and error even in this range which keeps the information transmission nearly constant? If this were so, it would allow us to summarize a good deal of traditional data on motor performance in a comparatively simple way, as was pointed out by Fitts [1954 a]. He ran three experiments on motor performance which gave similar results; we shall describe one of them (a summary can also be found in Fitts [1954 b]).

The subject sits before a panel on which there are two plates (cross hatched in Fig. 5) and for short periods he is alternately to tap these with a stylus. He was instructed to try for accuracy, but within that limitation he was to perform as rapidly as possible. The stylus closed an electric

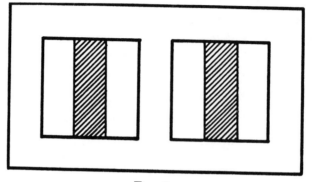

Fig. 5.

circuit when the cross hatched plate was touched, and another one which recorded errors when the outside region was touched. The variables controlled by the experimenter were the distance between the plates (i. e., the amplitude of the movement) and the size of the plate (i. e., the accuracy tolerance). The subject controlled the speed and accuracy of performance. Fitts' hypothesis was this: "If the amplitude and tolerance limits of a task are controlled by E, and S is instructed to work at his maximum rate, then the average time per response will be directly proportional to the minimum average amount of information per response demanded by the particular conditions of amplitude and tolerance." ([1954 a], p. 383).

On the basis of the continuous theory of information (see the appendix) he defined an index of difficulty

$$-\log_2 \frac{W}{2A} \text{ bits/response,}$$

where W is the tolerance and A the amplitude measured in the same units. His hypothesis was that this quantity is linearly related to the average time per response, i. e.,

$$\frac{1}{t} \log_2 \frac{W}{2A} \text{ bits/sec,}$$

where t the average time in seconds per movement, is a constant. The data roughly confirm this hypothesis, e. g., the range is 10.3 to 11.5 bits/sec. for one weight stylus. However, at the extremes of amplitude and tolerance he studied, there seemed to be some indication that the information transmitted was falling off. Two other experiments of a similar nature gave similar results.

Other Observed Rates of Information Transfer. Not all the experiments, or the observation taken, on rates of information transfer have resulted in rates as high as those described.

Evidently the mode of presentation of the information vitally affects the rate at which it can be handled; if this conclusion is true, then the naive program outlined at the beginning of this section for determining the channel capacity of a human being must be modified to some degree.

In this connection the results of an experiment performed by Klemmer and Muller [1953] are of interest. The stimuli consisted of five lights arranged in an arc; a corresponding set of telegraph keys was arranged under the subject's fingers. The subject was to press the keys corresponding to those lights which were on. By using various numbers of bulbs — the subjects were told which ones would be employed — 1, 2, 3, 4, and 5 bits could be achieved in the presentation. In addition, the stimulus cycle, which consisted of lights on 50 per cent of the cycle and off the last 50 per cent, was presented at a rate of 2, 3, 4, and 5 cycles per second. The subjects were all trained on the apparatus for several weeks, and the practice curves indicated that they had completely stabilized by the time the experiment was performed.

For a fixed number of bits in the stimulus, it was found that by varying the rate of information presented there was a nearly linear increase in the transmitted information until a peak was reached, after which the transmission rate fell markedly. The location of the peak, and hence its value, was found to be an increasing function of the number of bits in the stimulus.

The approximate values of the peaks were:

	Information presented in bits/stimulus				
	1	2	3	4	5
Peak Transmitted Info. in bits/sec ..	2.7	4.0	5.8	8.4	10.5

The decay of performance following the peak is remarkable. In the case of a stimulus with 5 bits, the peak of 10.5 bits/sec occurred when the input rate was approximately 13 bits/sec. When the rate was increased to 15 bits/sec, the transmitted information dropped to 6 bits/sec. This drop is, of course, due to a radical increase in the error rate.

It should be mentioned that I am reporting average results, and the authors present data to show that there is considerable individual variation.

Now, it is clear that the maximum rates found in this experiment are less than those described above. In many respects this experiment and its conclusions are more closely related to those to be described in the next Chapter on reaction times than it is to either the reading, typing, or music experiments. One important difference is that in the latter experiments the stimuli are before the subject at all times and hence the receptor mechanism can operate with a considerable lead over the response mechanism, whereas such a large lead was not possible in Klemmer and Muller's study. It therefore appears to be more nearly a "continuously" executed reaction-time experiment. This can be supported from data they present. Typical reaction-time experiments were run on the same subjects, and a comparison of the inverse of the reaction time to the stimulus rate (in stimuli/sec) at peak transmission is revealing:

	Bits in Stimulus				
	1	2	3	4	5
$1/RT$	3.8	2.6	2.6	2.4	2.4
Stimulus rate at peak transmission....	3.7	2.4	2.4	2.4	2.4

The Felton, Fritz, and Grier [1951] study of communications at Langley, discussed in Chapter 7, yields some data on operational rates of information handling. Using "information elements" on which to base their calculations, they found that during a single landing the following amounts and rates of information were employed by pilots and tower:

	Transmitted in bits	Rate in bits/sec
Air	114	8.4
Tower	133	10.3

However, it will be recalled that they determined that there was a very high redundancy in the transmission, and if only "new" information is considered, the table becomes:

	New Information Transmitted in bits	Rate of new information transmitted in bits/sec
Air............	22	1.6
Tower	29	2.2

Either set of rates is below that which we have seen is possible for speech.

Hick writes, "As a personal speculation from such data as are available, it seems likely that transmission rates fall into three fairly distinct classes: —

1. High rates of 10-15 bits per second.
2. Moderate — 5-6 bits per second.
3. Slow — 3-4 bits per second." ([1952b], p. 68.)

He feels that these rates are closely correlated to the mode of presentation of the information. High rates are obtained only through simple "imitation" codes of the type we learn in childhood. Moderate rates are typical of "arbitrary" specially learned codes in which each signal has a high information content. The low rates result from arbitrary codes having a low information content per signal and a high rate of presentation. As a partial and speculative explanation for rates less than full capacity Hick comments: "But for various reasons I am inclined to suspect — I would certainly not be more definite than that — that there is a tendency, overcome, if at all, only with long practice, to sidetrack one or two bits per discrete movement as a kind of monitoring feedback. It would be originally necessary in the course of developing the skill (the code being, as stated above, relatively arbitrary or 'unnatural'), and may be retained, perhaps as a habit, or perhaps to keep the skill up to full efficiency, for a long time after that." ([1952b,] pp. 70-71).

Experimental results of Fitts and his colleagues (Fitts and Seeger [1953], Fitts [1954], Fitts and Deininger [1954], and Deininger and Fitts [1955]) tend to support part of Hick's position. For example, if the stimulus set is a circle of eight lights and the subject is required to respond according to the corresponding clock positions, the rate of information transfer is significantly higher than if some arbitrary numbering of the lights is used. The one clearly has a well engrained cultural basis, and the other does not. Such results, while hardly surprising, serve as a check on those who have too easily lapsed into speaking of the information in the stimulus set as the determiner of information transfer. "[These results] indicate that it is not permissible to conclude that any particular set of stimuli, or set of responses, will provide a high rate of information transfer; it is the ensemble of $S—R$ combinations which must be considered." (Fitts and Seeger [1953], p. 209).

10. REACTION TIME AND INFORMATION TRANSFER(*)

OUR PRESENT TOPIC may, in a sense, be considered a continuation of the last Chapter on capacity; here we shall deal with what might be called "momentary" capacity. Previously we considered long samples of sequential stimuli to which the subject responded more or less continuously; now we shall consider his reaction time to a single isolated display. The question is what characteristics of the display need to be considered in order to account (simply) for the observed reaction times. The hypothesis, very generally, is that the information content of the display is the relevant variable and that the reaction time will turn out to be a very simple function of it — namely, linear.

There are, according to information theory, a number of ways in which the information transmitted can be varied: a) by varying the number of equi-probable alternatives, b) by altering the probabilities of the various choices, c) by introducing sequential dependencies between choices, and d) by allowing errors (noise) to occur. In the theory these are equivalent; whether they produce equivalent human responses is an empirical problem.

In the first experiment of the series of three I shall discuss, Hick [1952a] considered cases a and d. He presented subjects with a stimulus in which one of n equally likely alternatives would arise, and the subject had to respond as to which occurred. His hypothesis was that the reaction time (RT) would be proportional to the information in the stimulus, or, in other words, the rate of information transfer would be constant. There is, of course, a difficulty in assuming $RT = k \log n$, since when $n = 1$ this would require a zero reaction time. Hick suggests that there are really $n + 1$ alternatives, since we have ignored the case of no stimulus. Furthermore, he assumes that all $n + 1$ are equi-probable and that $RT = k \log (n + 1)$. This assumption is controversial and will be discussed below. Accepting it, he finds that data taken by Merkel [1885] are well fit by choosing $k = 0.626$ and that his own are fit with $k = 0.518$. Since a fixed delay, independent of n, seems plausible, the function $c + k \log n$ might seem intuitively more suited to fitting the data, but it does not fit either set of data as well. These fits were obtained with n in the range 1 to 10, i.e., up to a little more than 3 bits.

Turning to method d of varying the information, Hick points out, "...if the subject can be persuaded to react more quickly, at the cost of a proportion of mistakes, there will be a residual entropy which should vary directly with the reduction in the average reaction time." ([1952a], p. 15). An

(*) See Bricker [1955] for a survey of much the same material as discussed here.

experiment was performed in which the subjects were pressed, and the errors were taken into account by computing an equivalent error-free n, n_e. The reaction time data when plotted against n_e were found to be fit pretty well by the curve obtained for the errorless case.

In Hick's experiment the rate of information transfer was about 5.6 bits/sec, a value which is low compared with the largest obtained using a "continuous" stimuli presentation.

We must consider Hick's assumption that there are $n+1$, or in the more general case n_e+1, equiprobable alternatives. In a later paper [1954] he defends this choice as follows: "The discrimination between 'nothing' and 'something,' so to say, was practically perfect.

"But the discrimination between the n_e mathematical fictions was also perfect, by definition; and they are defined as equally probable. It is as if the subject were able to state with certainty — in an average sense, of course — which of the n_e+1 phases the environment was in. In other words, an impartial observer, having no reason to think one phase more probable than another, could receive $\log(n_e+1)$ units of information from him, per response. That is a fact, whatever the reaction time might happen to be, and it implies that the one extra possibility — that of no signal — can be regarded as having the same probability as any particular signal. Whether it really has is neither here nor there — the subject's channel capacity is such that it *can* have." ([1954], p. 400).

Mandelbrot(*) has suggested an alternative model based upon his theory discussed in Chapter 8. The fact that a response occurs, or doesn't, plays a special role, analogous to a space in ordinary language, which is quite different from the particular responses, which are treated as ordinary letters. Using his cost model, where reaction time is now the cost involved, the second approximation leads to

$$RT = \log(n+m) + T,$$

where m and T are unknown constants and n is the number of alternatives. This formula is related to, but different from, Hick's and it is not known whether it fits the data as well. The rationale for it, however, seems to me more substantial and better capable of being extended than does Hick's argument.

"The original evidence that the information measure was the appropriate one to use for interpreting choice-reaction times was simply that the logarithmic function occurs in both. This in itself is not strong, since logarithmic

(*) Personal communication.

relations occur rather often in biological measurement. The case became much stronger with Hick's finding that the reduction in response-time where errors are permitted obeyed the same law." (Crossman [1953], p. 41), Cronbach [1955] also stresses this important point, and he notes that the argument is made even stronger by Hyman's data, to which we turn now.

Hyman [1953] examined methods a, b, and c of varying the information when the performance was kept errorless. He states his hypotheses as,

"1) Reaction time is a monotonically increasing function of the amount of information in the stimulus series.

"2) The regression of reaction time upon amount of information is the same whether the amount of information per stimulus is varied by altering the number of equally probable alternatives, altering the relative frequency of occurrence of particular alternatives, or altering the sequential dependencies among occurrences of successive stimuli." ([1953], p. 189).

The stimuli were a matrix of lights with a range of 0 to 3 bits. The subjects responded by a vocal key, which seems to yield more precise measurements than the hand-operated key of Hick's experiment. The subjects were given complete statistical information about the stimuli and before each test run they were given sample sequences formed according to the appropriate statistics. Four subjects were used. The correlations reported below are the average of the four correlations computed for each subject separately.

In the first phase, the number of equi-probable alternatives were varied and a correlation of 0.983 was found between reaction times and information in the stimuli. This confirms Hick's results. In the second phase, when the relative frequencies were changed, an average correlation of 0.975 was found. In the third phase, introducing sequential dependencies resulted in a correlation of 0.938. The last correlation is significantly lower than the other two.

Hyman concludes from his data that his second hypothesis, while not acceptable at the 1 per cent level, is acceptable at the 5 per cent level. However, he points out two features in the data which suggest to him that the subjects did not react to the fine information structure of the experiment. In the third experiment there were cases where if a stimulus occurred, then in the next presentation it could not possibly occur, and the subjects knew this. Yet instead of reducing the reaction time, this increased it. This result seems disturbing.

He also raises this point: the reaction time to an event with probability p does not depend upon p alone, but also upon the probabilities of the other events in the display. Thus, although the average reaction time is determined by the average information in the display, the individual reaction times are not determined by the surprise — $\log_2 p$ — of the individual events. It is well to know this, but it does not seem to me to be either surprising or unfortunate, for the main thesis is that the subject responds to the overall statistical features of the display as described by the average information.

The relation between average reaction time and information has been further examined by Crossman [1953]. "When a subject responds to a sequence of signals all of which belong to a known set but some of which occur more frequently than others, his average response-time will be proportional to the average information per signal. This follows from the hypothesis that the subject deals with information at a constant rate." ([1953], p. 41). To test this he used a sorting task on ordinary playing cards. By varying the dimensions on which they were to be sorted he was able to examine the reaction times over a range of 0 to 2 bits/card. The correlation between reaction time and information per card was 0.86, and when the data are plotted it appears that no simple curve will fit them better than a straight line.

Crossman adduced evidence to show that the deviations from linearity were due to differential difficulties in discriminating the cards in different classes. On the basis of this he made the important observation that there is "...a major difficulty in the use of information theory in psychology, for information theory in the discrete case stated by Shannon says nothing about actual signals and the process of distinguishing them one from another; it deals only with abstract symbols already identified and distinct." ([1953], p. 49). This, of course, suggests carrying out a similar experiment using only one dimension of discrimination and causing the entropy to vary along it. This was done and the fit was improved.

On the basis of his data, Crossman concluded "... our hypothesis that rate is constant under variation of relative probabilities is upheld by these observations, with the proviso that 'discriminability' of signals should be equal in a sense yet to be precisely defined." ([1953], p. 50).

From these data it seems reasonable to conclude tentatively that the rate of information transfer in a reaction time experiment is constant when the information in the stimulus is in the range 0 to 3 bits. Since this conclusion is not in conformity with the observations made with a "continuous" stimuli presentation, it would certainly be interesting to see whether the rate remains constant when there are more than 3 bits in the stimulus, and also to see whether an experiment can be found with the rate constant, but much larger than 5 bits/sec, for the range 0 to 3 bits.

11. VISUAL THRESHOLD AND WORD FREQUENCIES

IN THE EARLY 1950's there were a series of experiments performed on the relation between the visual threshold of word recognition (as given by tachistoscopic measurements) and the frequency of their occurrence. Originally, the program stemmed from work on the Bruner-Postman hypothesis that sentences which relate to things liked are recognized with less difficulty than those relating to things disliked. Evidence has accumulated that the major relation is actually between recognition speed and the frequency of occurrence of the word in the language. Howes [1950] cites data involving sentences, and Howes and Solomon [1951] cite similar data involving only words. In the latter case, word frequency counts were obtained from Thorndike and Lorge [1944] and there was found to be a correlation of about −0.7 between recognition time and the logarithm of word frequency. Howes [1950] and Miller [1951 a] describe data taken by Solomon in which seven-letter Turkish words were used. These were written on cards which the subjects studied. Some words appeared on many cards, others on only a few, so there was differential exposure to these new words. A correlation of −0.96 was found between recognition time and log frequency. King-Ellison and Jenkins repeated Solomon's experiments with some slight variations, including the use of artificial five-letter words, and they obtained a correlation of −0.99. They point out a relationship to information theory is suggested, namely, that recognition time is a linear function of the information transmitted by a word. The earlier comment I quoted from Crossman is relevant here, namely, that logarithmic relations are so common in biology and psychology that more must be established before an information theoretic model is assumed.

On the other hand, one can argue that this result is *predicted* by Mandelbrot's model of language, provided that one is willing to make one assumption (see Mandelbrot [1954a]). It will be recalled that a central notion of his model is the cost C_r of a word of rank r, and this was left undefined in the general model. It is plausible that recognition time is this cost. If so, then by Zipf's relation, we know that a word of rank r has a probability

$$p_r = Pr^{-B},$$

or taking logarithms,

$$\log r = -\frac{1}{B} \log \frac{p_r}{P}.$$

But Mandelbrot showed, to a first approximation, that $C_r = \log r$, thus we conclude that recognition time should be negatively correlated to the logarithm of the probability of occurrence. The second approximation to the cost expression would lead to a slightly different prediction, and it would be of interest to see whether a careful experiment could discriminate between these two predictions in favor of the second and more exact one.

Work of Krulee, Podell, and Ronco [1954] is related to and consistent with the above data. They established the distance from the eye at which a symbol is first recognized and found a slight decrease in the mean distance as the number of alternatives was increased.

12. THE INFORMATION TRANSMITTED IN ABSOLUTE JUDGMENTS(*)

WHEN A SUBJECT is required to place stimuli varying along one dimension, such as size or loudness, into N simply ordered categories, such as the first N integers, then he is said to be making absolute judgments of the dimension of the stimuli. For example, the stimuli might be pure tones at $100, 150, 200, \ldots, 1,000$ cycles/sec. Each time a tone is presented he must place it in a category as accurately as he can. It is clear that in general errors will occur of the form: a tone with a lower frequency than another will be put in a higher number category. It is also clear that the error rate can probably be diminished by reducing the number of categories. For example, if he must place the above stimuli in 21 categories, we may expect more errors than if he need only report whether a signal is below or above 500 cycles/sec, for then there will be little ambiguity in his mind except for those stimuli near 500 cycles. Such experiments have a long history, but there has always been some difficulty in summarizing the data — just how should the error picture be presented?

Garner and Hake [1951] pointed out that the matrix relating input stimuli to response categories, with the entries the frequencies of pairings between a stimulus and a category, can be treated (with the obvious normalization) as a noise matrix for a communication system, where the communication is of selective information from the stimuli to the experimenter via the subject as a channel. We may, therefore, compute the information of the stimulus set (which, of course, depends on the relative frequencies of

(*) An excellent summary discussion, and interpretation, of much of the data in this and the following two chapters, plus some not so immediately related to information theory, has been presented recently by Miller [1956].

presentation of the different stimuli) and the equivocation of the transmission, and the difference is the information transmitted. If for a certain type of absolute judgement it is found that 21 categories allow the transmission of 3 bits, then in principle as much can be transmitted using only 8 unambiguous categories. Choosing the categories so that there is no ambiguity, i.e., no errors, may be difficult, but Garner and Hake point out that if the errors have a Gaussian distribution the condition is equivalent to a criterion of equal discriminability.

In another paper (Hake and Garner [1951]) they cite the difference between the usual error analysis for experiments of absolute judgments and the proposed information theory analysis. An error analysis ignores the fact that if the error distributions do not overlap, there will be no ambiguity. The information analysis takes this into account, but, unlike the error analysis, it completely ignores the magnitudes of the errors. There are some applications where it is preferable to have a multitude of small errors, provided that there is never a single major one.

A number of applications of this proposal have been made to different classes of absolute judgments. Pollack [1952a] studied tones spaced equidistantly on a logarithmic frequency scale from 100 to 8,000 cycles/sec. The subjects had to assign a number to each tone presented. When there were 2 and 4 tones in the stimulus set, the transmission was perfect, 1 and 2 bits respectively. But with 8 and 16 tones, the curve became flat, and the average maximum transmission was 2.3 bits, or the equivalent of perfect identification among 5 tones. The best subjects reached the equivalent of only 7 tones. On the grounds that there are known to be 40 to 60 identifiable sounds associated with speech and music, Pollack felt that there must have been a serious underestimation of the information transmitted, and so he performed a series of auxiliary experiments to attempt to raise the value. Six different partitions of the frequency space were examined, and the frequency range was varied with the bottom held at 100 cycles/sec and the top moved from 500, 2,000, 4,000 to 8,000 cycles/sec. These variations, and similar ones in a later paper (Pollack [1953]), resulted in only a few percentage points change in the information transmitted. He suggested that the result is so low because of the acute sensitivity of the information measure to error, which we have mentioned earlier (Chapter 4). However, later results which I shall present below show how more information can be transmitted and so suggest indirectly that the low value found may be realistic.

Halsey and Chapanis [1951] have presented similar data on the number of absolutely identifiable spectral hues, and though they did not apply an informational analysis, their findings are of some interest. The colors were identified sequentially from violet to red by numbers, and the subjects were familiarized with the number-color code until learning was completed. In a test using 10 hues and 20 judgments per hue, they found that two observers were correct in 97.5 per cent of the judgments. These hues were selected on the basis of several earlier experimental runs in which more hues were employed, but a lower accuracy was obtained. They note that absolute identifiability of 10 hues is considerably better than had been previously reported, but they attribute this mainly to different experimental conditions.

If we turn to the sense of taste, similar results hold except that the maximum amount of information transmitted is definitely less than for either pitch or hue. Beebe-Center, Rogers, and O'Connel [1955] report data for both sucrose and saline solutions with the number of stimuli varying from 3 to 17. The concentrations were chosen to be roughly equally spaced in jnd units. The information transmitted reached a peak of about 1.7 bits per judgement for sucrose and a range (for three subjects) from 1.6 to 1.8 bits per judgment with a saline solution. As the number of stimuli in the set were increased, there was a decrease in the information per judgment down to about 1 bit for 17 stimuli. The most notable aspect is that these data are equivalent to perfect discrimination among only three distinct stimuli, as compared with five to seven tones and possibly as many as 10 hues.

Hake and Garner [1951] applied an information theory analysis "... to determine the minimum number of different pointer positions which can be presented in a standard interpolation interval to transmit the maximum amount of information, not about which positions of the pointer are occurring, but about the event continuum being represented." (p. 358). Two variations were run: in the limited response case the subjects were told the values the pointer could assume and they were required to respond only with those numbers; in the unlimited response case no such restriction was made. 5, 10, 20, and 50 possible pointer positions were used, and the data are summarized below:

Information Transmitted in Bits

Number of Positions	5	10	20	50
Limited Response	2.31	3.14	3.16	3.19
Unlimited Response	2.29	3.03	3.11	3.41

We observe that beyond 10 pointer positions the amount of information transmitted is roughly constant — equivalent to about 10 errorless positions.

There seems to be little or no difference between limited and unlimited responses as far as this analysis is concerned, but Hake and Garner point out that an error analysis shows that the errors increase when the subjects are allowed unlimited response.

In a later paper, Garner [1953] comments: "A measure of information transmission provides a means of specifying perceptual and judgmental accuracy in situations where absolute judgments about various categories on a stimulus continuum are required. This measurement allows the determination of the maximum number of stimulus categories which could be used with perfect accuracy without the necessity of sampling all the possible numbers of categories. However, this use of information transmission requires the assumption that the inherent judgmental accuracy is independent of the number of stimulus categories used experimentally. Two experiments (Garner and Hake, and Hake and Garner) have shown that this assumption is quite valid for situations involving judgments of position in visual space, and Pollack's experiment demonstrates its validity for judgments of pitch" (p. 373). Garner then proceeded to examine its validity in judgments of loudness of tones using 4, 5, 6, 7, 10, and 20 stimulus categories and a corresponding number of response categories. He found that judgment accuracy was nearly perfect for 4 and 5 categories (perfect being 2 and 2.32 bits respectively), but that it had dropped to 1.62 bits for 20 categories, which is equivalent to perfect accuracy for only three categories. Thus, the assumption is apparently not valid for loudness.

He went on to show, however, that the information transmitted could be improved if both the observers, i.e., the subjects, and the stimuli were taken as inputs to the system and the responses as outputs. (See Chapter 5, Multivariate Theory, for the analysis procedure when there are more than two dimensions.) In other words, there was considerable variability among the subjects when a large number of categories were employed. A further raising of the information transmitted is achieved, so that there is no drop at all, if the stimuli, the observers, and the preceding stimulus are all taken as inputs to the system.

Ericksen and Hake [1955] have obtained data and given a similar analysis for judgments of size. Their interest was not so much with the value of the information transmitted as "...with the extent to which the number of absolutely discriminable stimulus categories can be affected by subjective anchoring effects associated with the range and density of the stimulus dimension and with the number of response categories available to Ss for expressing discriminations or judgments." (p. 323). Judgments were made of squares in two ranges, 2 to 82 mm and 2 to 42 mm, with 5, 11, and 21 stimuli in each range and using 5, 11, or 21 categories. All combinations of number of stimuli and number of categories were examined. It was found, as might be expected, that for a fixed number of stimuli and of response categories, discrimination was better for the larger range than for the smaller one; the difference was significant, but slight (about 0.2 bits).

The interaction between the number of stimuli and number of response categories is shown in the following table:

Information transmitted in bits per judgment

Number of Stimuli	5	11	21
Number of 5	2.08	1.65	1.49
Response 11	1.93	2.07	1.90
Categories 21	2.03	2.14	2.08

We observe that when the number of stimuli match the number of response categories, the information transmitted is constant, and it is nearly so when the number of response categories exceeds the number of stimuli. There is, however, a distinct reduction if there are more stimuli than response categories. This is not unreasonable since as the number of response categories is reduced, the possible response entropy is reduced, so the error entropy would have to diminish an equal amount in order to keep the information transmitted a constant. Detailed study of the data show this did in fact happen for the larger stimuli, but not for the smaller ones. An explanation is given, which we need not enter into here, in terms of the characteristic end (or anchoring) effects of the method of absolute judgments.

Klemmer and Frick [1953] carried out an experiment similar in method and analysis to those above, except that there were two and three stimulus dimensions instead of one. They flashed (0.03 sec) a display consisting of white dots on a black background to subjects who marked on answer sheet grids what they thought the position of the dots to be. The experiment was run both with and without grid lines on the black background, but appreciable differences were not found in the data. With the situation restricted to the presentation of one dot, the information in the stimulus could be varied by changing the order of the matrix of possible positions. From 3.2 bits (order 3) to 5.2 bits (order 6) there was an increase in information transmitted from 3.2 to 4.4 bits. From 5.2 bits to 8.6 bits (order 20) in the display, the information transmitted remained approximately constant.

In addition, the number of dots presented was varied, and it was found that by using 4 dots and a matrix of order 3 (7.0 bits), 6.6 bits were transmitted. Further, when from 1 to 4 dots were used, then a display having 8.0 bits resulted in almost perfect transmission — 7.8 bits. "It is clear that the maximum amount of information that can be assimilated from a brief visual exposure is a function of the type of encoding used. The question immediately arises as to whether or not there is a common metric which may be applied to the different message classes and which will correlate with the maximum information-carrying capacity of that class." (Klemmer and Frick [1953], p. 18). They observe that using only one dimension or coordinate (the location of a point on a line) Hake and Garner found a maximum transmission of 3.1 bits, and using the two coordinates of a matrix plus the one of the number of dots, they found 7.8 bits transmitted. This suggests that the maximum increases with the number of dimensions.

This supposition is confirmed in data taken by other experimenters, particularly those reported by Pollack and Ficks [1954]. In the first of these studies, Pollack [1953] presented auditory stimuli which varied both in pitch and loudness, each dimension being represented by five stimuli roughly spaced at subjectively equal intervals. It was found that the multiple absolute judgments caused a slight reduction in the information transmitted in each dimension, and that the total information transmitted was a little in excess of the sum of the two dimensions analyzed separately(*) and a little less than their sum for the judgments made separately on the two dimensions:

Condition	Information transmitted per judgment in bits
1. Frequency alone, no report on loudness..........................	1.8(†)
2. Frequency alone, loudness report given	1.6
3. Loudness alone, no report on frequency	1.7
4. Loudness alone, frequency report given.........................	1.3
5. Combined frequency and loudness reports	3.1
6. Sum of 1 and 3	3.5
7. Sum of 2 and 4	2.9

(†) Note, this value is not as large as the rate Pollack [1952 a] reported earlier.

Roughly similar results were found by Beebe-Center, Rogers, and O'Connel when they combined the several possible mixtures of sucrose and salt (holding the amount of solvent constant); however, in every case the subjects transmitted slightly more information for the compound stimuli than the sum of the information transmitted for the two dimensions separate-

(*) Recall that McGill's multivariate model (Chapter 5) shows that this is possible because of the interaction term $A(uvy)$.

ly. The excess ranged from 0.04 to 0.20 bits in a total value of roughly 2 bits.

The most vivid demonstration of the increase of information transmitted with increased dimensions is given by Pollack and Ficks [1954]. In one display there were eight dimensions, which were achieved by presenting the subject with a stimulus composed of a tone and noise alternating in time. The eight variables on which he had to report were: frequency range of the noise, loudness of the noise, frequency of the tone, the loudness of the tone, the rate of alternation between the tone and noise, the fraction of time the noise was on, the total duration of presentation of the display, and the direction within the room from which the sound originated. In each case he was asked only to make a binary decision: high or low, loud or soft, fast or slow, etc. In a second variation, only the interupted tone was used and so there were only the last six of the above dimensions; however, in addition to the binary classification on each dimension, subjects were also run having to classify each dimension into 3 and 5 categories.

The subjects were separated into three classes of equal size according to the amount of information transmitted. The results for the poorest and the best classes are given:

Steps per Dimension	Information Transmitted in Bits per Stimulus		
	Maximum possible	Poorest Third	Best Third
two	6	4.8	5.6
two	8	6.4	7.4
five.................	13.9	6.2	7.8

Two aspects of these data are striking. First, the total amount of information transmitted is much greater than was possible using one dimension. Second, increasing the number of classification steps per dimension increases the information only very little as compared with increasing the number of dimensions.

Pollack and Ficks present data on the information transmitted for each of the separate dimensions and there are considerable differences. In the eight dimensional case, direction conveys the most, 0.97 bits, and frequency of the noise least, 0.78 bits. Furthermore, by considering the data for the finer subdivision they find "In general, dimensions associated with a high informational transfer... show a progressive increase in transmission with finer subdivision, whereas dimensions associated with a low information transfer... may show a maximum transmission with a cruder subdivision. Thus, the effectiveness of subdividing dimensions of elementary multidimensional auditory displays is a function of the specific dimensions employ-ed." ([1954], p. 158).

It is reasonably certain that eight dimensions is not the limit to increased information transfer and it would be interesting to know just how far this can be effectively extended. Of course, as Pollack and Ficks point out, such a method of increasing the information transmitted may not be useful in practice. Their study completely ignores the time parameter and presum-ably as the number of dimensions is increased the rate of information trans-mitted reaches a peak. Judging by the earlier results presented on rates, this peak can be expected at about eight or ten binary dimensions.

These results appear to tie into some recent work in linguistics. Jakobson, Fant, and Halle [1952] have attempted to show that the various speech sounds of natural languages can be classified according to a number of elementary binary linguistic characteristics: nasal or not, stopped or not, etc. It is thought that discrimination of sounds occurs by recognizing which state obtains for each dimension. Certainly, the above data would indicate that this is the most efficient way to use the auditory characteristics of human beings. (Also see Osgood [1954]).

On the basis of the several experiments we have discussed, one can conclude that for objective ratings there is, up to a point, an increase in the information transmitted with an increase in the number of categories. After that point the information transmitted either remains constant or decreases. Bendig and Hughes [1953] raised this question: Is the same conclusion possible for ratings of subjective feelings? To study this, they had subjects evaluate, according to either 3, 5, 7, 9, or 11 categories, their knowledge of 12 different countries. Anchoring statements of the form "I know (a great deal) (something) (very little) about this country" were employed in three variations: center anchored, both ends anchored, and both ends and the center anchored. Information transmission, they found, was increased by an increase of number of scale categories, except that there was a decelera-tion in the step from 9 to 11 categories. This is reconfirmed by Bendig [1953b]. This effect is in accord with the diminishing return observed for objective scaling. Bendig [1954] points out that it is also consistent with the hypothesis that the information transmitted is a constant proportion of the maximum possible, and he reports further data which substantiates this assumption.

13. SEQUENTIAL DEPENDENCIES AND IMMEDIATE RECALL, OPERANT
CONDITIONING, INTELLIGIBILITY, AND PERCEPTION

ONE OF THE MAIN POINTS of the 1949 Miller and Frick paper was to bring to the attention of psychologists that in information theory they had a tool ideally suited to the characterization of sequential dependencies in the stimulus, in the response data, or in both. There appear to have been four areas of psychological study to which this observation has been applied: to the learning of written material as a function of the statistical dependencies in those materials, to the sequential responses obtained in operant conditioning, to the intelligibility of verbal material as a function of statistical dependencies within the material, and to the ability of subjects to perceive statistical dependencies in materials. I shall discuss them in that order.

Immediate Recall. "Briefly stated, the problem... is, How well can people remember sequences of symbols that have various degrees of contextual constraint in their composition? The experimental literature contains considerable evidence to support the reasonable belief that nonsense is harder to remember than sense. This evidence has suffered, however, from a necessarily subjective interpretation of what was sensible" (Miller and Selfridge [1950]). Using Shannon's method, Miller and Selfridge prepared N^{th} order approximations to English in the following manner: A sequence of N successive words was chosen at random from a connected text, and a subject was asked to imbed the passage in a meaningful sentence. The first word in his sentence following the original group of N words was recorded. The next subject was presented with the last $N-1$ words of the original passage plus the new word, and he placed this N-word passage in a sentence. The first word after the passage was recorded, and so on. In this manner they generated approximations of order $0, 1, 2, 3, 4, 5$, and 7 in passages of $10, 20, 30$, and 50 words in length. Using these approximations to English, plus meaningful text, a standard recall experiment was executed. With the passage length held constant, they found that the percentage of recall increases with an increase in the order of approximation to English. In particular, for the 30 and 50 word passages the recall of the 5th and 7th order approximations to English is very little different from the recall of text material of the same length — this notwithstanding the fact that the 5th order is quite nonsensical and the 7th order by no means would be considered English. With shorter passages, recall comparable to that of text was achieved for even lower values of N.

"The results indicate that meaningful material is easy to learn, not because it is meaningful *per se*, but because it preserves the short range associations that are familiar to the *Ss*. Nonsense materials that retain these short range associations are also easy to learn. By shifting the problem from 'meaning' to 'degree of contextual constraint' the whole area is reopened to experimental investigations." (Miller and Selfridge [1950], p. 183). For example, one may ask whether their conclusion is valid for the whole memory decay curve, or whether it holds only for short term memory.

Similar results have been found by Aborn and Rubenstein [1952] in a slightly different experimental situation. They devised an "alphabet" of 16 nonsense syllables which fell into four easily distinguished classes of four syllables each; this classification was shown to the subjects. From these syllables six classes of passages of 30-32 syllables were constructed. The members of the first class were formed by random selection of syllables, and the others had increasing amounts of organization. For example, class four passages were marked by commas into groups of four syllables, and the first syllable of each group was chosen from class one, the second from class two, etc. The subjects were allowed 10 minutes to study the formal organization of the passage on which they would be tested and then three minutes to learn the actual passage, after which they were asked to reproduce it as accurately as possible. The authors had two hypotheses: "(a) The amount of learning in terms of syllables recalled is greater as the organization of the passage is greater, i.e., as the average rate of information is smaller. (b) The amount of learning in terms of the information score, computed as the product of the number of syllables recalled and the average rate of information, is constant for all passages." ([1952], p. 261). The data verified the first hypothesis, but not the second. For the first four passages the total amount of information learned was constant, but it dropped in passage 5 and even more so in passage 6. The breaking point was between 1.5 and 2 bits/syllable. This result simply means that the subjects were unable to memorize enough syllables to keep the information score high when the information per syllable was very low. Both these findings are in conformity with those of Miller and Selfridge above.

These same authors have pushed the problem further in a later paper (Rubenstein and Aborn [1954]). They conjectured that the lack of constancy in the information learned as the degree of organization changed was due to both inadequate training and too short study periods. Using the same materials to form passages of from 1 to 4 bits per symbol and of length 80 symbols, they repeated their experiment with a 10-hour training period and varied the study periods from 1 to 20 minutes. The previous results were not only reconfirmed, but strengthened: the amount of information recalled decreased with every increase of the degree of organization within the message, holding the study time constant. This was not merely a trend, but it was strictly true for each length study period. Consider two passages: it was found that the ratio of information recalled in the one of higher degree of organization to the one of lower degree is less than the ratio of the information per symbol in the two passages. And finally, the information recalled per unit of study time was a decreasing function of the total length of study time.

One appears to be able to conclude that meaningful text is made easy to recall (at least in part) by its redundancy, but that it is not correct to state that holding other things constant the amount of information recalled is constant.

Operant Conditioning. Frick and Miller [1951] have reported an application of their earlier ideas for the measurement of stereotypic behavior (Miller and Frick [1949]) to the operant conditioning of rate in a Skinner box. Two responses were observed: approach to food (A) and bar pressing (B). "Instead of the usual analysis in terms of the *rate* of responding to the bar, the results are analyzed here in terms of the *patterns* of responses" ([1951], p. 21). Three experimental phases were considered separately in the analysis: a) behavior prior to conditioning (operant level), b) conditioning behavior, and c) extinction behavior. During phase b a total of 300 reinforcements were applied.

In all phases the behavior was recorded as sequences of A's and B's, and the uncertainties — in terms of the index of behavioral stereotypy (redundancy) — were computed. It was found that "intersymbol" influences did not extend appreciably. beyond two symbols, and the value of the uncertainty in phase a was 0.408 for two symbols. Such a high value when there has been no conditioning is a consequence of the fact that such a sequence as $AAAA$ had a probability of 0.732 of occurring; indeed, the behavior of the rats was more stereotyped before conditioning than after. "The training-period did not introduce order into randomness, but rather caused the animal to abandon one well organized pattern of behavior for another. This needs some qualification. The lower stereotypy after conditioning appears when we consider only the temporal order; when we try to predict which response comes next. If we tried to predict also when the next response would occur and how long it would last, then the conditioned

behavior would look less random than the pre-conditioned behavior."
([1951], p. 25).

Another simple way the data may be described is as points in a two-dimensional plot of $p(B|B)$ vs $p(A|A)$. In phase a of the experiment the rats were approximately at the point (0.9, 0.75). This high perseveration is, in large part, simply a reflection of the topography of the Skinner box, as can be seen from the fact that 96 per cent of the responses separated by less than 10 seconds are of the form AA and BB, while this is reduced to 52 per cent for responses separated by more than 80 seconds.

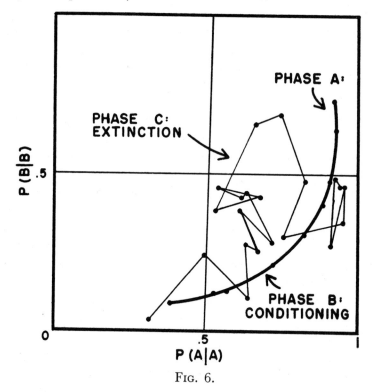

FIG. 6.

During conditioning, phase b, the rats initially move down the plot and then curve slowly over to an equilibrium point of about (0.4, 0.1), as shown in Fig. 6. During the extinction period the movement of a rat in this space is not very clear. There appears to be an initial tendency toward the center (0.5, 0.5) of the plot, or random behavior, but there is considerable random variation over a large portion of the plot. Over a 36-hour period there is a drift toward the initial resting point, but no stability is achieved in that period comparable to that prior to conditioning. It was not determinable from these data how long it takes for the effects of reinforcement to wear off. As in phase a, there is little difference between the uncertainty determined from two successive responses and from more than two, and after some extinction there is little or no difference in the index based on a single response and that based on successive pairs of responses.

"The data presented and analyzed [in this paper] do not provide any startling new insights into operant conditioning. Most of the conclusions seem perfectly reasonable and obvious to anyone who has worked with rats in a similar situation and observed their general behavior closely. The impressive feature of such an analysis is the extent to which the qualitative aspects of the behavior can be incorporated into a completely quantitative account." ([1951], p. 35).

Intelligibility. The data on the effects of sequential dependencies on intelligibility are less detailed than for learning. There is an experiment by Miller, Heise, and Lichten [1951] in which certain gross effects were examined. They explored the effects of three different contexts on intelligibility, namely: 1) the test item is known to be one of a small vocabulary of possible items, 2) the test item is imbedded in either a word or a sentence, and 3) the test item is known to be a repetition of the preceding item. The materials used were digits, words in sentences, and nonsense syllables, and it was found that intelligibility decreased in that order. Further, the intelligibility of monosyllables, isolated words, and words in sentences was found to increase in each case as the domain of possible items was decreased. Only a very slight increase in intelligibility resulted from the knowledge that the item was a repetition of the preceding one. "The results indicate that far more improvement in communication is possible by standardizing procedures and vocabulary than by merely repeating all messages one or two times." ([1951], p. 335). This conclusion seems to confirm the military practice of using standardized languages when conditions are adverse, as in air traffic control (see Chapter 7).

Perception of Statistical Dependencies. Hake and Hyman [1953] raised the question of just how well and in what way people perceive sequential dependencies that are built into a set of stimuli. They chose to summarize their results in terms of certain conditional uncertainties — entropies — of the subject's responses. Their experiment was divided into four series of runs. Each run consisted of 240 presentations of one or the other of two symbols (H and V), and these presentations were generated according to the following probabilities and conditional probabilities:

	Series			
	1	2	3	4
$p(H)$	.50	.50	.75	.75
$p(H|H)$	.50	.80	.75	.90
$p(V)$	.50	.50	.25	.25
$p(V|V)$	.50	.80	.25	.70

Prior to each presentation, a subject was required to predict, or guess, which symbol would occur. The problem of analysis is to determine how accurately we can predict his guess provided we know certain past events such as his previous guesses and the symbols which actually occurred. For the last 120 trials the following conditional entropies were examined: the entropy of the guess y when only the distribution of y is known — $H(y)$, the entropy of y when the distribution of y and the previous guess are known — $H_y(y)$, the entropy of y when the distribution of y, the previous guess, and the previous occurrences are known — $H_{xy}(y)$, the entropy of y when the distribution of y and the previous occurrence are known — $H_x(y)$, and the analogues of each of the last three for the two preceding trials, instead of just one. These data are summarized:

	Series			
	1	2	3	4
$H(y)$	1.00	1.00	.76	.80
$H_y(y)$	1.00	.83	.72	.75
$H_x(y)$.............	.99	.69	.74	.70
$H_{xy}(y)$	.98	.54	.68	.55
$H_{y,y}(y)$	1.00	.83	.72	.73
$H_{x,x}(y)$	.98	.55	.70	.56
$H_{xy, xy}(y)$	.95	.52	.66	.55

It is clear that the best prediction of the subject's guess, i.e., the lowest entropy, is obtained when both his guesses and the actual occurrences on the two preceding trials are known, but a knowledge of his guess and the actual occurrence on the single preceding trial yields a prediction which is nearly as good, and knowledge of just the occurrence on the two preceding trials is only slightly worse. It thus follows that a subject responded not only to the actual events which occurred but also to his predictions about them. This can be made quite apparent by computing the probability of a guess of H when on the preceding trial a *correct* guess of H was made. For series one this conditional probability is about 0.5, but for the other three series it rises over trials and from trial 100 on it remains approximately constant with a value of 0.9. When the probability of an H guess following two successive correct *H* guesses is plotted, the curves rise more rapidly, and even in series one there is a rise from 0.5 to about 0.75.

"We conclude from our evidence that *Ss* do not, in fact, perceive the probability rules by which the series of events was generated. They do perceive, instead, those short sequences of events which precede each prediction, which can be discriminated from other possible sequences, and which are found to provide some information about the future behavior of the symbol series. There are several interesting conclusions which we can make about the way in which *Ss* perceive these previous events.

"1. All combinations of possible previous events were not discriminated with equal ease. Some previous events, especially homogeneous runs of the same symbol, were more easily discriminated and consistently responded to than were others.

"2. The previous events to which our *Ss* responded on each trial included more than just the symbols which had been appearing. They included also the previous predictions of *Ss* and the degree of correspondence between their predictions and the symbols which appeared on previous trials.

"3. There was considerable agreement among our *Ss* as to *when* a particular symbol should be predicted. They tended to respond to some similar or identical previous events in the same way, no matter which series they were predicting..." (Hake and Hyman [1953], p. 72).

Bennett, Fitts, and Noble [1954] report an experiment similar to, but more complicated than Hake and Hyman's. The general structure was the same except that there were five symbols — in this case lights — rather than two to predict. Throughout the experiment the probabilities of the several symbols were held constant, but the digram and trigram frequencies were varied. First, they used one group of subjects to obtain information about sequential guessing habits, which the Hake and Hyman experiment (among others) indicated. The stimulus series consisted of independent selections; however, the subjects' response patterns differed both from independence and from the objective probabilities of the symbols. These data were used to generate conditional probabilities in the stimuli for the succeeding experiments — one sequence, called the concordant one, had sequential dependencies compatible with the observed guessing habits; the other, the discordant one, was designed to be incompatible with those habits. Using different subjects, learning was observed when better than chance behavior was possible if digrams were taken into account but not if only trigrams were considered. It was found that considerable learning did occur in 250 trials with the digrams, and that although there was some initial difference between the concordant and discordant passages, it was not sustained. Using 500 trials and the trigrams, no learning was apparent. However, behavior for the two types of passages was sharply different: the concordant one elicited a larger number of correct predictions. The last experiment was repeated but extended to 1000 trials and the statistical structure of the passages was explained to the subjects. The differences between the two groups were markedly reduced and there seemed to be some slight indication of learning in the last 250 trials.

The authors point out that one must not conclude from these data that trigrams cannot be learned. With five symbols there are only 25 digrams as compared with 125 trigrams, which is a factor of 5. It is known from other studies that the number of trials required for learning goes up somewhat more rapidly than linearly with the number of stimuli. Furthermore, the four-second interval between trials during which the subject responded tends to prevent natural groupings such as are found in language, so the trigrams cannot easily be dealt with as a whole. "One implication of this line of reasoning, which may have important implications for skill learning, is that when sequences (of stimuli or movements) of a statistical nature have to be learned, it may be very important to give knowledge of results in such a way that Ss can observe entire sequences of events." ([1954], p. 311).

14. IMMEDIATE RECALL OF SETS OF INDEPENDENT SELECTIONS

THE SUBJECT OF THIS chapter is closely related to the first part of Chapter 13. The main emphasis of that Chapter was on the effects that inter-symbol dependencies have on immediate recall, whereas here we shall examine the effects of message length and the bits per symbol on immediate recall when there are no dependencies among symbols. Pollack [1952b] prepared messages of from 4 to 24 symbols from sets of $2, 4, 8, 16$, and 30 equi-probable Latin consonants and numerals. These were read in a uniform manner to subjects who were told in advance both the set of symbols and the message length. They were required to reproduce them as accurately as possible. When an error was made, the subject was requested to guess as many times as was necessary to obtain the correct response. In one version of the experiment, reading rates were varied, but "Rate of presentation of stimulus materials (over the range considered) appears as a variable with little significance for immediate recall under the conditions considered here" ([1952b] II, p. 13).

The data show that the error entropy per message unit increases both with message length and with an increase in bits per symbol. But, for a message of given length, the percentage of presented information which is lost is approximately independent of the number of bits per symbol. This percentage is, however, an increasing function of the length of the message. The error entropy increased in such a manner that the total information transmitted increased as the message length was increased from 4 to about 10 symbols, it remained roughly constant in the range of 10 to 16 or 18 symbols per message, and it decreased for longer messages. The curves are displaced upward with an increase in bits per symbol, but they are of remarkably similar shape. "The main generalization is that one cannot obtain simultaneously both minimum information loss and maximum information gain by simply varying either the length of a message or the number of possible alternatives per message-unit." "These relations stem from the fact that the percentage of the information presented that is lost or gained is independent of the number of alternatives per unit and is simply a function of the length of the message." ([1952b], I, p. 12).

It is useful to transform these data into plots of error entropy and information transmitted *vs* total informational input. It is then found that for a fixed input, the error entropy is smaller and the information transmitted is larger the greater the number of bits per symbol. Thus, as Pollack points out, if one is interested in the optimal encoding characteristics for messages of fixed length, there are two answers depending upon whether a high error count is tolerable or not. If, however, the question is "What are the optimal encoding characteristics (for immediate recall) for messages of fixed informational content?" then the answer is unequivocal: short messages with a large number of alternatives for each message unit.

In parts III and IV of his report, Pollack systematically studied the error behavior of his subjects. First, his data confirm the familiar finding of this type of experiment that the subjects are most uncertain about the middle portion of the message. For messages of length 7, the relative uncertainty of the middle symbols is slightly higher than the end uncertainty, but it never exceeds .30. However, for messages of length 24, there is a broad plateau in the middle of the message which has a relative uncertainty of about .80. The broadness of this plateau Pollack attributed to the great sensitivity of the information measure to errors. He noted that the uncertainty curve alters its character with increasing message length: for short messages it is positively skewed and for long ones it is negatively skewed.

In the fourth part of the report, he established the conclusion that there is still information transmitted (as compared with chance responses) by the subjects on the second and third guesses following an incorrect response. "In general, the additional information recovered per message increases as the degree of analysis of the multiple response data becomes more exhaustive. Stated otherwise, we recover more information from the distribution of responses if we utilize the first response following the initial incorrect reproduction, still more if we utilize the first and second responses following the initial incorrect reproduction, and still more if we utilize the first through the third responses following the initial incorrect reproduction. The magnitude of the information increases as the number of alternatives per message-unit increases and is, roughly, independent of message-length (for messages greater than 7 units in length)" ([1952b], IV, p. 8). As would be expected, this effect is a decreasing one, but the decrease is less rapid with larger numbers of alternatives per message-unit.

15. CONCEPT FORMATION

CONSIDER THE EIGHT objects that are characterized by the three "dimensions": triangles or circles, large or small, and black or red. One may attempt to convey to a subject a concept, such as red triangle, by showing him the objects one at a time and stating whether or not they are examples of the desired concept. A positive instance of the concept red triangle is "large red triangle," whereas "small black triangle" or "large red circle" are negative instances. Such experiments in concept learning have long been performed, and the conclusion has been drawn that negative instances are of little value in learning the correct concept. Hovland [1952], however, has raised a question about this conclusion — a question which stems from an information analysis of the situation. "What is not clear...is whether the ineffectiveness of negative instances is primarily attributable to their low value as carriers of information, or whether it is primarily due to the difficulty of assimilating the information which they do convey" ([1952], p. 461).

Certainly it is clear from the above example that positive and negative instances do not transmit the same information, since only two positive ones are required to specify the concept, as compared with six negative. It is, of course, possible to design a situation where the negative instances carry as much or more information as the positive ones. For certain simple general situations, of which the above example is illustrative, Hovland has given formulae for the total number of positive and negative instances required to specify the concept. In an experimental paper, he and Weiss [1953] examined the effect of positive and negative instances when both the number of instances and the amount of information are held constant, and they conclude that even so the negative instances do not contribute as effectively to learning. "At the same time the data disprove the generalization often cited that negative instances have no value in the learning of concepts. Under appropriate conditions over half of the *Ss* were able to reach the correct solution solely on the basis of negative instances." ([1953], p. 181).

Archer, Bourne, and Brown [1955] establish that additional but irrelevant information of from 1 to 3 bits diminish the rate at which a concept is achieved — the more irrelevant information, the slower the rate.

Bendig [1953a] conducted an experiment which is closely related to concept formation, namely, the identification of a concept after the manner of the game "20 questions." In the experiment, four questions were employed to isolate an animal topic. One experimenter asked the questions in fixed order of another who answered "yes" or "no" according to the topic. Following each question, the subjects were required to guess the concept. The information transmitted by each question was calculated, and theoretically each should have conveyed one bit, but in actuality 0.83, 0.91, 0.21, and 0.78 bits were transmitted. The central conclusion seemed to be that the third question was unfortunately phrased, since answers to it failed to convey much information.

16. PAIRED ASSOCIATES LEARNING

As A FINAL APPLICATION of information ideas, I shall consider a learning situation where one class of objects — usually words — known as "responses" have been placed by the experimenter in one-to-one correspondence with another class of objects known as "stimuli." Initially, the subject knows nothing of the pairing and he can only guess at the appropriate response to a given stimulus; if he is correct, he is told this, if not, he is told the correct response. After a number of repetitions, R, of the stimulus class, the subject begins to learn the correct pairing, and he obtains a certain number of correct bonds, say C, out of the total of N. The function $C(R)$ is known as his "learning curve" for the paired associates. Several theories, and formulae, for this learning phenomenon have been put forth and are summarized by Rogers [1952] in a thesis in which he introduces a new learning theory based in part on information theory.

He makes two central assumptions. First, he supposes that the uncertainty which a subject entertains about the stimulus class after R repetitions of the stimulus class is a function of R alone. In particular, he supposes that it is constant — U_{ck} — for the first b repetitions, where b is a "set" parameter which tells when the learning begins, and that from b on it is a linear function of R, i.e.,

$$U_k = U_{ck} - a\,(R-b), \text{ for } R \geq b.$$

Second, let B be the total number of bonds which the subject knows after R repetitions. Rogers shows this is one less than the expected value of the observable C. Let k be a stimulus not among the B that are known, and let i be any response which is not associated with one of the B known stimuli. Then he supposes that the probability that i is the response when k is given is $1/(N-B)$. In other words, the subject is assumed to distribute his response choices without preference over all the available response elements.

From this second assumption, it is not difficult to obtain an expression for the uncertainty in terms of N and B. Equating this to the assumed expression in terms of R gives an equation between B and R, and so between C and R. This may be solved for C:

$$C = \begin{array}{l} (N-1)\,\{\,1-exp[-\delta a(R-b)]\,\} + 1, \text{ for } R \geq b, \\ 1 \qquad\qquad\qquad\qquad\qquad\qquad\quad , \text{ for } R < b \end{array}$$

where $\delta = \log_2 e$. It has long been noted that many learning data are approximately fit by such an exponential learning curve, though in general this has been an empirical observation which was not deduced from other assumptions.

To test the merits of this theory, Rogers drew certain conclusions from it which could be confronted by data. These conclusions were sustained by his data. Three related experiments were performed. 1) Correlated Structure. Stimuli — playing cards having two easily recognized dimensions, suits and denominations — were associated with nonsense syllables of the form consonant-vowel-consonant in a correlated manner. The first letter always corresponded to the denomination and the last to the suit. 2) Unstructured. Pictures of diverse household objects were paired in an arbitrary manner with nonsense syllables. 3) Uncorrelated Structured. The same materials as in 1 were used (so both the stimulus class and the response class were structured) but there was no systematic relation in the pairing between the stimulus class and the response class. He then examined what two classical theories — Gestalt and the transfer theory of meaning — and what his own information theory of learning predict as to the learning rates in these three cases. Gestalt theory, according to his interpretation, ranks them 1, 3, 2 in order of increasing difficulty, transfer theory gives an ordering of 1, 2, 3, while information theory predicts that 1 and 2 should be equally easy and 3 more difficult. His data are consistent with only the last prediction.

Attempts to fit the learning curve to the data were for the most part successful, although one can note a consistent '*S*' character to the data, which, of course, the exponential does not possess. He points out that if the linear assumption were replaced by an appropriate non-linear one, one could easily produce a learning curve with an '*S*' shape — or, I might add, practically any other shape, for that matter.

APPENDIX

THE CONTINUOUS THEORY

MUCH COMMUNICATION can best be thought of as the transmission of a continuous signal and not as a sequence of temporally ordered selections from a finite set of possible elements. For the most part, as we have seen, the continuous theory has been of little importance in behavioral applications, though it is of considerable importance in electrical ones. I shall, therefore, briefly sketch the theory. This presentation follows Shannon's [1948] closely.

The Continuous Source. A source is said to be continuous if, in effect, it makes but one selection from a continuum of elements; specifically, if it chooses one number from the set of all real numbers. I shall suppose that this selection is characterized by a probability density $p(x)$ over the real numbers x. Since p is a density, $\int_{-\infty}^{\infty} p(x)dx = 1$ and furthermore for any $\epsilon > 0$, no matter how small, one can find finite a and b such that $1 - \epsilon < \int_{a}^{b} p(x)\,dx \leq 1$.

Now, for such a and b we may divide the interval from a to b into n equal intervals, and we can treat each of the intervals as an element from a finite set, with probability $\int_{x_i}^{x_{i+1}} p(x)\,dx$ of being selected. All the continuum not in a to b is an $(n+1)^{st}$ element with probability $1 - \int_a^b p(x)\,dx$. Thus we have approximated the continuous source by a discrete one and for each n we can compute a corresponding entropy H_n. As we let n approach infinity, the approximation is better and better, but unfortunately H_n also approaches infinity. This, of course, is reasonable considering the basis of the discrete entropy concept, but that does not make the approach any more satisfactory as a way to compare continuous sources.

In such situations very often the difference between the quantity desired and another quantity, which tends to infinity with increasing n, will itself tend to a finite limit. If this second quantity can be chosen to be the same for all sources, then the resulting differences afford a perfectly acceptable comparison for continuous sources. As before, we choose a and b and we divide the interval from a to b into n equal intervals. Each of these intervals is of length $\Delta x = (b-a)/n$. Whereas before we tried to generalize

$$ -\sum_{i=1}^{n} p(x_i)\,\Delta x \log_2 [p(x_i)\,\Delta x] $$

and got into trouble, we now examine the entropy of the finite approximation minus the most that approximation might have been, i.e.

$$ \log_2 \Delta x - \sum_{i=1}^{n} p(x_i)\,\Delta x \log_2 [p(x_i)\,\Delta x]. $$

It is not difficult to show that

$$ \lim_{\substack{b\to\infty\\ a\to-\infty}} \lim_{\substack{n\to\infty\\ \Delta x\to 0}} \left\{ \log_2 \Delta x - \sum_{i=1}^{n} p(x_i)\,\Delta x \log_2 [p(x_i)\,\Delta x] \right\} $$

$$ = -\int_{-\infty}^{\infty} p(x) \log_2 p(x)\,dx. $$

This quantity, which is denoted by $H(x)$, is called the *entropy* of a continuous source. It is well to keep in mind that the continuous entropy is not an exact analogue of the discrete entropy, and so certain differences in properties may be anticipated. The surprising thing is how many of the results are independent of the base-line from which the discrete entropy is measured.

If there are two arguments x and y to the distribution (as in the case of noise), the joint and conditional entropies are defined by

$$H(x,y) = -\iint p(x,y) \log_2 p(x,y) \, dx \, dy$$

$$H_x(y) = -\iint p(x,y) \log_2 \frac{p(x,y)}{p(x)} \, dx \, dy$$

$$H_y(x) = -\iint p(x,y) \log_2 \frac{p(x,y)}{p(y)} \, dx \, dy,$$

where

$$p(x) = \int p(x,y) \, dy$$

$$p(y) = \int p(x,y) \, dx.$$

Many of the theorems of the discrete case carry over — usually quite directly — to the continuous case, but in addition there are certain new theorems which rest heavily on the existence of a coordinate system. I shall list some of the more important ones, of which the first is familiar and the other four are new.

1. $H(x,y) \leq H(x) + H(y)$,
   $H(x,y) = H(x) + H_x(y) = H(y) + H_y(x)$,
   $H_x(y) \leq H(y)$.
2. If $p(x) = 0$ except on an interval of length v, then $H(x)$ is a maximum $(= \log_2 v)$ when $p(x) = 1/v$ for x in the interval.
3. Of the class of all continuous one-dimensional distributions with variance σ^2, the normal, or Gaussian, is the one having maximum entropy. The value of the maximum is $\log_2 (2\pi e)^{1/2} \sigma$.
4. Of the class of all continuous one-dimensional distributions with mean $a > 0$ and with $p(x) = 0$ for $x \leq 0$, the exponential is the one having maximum entropy. The value of the maximum is $\log_2 ea$.
5. Unlike the discrete case, in which entropy measures the randomness in an absolute way, the continuous entropy is a measure which is relative to a coordinate system. If the coordinate system is changed, the entropy is changed. This is not serious, however, since both the channel capacity and the rate of information transfer depend upon the difference between two entropies, and so they are invariant under coordinate transformation. Reich [1951 a] states that he has shown the definition of information rate used by

Shannon is the only one of a broad class of possible definitions which is invariant under coordinate transformation.

The Channel Capacity. As in the discrete noisy case, the channel capacity C is defined to be the maximum rate of transmission $R = H(x) - H_y(x)$ obtained by considering all possible distributions. This is easily shown to be

$$C = \lim_{T \to \infty} \max_{p(x)} \frac{1}{T} \iint p(x, y) \log_2 \frac{p(x, y)}{p(x)p(y)} \, dx \, dy.$$

One particularly important case in applications is that in which the noise is simply added to the signal and is independent of it. In that case the entropy of the noise can be computed. If we denote it by $H(n)$, then

$$C = \max_{p(x)} H(y) - H(n).$$

Of course, if there are restraints on the class of admissible signals, the maximization is taken subject to these restraints.

A simple, but very important, electrical application of the above theorem is to the case of a channel which has a bandwidth of W cycles per second (e.g., a telephone which will pass from 500 to 3,500 cycles per second has a bandwidth of 3,000 cycles per second), in which the transmitter has an average power output of P and the noise is white thermal noise (i.e., all frequencies are equally represented) of average power N. In this case the channel capacity in bits per second is

$$C = W \log_2 \left(1 + \frac{P}{N}\right)$$

Rate of Transmission. "In the case of a discrete source of information we were able to determine a definite rate of generating information, namely the entropy of the underlying stochastic process. With a continuous source the situation is considerably more involved. In the first place a continuously variable quantity can assume an infinite number of values and requires, therefore, an infinite number of binary digits for exact specification. This means that to transmit the output of a continuous source with *exact recovery* at the receiving point requires, in general, a channel of infinite capacity (in bits per second). Since, ordinarily, channels have a certain amount of noise, and therefore a finite capacity, exact transmission is impossible.

"This, however, evades the real issue. Practically, we are not interested in exact transmission when we have a continuous source, but only in transmission to within a certain tolerance. The question is, can we assign a definite rate to a continuous source when we require only a certain fidelity of recovery, measured in a suitable way. Of course, as the fidelity requirements are increased the rate will increase. It will be shown that we can, in very general cases, define a rate, having the property that it is possible, by properly encoding the information, to transmit it over a channel whose capacity is equal to the rate in question, and satisfy the fidelity requirements. A channel of smaller capacity is insufficient." ([Shannon and Weaver], 1949, p. 74).

The noise character of the whole system is, as before, given by a distribution $p(x,y)$ which states the probability density that the signal y is received when x is sent. The fidelity of the system is, roughly, an evalution of how different y is on the average from x. It is assumed to be a function of the noise, that is, if it is measured by a real number it can be written in the form $v[p(x,y)]$. Under quite broad conditions, which I shall not attempt to state here (see [Shannon], 1948), it can be shown that v can be represented as

$$v[p(x,y)] = \iint p(x,y)\,\rho(x,y)\,dx\,dy.$$

The real-valued function $\rho(x,y)$ is essentially a measure of the difference between x and y and in computing the fidelity it is weighted according to the probability density of the joint occurrence of x and y. It may be illuminating to consider two very common electrical criteria of fidelity. The first is the root-mean-square criterion, namely,

$$\rho(x,y) = \frac{1}{T}\int_0^T [x(t)-y(t)]^2\,dt,$$

and the second is the absolute error criterion, namely,

$$\rho(x,y) = \frac{1}{T}\int_0^T |x(t)-y(t)|\,dt.$$

Now, the rate R of generating information corresponding to a given quality of reproduction (fidelity) v is defined to be the minimum R which is obtained by varying $p(y|x)$ with v held constant, i.e.,

$$R = \operatorname*{Min}_{p(y|x)} \iint p(x,y) \log_2 \frac{p(x,y)}{p(x)\,p(y)}\,dx\,dy$$

subject to

$$v = \iint p(x,y)\, \rho(x,y)\, dx\, dy.$$

With this definition, and with that of channel capacity given earlier, it can be shown that if a source has a rate R for a valuation of fidelity v, then it is possible to encode the output of the source and to transmit it over a channel with capacity C in such a manner that the fidelity is arbitrarily near v if and only if $R \leq C$. This is the fundamental theorem for the transmission of information in the continuous case.

BIBLIOGRAPHY

The following papers and books were examined in preparing this essay, and many — though not all — have been mentioned in the text. They include the central works on information theory and all of the published reports I have been able to find (as of early 1956) concerned with its application in psychology. The bibliography prepared by Stumpers (1953) is more general than this one in that it covers the whole area of Cybernetics and the applications of information theory in engineering and in the several behavioral sciences (as of early 1953), but it is not so complete for psychological applications.

Aborn, M., and Rubenstein, H., "Information Theory and Immediate Recall," *J. exp. Psychol.*, 44, 1952, 260—266.

Adelson, M., Muckler, F. A., and Williams, A. C., Jr., "Verbal learning and message variables related to amount of information," *Information Theory in Psychology* (H. Quastler, ed.), The Free Press, Glencoe (1955), 291—299.

Alexander, L.T., and Garner, W. R., "Information transmission in a tracking task," *Amer. Psychologist*, 7, 1952, 276 (abstract).

Archer, E. J., Bourne, L. E., Jr., and Brown, F. G., "Concept identification as a function of irrelevant information and instructions," *J. exp. Psychol.*, 49, 1955, 153—164.

Attneave, F., "The estimation of transmitted information when conditional probabilities are interdependent," *Information Theory in Psychology* (H. Quastler, ed.), The Free Press, Glencoe (1955), 118—122.

Augenstine, L., "The use of Illiac in determining distributions for information functionals," *Information Theory in Psychology* (H. Quastler, ed.), The Free Press, Glencoe (1955), 109—115.

Bar-Hillel, Y., "An examination of information theory," *Phil. Sci.*, 22, 1955, 86—105.

Bar-Hillel, Y., and Carnap, R., "Semantic information," *Communication Theory* (Willis Jackson, ed.), Academic Press, New York (1953), 503—511.

Beebe-Center, J. G., Rogers, M. S., and O'Connel, D. N., "Transmission of information about sucrose and saline solutions through the sense of taste," *J. Psychol.*, 39, 1955, 157—160.

Bell, D. A., "The 'internal information' of English words," *Communication Theory* (Willis Jackson, ed.), Academic Press, Inc., New York (1953), 383—391.

Bendig, A. W., "Twenty questions: an information analysis," *J. exp. Psychol.*, 46, 1953 a, 345—348.

—, "The reliability of self-ratings as a function of the amount of verbal anchoring and of the number of categories on the scale," *J. Applied Psychol.*, 1953 b, 37, 38—41.

—, "Transmitted information and the length of rating scales," *J. exp. Psychol.*, 47, 1954, 303—308.

—, and Hughes, J. B., "Effect of amount of verbal anchoring and number of rating-scale categories upon transmitted information," *J. exp. Psychol.*, 46, 1953, 87—90.

Bennett, W. F., Fitts, P. M., and Noble, M., "The learning of sequential dependencies," *J. exp. Psychol.*, 48, 1954, 303—312.

Birdsall, T. G., "The theory of signal detectability," *Information Theory in Psychology* (H. Quastler, ed.), The Free Press, Glencoe (1955), 391—402.

Blachman, N. M., "Minimum-cost encoding of information," *Transactions of the Institute of Radio Engineers, Professional Group on Information Theory*, 3, 1954, 139—149.

Black, J. W., "The information of sounds and phonetic diagrams of one- and two-syllable words," *J. Speech Hearing Disorders*, 19, 1954, 397—411.

Blackwell, D., and Girshick, M. A., *Theory of Games and Statistical Decisions*, John Wiley & Sons, New York (1954).

Blank, A. A., and Quastler, H., *Notes on the estimation of information measures*, Control Systems Laboratory Report R—56, University of Illinois, 1954.

Bricker, P. D., "Information measurement and reaction time: a review," *Information Theory in Psychology* (H. Quastler, ed.), The Free Press, Glencoe (1955), 350—359.

Carnap, R., and Bar-Hillel, Y., *An outline of a theory of semantic information*, Research Laboratory of Electronics, Technical Report 247, M. I. T., 1952.

Chapanis, A., "The reconstruction of abbreviated printed messages," *J. exp. Psychol.*, 48, 1954, 496—510.

Cherry, E. C., "A history of the theory of information," *Proceedings of the Institution of Electrical Engineers*, III, 98, 1951, 383—393; and *Transactions of the Institute of Radio Engineers, Professional Group on Information Theory*, 1, 1953, 22—43.

—, "Organisms and mechanisms — an introductory survey," *The Advancement of Science*, 40, 1954, 393—397.

—, Halle, M., and Jakobson, R., "Toward the logical description of languages in their phonemic aspect," *Language*, 29, 1953, 34—46.

Cronbach, L. J., *A generalized psychometric theory based on information measure*, Bureau of Research and Service, College of Education, University of Illinois, 1952 (mimeographed).

Cronbach, L. J., *A consideration of information theory and utility theory as tools for psychometric problems*, Bureau of Educational Research, University of Illinois, 1953 (mimeographed).

—, "On the non-rational application of information measures in psychology," *Information Theory in Psychology* (H. Quastler, ed.), The Free Press, Glencoe (1955), 14—26.

Crossman, E. R. F. W., "Entropy and Choice time: the effect of frequency unbalance on choice response," *Quart. J. exp. Psychol.*, 5, 1953, 41—52.

Davis, H., "Applications of information theory to research in hearing," *J. Speech Hearing Disorders*, 17, 1952, 189—197.

Deininger, R. L., and Fitts, P. M., "Stimulus-response compatibility, information theory, and perceptual-motor performance," *Information Theory in Psychology* (H. Quastler, ed.), The Free Press, Glencoe (1955), 316—341.

Dewey, G., *Relative Frequency of English Speech Sounds*, Harvard University Press, Cambridge (1923).

Dolanský, Ladislav, and Dolanský, M. P., *Table of* $\log_2 \frac{1}{p}$*, and* $p\log_2 \frac{1}{p} + (1-p)\log_2 \frac{1}{1-p}$*,* Technical Report 227, Research Laboratory of Electronics, M. I. T., 1952.

Elias, Peter, "A note on autocorrelation and entropy," *Proceedings of the Institute of Radio Engineers*, 39, 1951, 839.

Eriksen, C. W., and Hake, H. W., "Absolute judgments as a function of stimulus range and number of stimulus and response categories," *J. exp. Psychol.*, 49, 1955, 323—332.

Fano, R. M., *The Transmission of Information*, Research Laboratory of Electronics, Technical Report 65, M. I. T., 1949.

—, *The Transmission of Information — II*, Research Laboratory of Electronics, Technical Report 149, M. I. T., 1950 a.

—, "The information theory point of view in speech communication," *J. acoust. soc. Amer.*, 22, 1950 b, 691—696.

—, *Information theory, past, present and future*, M. I. T., 1954 (dittoed).

Faverge, J. M., and Patin, J., "Recherche sur la notation des épreuves composées de questions en vue d'améliorer la validité," *Travail hum.*, 17, 1954, 86—91.

Feinstein, A., "A new basic theorem of information theory," *Transactions of the IRE, Professional Group on Information Theory*, 4, 1954, 2—22.

Felton, W. W., Fritz, E., Grier, G. W., Jr., *Communications measurements at the Langley Air Force Base*, Human Resources Research Laboratory Report No. 31, 1951.

Fitts, P. M., "The information capacity of the human motor system in controlling the amplitude of movement," *J. exp. Psychol.*, 47, 1954 a, 381—391.

—, "The influence of response coding on performance in motor tasks," *Current Trends in Information Theory* (R. A. Patton, ed.), U. of Pittsburgh Press, Pittsburgh (1954 b), 47—75.

—, and Seeger, C. M., "S-R compatability: spatial characteristics of stimulus and response codes," *J. exp. Psychol.*, 46, 1953, 199—210.

Fitts, P. M., and Deininger, R. L., "S-R compatability: correspondence among paired elements within stimulus and response codes," *J. exp. Psychol.*, 48, 1954, 483—491.

Frick, F. C., "Some perceptual problems from the point of view of information theory," *Current Trends in Information Theory* (R. A. Patton, ed.), U. of Pittsburgh Press, Pittsburgh (1954), 76—91.

—, and Miller, G. A., "A statistical description of operant conditioning, *Amer. J. Psychol.*, 64, 1951, 20—36.

—, and Sumby, W. H., "Control tower language," *J. acoust. Soc. Amer.*, 24, 1952, 595—597.

Fritz, E. L., and Grier, G. W., Jr., "Pragmatic communications: a study of information flow in air traffic control," *Information Theory in Psychology* (H. Quastler, ed.), The Free Press, Glencoe (1955), 232—243.

Gabor, D., "Theory of communications" *Journal of the Institution of Electrical Engineers*, 93, III, 1946, 429—456.

—, "New possibilities in speech transmission," *Journal of the Institution of Electrical Engineers*, 94, III, 1947, 369—390.

—, *Lectures on communication theory*, Research Laboratory of Electronics, Technical Report 238, M. I.T., 1952.

—, "Communication theory, past, present, and prospective," *Transactions of the Institute of Radio Engineers, Professional Group on Information Theory*, 1, 1953 a, 2—4.

—, "A summary of communication theory," *Communication Theory* (Willis Jackson, ed.), Academic Press, Inc., New York (1953 b), 1—23.

—, "Communication theory and physics," *Transaction of the Institute of Radio Engineers, Professional Group on Information Theory*, 1, 1953 c, 48—59.

Garner, W. R., "An informational analysis of absolute judgments of loudness," *J. exp. Psychol.*, 46, 1953, 373—380.

—, and Hake, H. W., "The amount of information in absolute judgments," *Psychol. Rev.*, 58, 1951, 446—459.

—, and McGill, W. J., "The Relation between information and variance analysis," *Psychometrika*, 21, 1956, 219—228.

Glaser, R., and Schwarz, P. A., "Scoring problem-solving test items by measuring information," *Educ. psychol. Measmt.*, 14, 1954, 665—670.

Goldman, S., *Information Theory*, Prentice-Hall, New York (1953).

Grant, D. A., "Information theory and the discrimination of sequences in stimulus events," *Current Trends in Information Theory* (R. A. Patton, ed.), U. of Pittsburgh Press, Pittsburgh (1954), 18—46.

Hake, H. W., "The perception of frequency of occurrence and the development of 'expectancy' in human experimental subjects," *Information Theory in Psychology* (H. Quastler, ed.), The Free Press, Glencoe, (1955 a), 257—277.

—, "A note on the concept of 'channel capacity' in psychology," *Information Theory in Psychology* (H. Quastler, ed.), The Free Press, Glencoe (1955 b), 248—253.

—, and Garner, W. R., "The effect of presenting various numbers of discrete steps on scale reading accuracy," *J. exp. Psychol.*, 42, 1951, 358—366.

—, and Hyman, R., "Perception of the statistical structure of a random series of binary symbols," *J. exp. Psychol.*, 45, 1953, 64—74.

Halsey, R. M., and Chapanis, A., "On the number of absolutely identifiable spectral hues," *J. opt. Soc. Amer.*, 41, 1951, 1057—1058.

Hartley, R. V. L., "Transmission of information," *Bell System Tech, J.*, 7, 1928, 535—563.

Hick, W. E., "Information theory and intelligence tests," *British J. Psychol.*, 4, 1951, 157—164.

—,   "On the rate of gain of information," *Quart. J. exp. Psychol.*, 4, 1952 a, 11—26.

—,   "Why the human operator?" *Transactions of the Society of Instrument Technology*, 4, 1952 b, 67—77.

—,   "Information theory in psychology," *Transactions of the Institute of Radio Engineers, Professional Group on Information Theory*, 1, 1953, 130—133.

—,   "The impact of information theory on psychology," *The Advancement of Science*, 40, 1954, 397—402.

Hockett, C. F., "An approach to the quantification of semantic noise," *Phil. Science*, 19, 1952, 257—261.

—,   "A review of Shannon and Weaver: the mathematical theory of communication," *Language*, 29, 1953, 69—93.

Hovland, C. I., "A 'communication analysis' of concept learning," *Psychol. Rev.*, 59, 1952, 461—472.

—,   and Weiss,W., "Transmission of information concerning concepts through positive and negative instances," *J. exp. Psychol.*, 45, 1953, 175—182.

Howes, D. H., *The definition and measurement of word probability*, Ph D. Thesis, Harvard University, 1950.

—,   and Solomon, R. L., "Visual duration threshold as a function of word probability," *J. exp. Psychol.*, 41, 1951, 401—410.

Hyman, R., "Stimulus information as a determinant of reaction times," *J. exp. Psychol.*, 45, 1953, 188—196.

Jackson, Willis (Editor), "Report of proceedings, Symposium on Information Theory, London, 1950," *Transactions of the Institute of Radio Engineers Professional Group on Information Theory*, 1, 1953 a.

—,   *Communication Theory*, Academic Press, Inc., New York, (1953 b).

Jacobson, H., "The informational capacity of the human ear," *Science*, 112, 1950, 143—144.

—,   "Information and the human ear," *J. acoust. Soc. Amer.*, 23, 1951 a, 463—471.

—,   "The informational capacity of the human eye," *Science*, 113, 1951 b, 292—293.

Jakobson, H., Fant, C. G. M., and Halle, M., *Preliminaries to speech analysis*, Technical Report 13, Acoustics Laboratory, M. I. T., Cambridge, 1952.

King-Ellison, Patricia, and Jenkins, J. J., *Visual duration threshold as a function of word frequency: a replication*, The Role of Language in Behavior, Technical Report Number 6, University of Minnesota, Contract No. N8 onr—66216.

Klemmer, E. T., "Tables for computing informational measures," *Information Theory in Psychology* (H. Quastler, ed.), The Free Press, Glencoe (1955), 71—77.

—,   and Frick, F. C., "Assimilation of information from dot and matrix patterns," *J. exp. Psychol.*, 45, 1953, 15—19.

—,   and Muller, P. F., Jr., *The rates of handling information: key pressing responses to light patterns*, HFORL memo Report No. 34, 1953.

Krulee, G. K., "Information theory and man-machine systems," *J. Operat. Res. Soc. Amer.*, 2, 1954, 320—328.

—,   and Sinclair, E. J., *Some behavioral implications of information theory*, Report 4119, Naval Research Laboratory, Washington, D. C., 1953, 11 pp.

—,   Podell, J. E., and Ronco, P. C., "Effect of numbers of alternatives and set on the visual discrimination of numerals," *J. exp. Psychol.*, 48, 1954, 75—80.

Kullback, S., "An application of information theory to multivariate analysis," *Ann. math. Statist.*, 23, 1952, 88—102.

—,   and Leibler, R. A., "On information and sufficiency," *Ann. math. Statist.*, 22, 1951, 79—86.

Leonard, J. A., *The effect of partial advance information*, British Medical Research Council, A. P. U. report 217/54, 1954.

—,   "Factors which influence channel capacity," *Information Theory in Psychology* (H. Quastler, ed.), The Free Press, Glencoe (1955), 306—314.

Licklider, J. C. R. (Editor), *Problems in human communications and control*, Paraphrased transcription of a conference sponsored by the National Science Foundation, 1954, M. I.T., Cambridge, dittoed, 203 pp.

—,   "Quasi-linear operator models in the study of manual tracking," this volume, 1960.

—,   and Miller, G. A., "The perception of speech," *Handbook of Experimental Psychology* (S. S. Stevens, editor), John Wiley & Sons, (1951), 1040—1074.

Lord, F. M., "Scaling," *Rev. educ. Res.*, 24, 1954, 375—392.

Luce, R. D., *Individual Choice Behavior*, John Wiley & Sons, (1959).

MacKay, D., "Quantal aspects of scientific information," *Philosophical Magazine* (series 7), 41, 1950, 289—311; and *Transactions of the Institute of Radio Engineers, Professional Group on Information Theory*, 1, 1953, 60—80.

—,   "The nomenclature of information theory," *Cybernetics* (Heinz von Foerster, ed.), Josiah Macy, Jr. Foundation, New York, (1951 a), 222—233; and *Transactions of the Institute of Radio Engineers, Professional Group on Information Theory*, 1, 1953, 9—21.

—,   "In search of basic symbols," *Cybernetics* (Heinz von Foerster, ed.), Josiah Macy, Jr. Foundation, New York (1951 b), 181—221.

Mandelbrot, Benoît, "Contribution à la théorie mathématique des jeux de communication, "*Publications de l'Institut de Statistique de l'Université de Paris*, 2, 1953 a, 1—124.

—,   "An informational theory of the statistical structure of language," *Communication theory* (Willis Jackson, ed.), Academic Press, New York (1953 b), 486—502.

—,   "Structure formelle des textes et communication: deux études," *Word*, 10, 1954 a, 1—27.

—,   "Simple games of strategy occurring in communication through natural languages," *Transactions of the Institute of Radio Engineers, Professional Group on Information Theory*, 3, 1954 b, 125—137.

—,   "On recurrent noise limiting coding," *Proceedings of the Symposium on Information Networks*, Microwave Research Institute, Polytechnic Institute of Brooklyn, New York (1954 c), 205—221.

McGill, W. J., *Multivariate transmission of information and its relation to analysis of variance*, Report No. 32, Human Factors Operations Research Laboratory, M. I. T., 1953.

—, "Multivariate information transmission," *Psychometrika*, 19, 1954, 97—116; and *Transactions of the IRE, Professional Group on Information Theory*, 4, 1954, 93—111.

—, "Isomorphism in statistical analysis," *Information Theory in Psychology* (H. Quastler, ed.), The Free Press, Glencoe (1955 a), 56—62.

—, "The relation between uncertainty and variance," *Proc. 1954 Conf. Test Probl. Educ. Test. Serv.*, 1955 b, 37—42.

—, and Quastler, H., "Standardized nomenclature: an attempt," *Information Theory in Psychology* (H. Quastler, ed.), The Free Press, Glencoe (1955), 83—92.

McMillan, B., "The basic theorems of information theory," *Ann. math. Statist.*, 24, 1953, 196—219.

—, "Mathematical aspects of information theory," *Current Trends in Information Theory* (R. A. Patton, ed.), U. of Pittsburgh Press, Pittsburgh (1954), 1—17.

Merkel, J., "Die zeitlichen Verhältnisse der Willensthätigkeit," *Philos, St.*, 2, 1885, 73—127.

Miller, G. A., "Language engineering," *J. acoust. Soc. Amer.*, 22, 1950, 720—725.

—, *Language and Communication*, McGraw-Hill, New York (1951 a).

—, "Speech and language," *Handbook of Experimental Psychology* (S. S. Stevens, ed.), John Wiley & Sons (1951 b), 789—810.

—, "What is information measurement?" *Amer. Psychologist*, 8, 1953, 3—11.

—, "Communication," *Annual Review of Psychology*, 5 (Stone, C, P., and McNemar, Q., eds.), Annual Reviews, Inc., Stanford (1954 a), 401—420.

—, "Information theory and the study of speech," *Current Trends in Information Theory* (R. A. Patton, ed.), U. of Pittsburgh Press, Pittsburgh (1954 b), 119—139.

—, "Note on the bias of information estimates," *Information Theory in Psychology* (H. Quastler, ed.), The Free Press, Glencoe (1955), 95—100.

—, "The magical number seven, plus or minus two: some limits on our capacity for processing information," *Psychol. Rev.*, 63, 1956, 81—97.

—, and Frick, F. C., "Statistical behavioristics and sequences of responses," *Psychol. Rev.*, 56, 1949, 311—324.

—, Heise, G. A., and Lichten, W., "The intelligibility of speech as a function of the context of the test materials," *J. exp. Psychol.*, 41, 1951, 329—335.

—, and Madow, W. G., *On the maximum likelihood estimate of the Shannon-Wiener measure of information*, Air Force Cambridge Research Center, Technical Report, 54—75, 1954.

—, and Selfridge, J. A., "Verbal context and the recall of meaningful material," 63, *Amer. J. Psychol.* 1950, 176—185.

Munsow, W. A., and Karlin, J. E., "Measurement of human channel transmission characteristics," *J. Acoust. Soc. Amer.*, 26, 1954, 542—553.

Newman, E. B., "Computational methods useful in analysing series of binary data," *Amer. J. Psychol.*, 64, 1951 a, 252—262.

Newman, E. B., "The pattern of vowels and consonants in various languages," *Amer. J. Psychol.*, 64, 1951 b, 369—379.

—, and Gerstman, C. J., "A new method for analysing printed English," *J. exp. Psychol.*, 44, 1952, 114—125.

Osgood, C. E. (Editor), "Psycholinguistics: a survey of theory and research problems," *J. abnorm. soc. Psychol.*, 49 (4, pt. 2 — suppl.), 1954, 203 pp.

—, "Fidelity and reliability," *Information Theory in Psychology* (H.Quastler, ed.), The Free Press, Glencoe (1955), 374—384.

Patton, R. A., (Editor), *Current Trends in Information Theory*, Univ. of Pittsburgh Press, Pittsburgh (1954).

Peterson, G. E., "Applications of information theory to research in experimental phonetics," *J. Speech Hearing Disorders*, 17, 1952, 175—188.

Pollack, Irwin, "Information of elementary auditory displays," *J. Acoust. Soc. Amer.*, 24, 1952 a, 745—750.

—, *The Assimilation of sequentially-encoded information. 1. Methodology and an illustrative experiment. 2. Effect of rate of information presentation. 3. Serial position analysis. 4. The informational contribution of "wrong" responses.* Human Resources Research Laboratories, Memo Report No. 25, Washington, 1952 b.

—, "The information of elementary auditory displays. II," *J. Acoust. Soc. Amer.*, 25, 1953, 765—769.

—, and Ficks, L., "Information of elementary multidimensional auditory displays," *J. Acoust. Soc. Amer.*, 26, 1954, 155—158.

Pratt, Fletcher, *Secret and Urgent*, Blue Ribbon Books, Garden City (1942).

Proceedings of the London Symposium on Information Theory, 1950, see Jackson [1953 a].

Proceedings of the London Symposium on Information Theory, 1952, see Jackson [1953 b].

Proceedings of the Symposium on Information Networks, Microwave Research Institute. Polytechnic Institute of Brooklyn, New York (1955).

Quastler, Henry (Editor), *Essays on the Use of Information Theory in Biology*, University of Illinois Press, Urbana (1953).

—, *Information Theory in Psychology*, The Free Press, Glencoe (1955 a).

—, "Approximate estimation of information measures," *Information Theory in Psychology* (H. Quastler, ed.), The Free Press, Glencoe (1955 b), 124—139.

—, "Information theory terms and their psychological correlates," *Information Theory in Psychology* (H. Quastler, ed.), The Free Press, Glencoe (1955 c), 143—171.

—, and Wulff, V. J., *Human performance in information transmission*, Control Systems Laboratory Report No. 62, University of Illinois, 1955.

Rappaport, M., *The role of redundancy in discrimination of visual forms*, Ph. D. dissertation, The Ohio State University, 1954.

Reich, E., "Definition of information," *Proceedings of the Institute of Radio Engineers*, 39, 1951 a, 290.

—, "The game of 'gossip' analysed by the theory of information," *Bulletin of Mathematical Biophysics*, 13, 1951 b, 313—318.

Rogers, M. S., *An application of information theory to the problem of the relationship between meaningfulness of material and performance in a learning situation*, Ph. D. thesis, Princeton University, 1952, mimeographed.

Rogers, M. S., and Green, B. F., "The moments of sample information when the alternatives are equally likely," *Information Theory in Psychology* (H. Quastler, ed.), The Free Press, Glencoe (1955), 101—108.

Rubenstein, H., and Aborn, M., "Immediate recall as a function of degree of organization and length of study period," *J. exp. Psychol.*, 48, 1954, 146—152.

Savage, L. J., *The Foundations of Statistics*, John Wiley & Sons, New York (1954).

Schafer, T. H., "A basic experiment in detection," *Information Theory in Psychology* (H. Quastler, ed.), The Free Press, Glencoe (1955), 415—418.

Schützenberger, M. P., "Sur les rapports entre la quantité d'information au sense de Fisher et au sens de Wiener," *Comptes Rendus de l'Académie des Sciences*, 233, 1951, 925—927.

Senders, J. W., "Man's capacity to use information from complex displays," *Information Theory in Psychology* (H. Quastler, ed.), The Free Press, Glencoe (1955), 360—363.

—, "The effect of number of subjects on the estimate of transmitted information," *Information Theory in Psychology* (H. Quastler, ed.), The Free Press, Glencoe (1955), 368—372.

—, and Cohen, J., "The effects of sequential dependencies on instrument reading performance," *Information Theory in Psychology* (H. Quastler, ed.), The Free Press, Glencoe (1955), 282—289.

Shannon, C. E., "A mathematical theory of communication," *Bell System Tech. J.*, 27, 1948, 379—423 and 623—656.

—, "Communication theory of secrecy systems," *Bell System Tech. J.*, 28, 1949, 656—715.

—, "The redundancy of English," *Cybernetics* (H. von Foerster, ed.), Josiah Macy, Jr. Foundation, New York (1950), 123—158.

—, "Prediction and entropy of printed English," *Bell System Tech. J.*, 30, 1951, 50—64.

—, "Communication theory, exposition of fundamentals," *Transactions of the Institute of Radio Engineers, Professional Group on Information Theory*, 1, 1953 a, 44—47.

—, "General treatment of the problem of coding," *Transactions of the Institute of Radio Engineers, Professional Group on Information Theory*, 1, 1953 b, 102—104.

—, "The lattice theory of information," *Transactions of the Institute of Radio Engineers, Professional Group on Information Theory*, 1, 1953 c, 105—107.

—, and Weaver, Warren, *The Mathematical Theory of Communication*, University of Illinois Press, Urbana (1949).

Simon, H. A., "On a class of skew distribution functions," *Biometrika*, 42, 1955, 425—440.

Slepian, D., "Information theory," *Operations Research for Management* (J. F. McCloskey and F. N. Trefethen, eds.), The Johns Hopkins Press, Baltimore (1954), 149—167.

Stumpers, F. L., "A bibliography of information theory (communication theory — cybernetics)," *Transactions of the Institute of Radio Engineers, Professional Group on Information Theory*, 2, 1953; and Research Laboratory of Electronics, Technical Report, M. I. T., 1953.

Tanner, W. P., Jr., "On the design of psychophysical experiments," *Information Theory in Psychology* (H. Quastler, ed.), The Free Press, Glencoe (1955), 403—414.

Thorndike, E. L., and Lorge, I., *The teacher's word book of 31,000 words*, Bureau of Publications, Teachers College, Columbia University, New York (1944).

Transactions of the Institute of Radio Engineers, Professional Group on Information Theory, 1 (see Jackson [1953 a]); 2 (see Stumpers [1953]); 3 (1954); 4 (1955).

Van Meter, D., and Middleton, D., "Modern statistical approaches to reception in communication theory," *Transactions of the IRE, Professional Group on Information Theory*, 4, 1954, 119—145.

Wald, A., *Sequential Analysis*, John Wiley & Sons, New York (1947).

Watanabe, S., "A study of ergodicity and redundancy based on intersymbol correlations of finite range," *Transactions of the IRE, Professional Group on Information Theory*, 4, 1954, 85—92.

Weaver, W., Peterson, G. E., and Davis, H., "Information theory: 1) Information theory to 1951 — a non-technical review, 2) Applications of information theory to research in experimental phonetics, 3) Applications of information theory to research in hearing," *J. Speech Hearing Disorders*, 17, 1952, 166—197.

Weinstein, M., *Stimulus complexity and the recognition of visual patterns*, Ph. D. dissertation, The Ohio State University, 1955.

Wiener, Norbert, *Cybernetics*, John Wiley & Sons, New York (1948).

—, *Extrapolation, Interpolation, and Smoothing of Stationary Time Series*, John Wiley & Sons, New York (1949).

Willis, R., "Estimating the scalability of a series of items — an application of information theory," *Psychol. Bull.*, 1954, 51, 511—516.

Wilks, S. S., "The likelihood test of independence in contingency tables," *Ann. math. Statist.*, 6, 1935, 190—196.

Woodward, P. M., *Probability and Information Theory, with Applications to Radar*, McGraw-Hill, New York (1953).

Zipf, G. K., *Human Behavior and the Principle of Least Effort*, Addison-Wesley Press, Cambridge (1949).

PART TWO

A Survey of

Mathematical Learning Theory

By ROBERT R. BUSH

UNIVERSITY OF PENNSYLVANIA

Contents

THIS PAPER(*) is a survey of recent attempts to develop mathematical theory in the psychology of learning. It is written primarily for mathematicians and for social scientists who are not familiar with the field of learning but who have an interest in mathematical models and theories. The organization of the material is problem oriented; the list of sections parallels the chapter headings in several current books on learning. No attempt is made to present a systematic mathematical theory.

Each section begins with a brief statement of the empirical phenomena to be discussed and a description of some of the relevant experiments and psychological theories. These parts are far from exhaustive, for they are intended only to set the stage for the discussions of the mathematical formulations. More complete discussions can be found in psychological texts (e.g., Deese [1952] and Hilgard and Marquis [1940]). Following these introductory remarks are discussions of proposed models but details are omitted and no formal proofs are included. Finally, suggestions for what needs to be done and, in a few cases, how it might be done, are made. Problems in statistical estimation which are very important in applying models to actual data analysis are not included, mainly because no new statistical developments have grown out of work on learning models although several unsolved problems have been posed by them.

The goal of this paper is to give the reader a broad picture of mathematical developments in learning rather than to mention everyone who has ever worked in the area. As a result, not even the bibliography is complete.(†)

1. HISTORICAL INTRODUCTION

THE PSYCHOLOGY of learning is concerned with how behavior patterns of individuals get established and changed. Since its childhood, learning has

(*) The writer is indebted to A. H. Black, W. K. Estes, J. Engler, F. W. Irwin, R. D. Luce, F. Mosteller, and F. Restle for critically reading the manuscript.

(†) No references to publications that appeared after 1955 are included.

been an experimental science, and so today a tremendous body of data is available. Moreover, a number of theories for explaining these results have been developed. Two basic concepts in all these theories are those of *stimulus* and *response*. Ordinarily, a stimulus is considered to be an environmental event such as a light or buzzer controlled by an experimenter, whereas a response is an act or movement made by the organism which received the stimulation. Psychologists have extensively studied the laws governing relations among stimuli, among responses, and between stimuli and responses. Many species of organisms from earthworms to college students have served as subjects in learning experiments. Perhaps the most popular subject is the white rat.

The analysis of data obtained in learning experiments has, on the whole, followed rather conventional lines. Means for groups of animals are plotted against some experimental variable, and *t*-tests between groups are made. Learning does not possess its own statistical methodology comparable to that developed for genetics or quality control. Sequential analyses are rarely made, even though the nature of the data might suggest such an approach.

Since the turn of the century, mathematical formulations of one type or another have been proposed for describing learning. The earliest attempts (Thurstone [1919], Ettlinger [1926]) were concerned with finding *the* learning function, an analytically defined function to describe how some measure of performance of a task increased with some measure of practice. The meaning of these two variables was clear enough from the beginning; the quality of a child's piano playing improves with each lesson, for example. However, the actual measures of performance and practice used varied considerably from study to study.

Several analytic functions were proposed for the learning curve, the most common ones being a hyperbola, the arc cotangent, and an exponential. In general, one wanted a function that was monotonically increasing and had an asymptote corresponding to the best possible performance. Whether or not the function was initially accelerating was much debated in the psychological literature. This search for the correct learning function began by *ad hoc* proposals and by curve fitting to experimental data, but later there appeared several attempts to derive the function from "rational" considerations. This was the beginning of formal models for learning. Perhaps the first *stochastic*(*) model was published by Thurstone

(*) According to J. E. Walsh of Houghton Library, Harvard University, the word "stochastic" was derived from the Greek word "στοχαζομαι" which means "to aim or shoot at" (a target or some object), but it later came to mean "to guess." In modern mathematical literature, the term is used almost as a synonym of "probabilistic" or "random" but usually implies that a time variable is present.

[1930], and later Gulliksen [1934] presented a modified version. In these early attempts, however, the goal was to derive the learning function — the curve of *mean* performance versus practice units. No other properties of the stochastic process were investigated. The mathematical tools used in these studies were those of simple probability theory and differential equations.

Without a doubt, Clark Hull was the leading proponent of formal theory in learning for many years. In his *Principles of Behavior*, Hull [1943] presented a formal system for describing a wide range of experiments in animal and human learning. The system contains sixteen "postulates" and five major "corollaries." However, the postulates are really empirical generalizations, and many psychologists have tried to test these so-called postulates by various kinds of experiments. For several of his postulates, Hull provides a mathematical (or at least symbolic) translation. As an example, consider Hull's postulate (4) (p. 178). He begins by introducing a symbolic construct which he calls "habit strength" and denotes by $_sH_R$. (Basic to Hull's theory is the concept of reinforcement; operationally it means giving food to a hungry rat, water to a thirsty one, etc.) Hull notes the following experimental observations:

(1) In Pavlovian conditioning experiments, the amplitude of a galvanic skin reaction increases with the number of reinforcements, rapidly at first, and then flattens off to some upper limit.

(2) In rote learning experiments, the mean reaction time for verbal responses decreases exponentially with the number of reinforcements.

(3) In bar-pressing experiments on rats, the "resistance to extinction" (as measured by total number of responses made after reinforcement ceases) increases with the number of preceding reinforcements, rapidly at first, but approaches an asymptote.

(4) In choice situations, the proportion of "correct" responses increases with the number of reinforcements, approaching 1.0 as a limit.

Hull then argues that the above four measures are indices of a more general behavioral variable he calls habit strength. He assumes that it increases with the number of reinforcements, N, according to the equation,

$$_sH_R = m\left(1 - e^{-iN}\right),$$

where m and i are positive constants.

In his ninth chapter, Hull argues that the upper limit of various indices of $_sH_R$ increases as the amount of the reinforcing agent (e.g., food) is increased. He cites two experiments which suggest this. As a result, Hull decides that m, in the preceding equation, depends upon the amount of reward, w, as follows:

$$m = m'\left(1 - e^{-kw}\right),$$

where m' and k are new constants. Next, in Chapter 10, Hull infers from experiments that m, the upper limit of habit strength, decreases as the time, t, between the response and the reinforcement is increased. Again he postulates an exponential law and lets

$$m' = m''e^{-jt},$$

where m'' and j are more new constants. Finally, in Chapter 11, Hull asserts that in Pavlovian conditioning the maximum habit strength decreases when the time, t', between the conditioned and unconditioned stimuli increases, i.e., he assumes

$$m'' = Me^{-ut'},$$

where M and u are two additional constants.

When the preceding four equations, assumed by Hull, are combined, one obtains the formal statement of his postulate (4):

$$_sH_R = M\left(1 - e^{-kw}\right)e^{-jt}e^{-ut'}\left(1 - e^{-iN}\right).$$

The right-hand side of this equation involves four experimental variables, w, t, t', and N, and five constants that must be estimated from data. This postulate essentially summarizes the first half of the book.

Many deductions from these postulates were made by Hull, Spence [1951], and others and this led to a vast amount of experimental work. Although no mathematician or logician would be satisfied with Hull's postulates as an axiom system or with the process used for deriving theorems, Hull's work did constitute a pioneer attempt in psychology. Hull devoted his life to making psychology a "hard" science. His influence is still strongly felt among experimenters and theorists in the field of learning. Hull's critics usually debated specific assumptions and concepts such as the physiological nature of some of his basic postulates or his emphasis on drive reduction as the mechanism of reinforcement, but most students of the science of behavior agree that Hull's general approach was sound. A notable exception is Skinner, whose main argument is that the time for such formal theorizing is not yet here. More basic data are needed first, argues Skinner [1950].

To a mathematician, Hull's theory is rather barren. In many cases his postulates are not stated in mathematical form. With a few exceptions, Hull did no mathematical analyses; he merely wrote down an exponential function to relate two variables. Like Thurstone and Gulliksen, Hull was primarily concerned with *mean* measures of performance. The theory has little to say about the sequential aspects of learning data, about the possible range of variation in a group of subjects, or, more generally, about the details of learning data.

Hull's chief contemporaries were Lewin, Tolman, Guthrie, and Skinner. These leading theorists made little use of mathematics, although Lewin gave psychological connotations to numerous mathematical terms like "field" and "vector."

Virtually independent of Hull and his collaborators and, in fact, independent of the bulk of research in psychology, work in mathematical biology has led to models for learning. Rashevsky [1951] and others have published several papers and books that give mathematical descriptions of learning processes, but they had little or no influence on psychological research. This lack of influence seems to stem from the fact that Rashevsky has not been concerned with learning data obtained by, or theoretical problems posed by, psychologists. Furthermore, Rashevsky's work has not led to new experiments nor opened up new theoretical issues in learning. For the most part, Rashevsky has been concerned with deriving learning functions from physiological models rather than with the relations among behavioral variables.

In 1949, the present growth of mathematics applied to learning began. Almost simultaneously, three independent programs were initiated. Estes [1950] started by trying to formalize some of the basic ideas of conditioning theory. Miller and Frick [1949] began by studying some of the sequential aspects of behavior and their relation to information theory. Bush and Mosteller [1951a] started to investigate the use of linear operators in analyzing learning data. During the following several years, close collaboration among these persons developed. In several instances, problems arose which required the talents of more skilled mathematicians. In addition, a fairly large number of experimental studies have resulted directly from this work on mathematical models for learning. The balance of this paper will deal primarily with these models, the problems they have handled, and many they have not.

2. ACQUISITION

THE MAJORITY of the model work done in recent years has been on the process of acquisition. How does a rat learn to turn right instead of left in a maze (Brunswik [1939])? How does a person learn one of two responses in a prediction experiment (Humphreys [1939], Goodnow and Postman [1955])? How does a dog learn to jump over a barrier to avoid an electric shock (Solomon and Wynne [1953])? These are typical of the kinds of questions asked. There exists a rather large body of experimental literature on such problems and it seems clear that they are a first order of business for any detailed mathematical learning theory.

Most acquisition experiments are readily considered to be choice situations. A person or an animal is confronted with a choice between two or more responses on each trial of a long sequence. For example, on each trial a rat turns right or left, a person guesses yes or no, or the dog jumps soon enough to avoid shock or it does not. These responses have certain specifiable outcomes for the subject, and behavior on future trials is altered as a result. If acquisition in fact occurs, one response becomes more frequent and others less so, but not in all experiments does one response tend to occur on 100 per cent of the trials asymptotically. The relative frequency may tend to stabilize at some other value.

On each trial of a learning experiment, the animal or human subject is exposed to a fixed stimulus situation — a piece of apparatus in an experimental room with constant lighting, temperature, and sounds — but only some of the stimuli are perceived by the subject on any given trial. In stimulus-response theories, stimuli become conditioned to certain responses; that is, they tend to evoke those responses. The mechanism by which this conditioning occurs marks the differences among the several theories, but all agree that somehow stimuli and responses do get connected or associated as a habit is acquired.

In the conditioning theory developed by Estes [1950, 1954], by Estes and Burke [1953], and by several of their students, the stimulus population is of central importance. It is represented in their formal model by a set of abstract elements. On each trial the subject samples from this set. Elements are conditioned to one response or another; that is, they are postulated to exist in one of several states corresponding to the response classes that are experimentally defined. One of Estes' main axioms is that the probability of a response is equal to the number of sampled stimulus elements conditioned to that response divided by the total number of elements sampled. In a minor generalization of Estes' theory, Bush and Mosteller [1951b, 1955] introduce a measure function on the set of stimulus elements (relative weights to the elements) and thereby replace "number of elements" with "measure of elements" in Estes' axiom.

A rather direct test of this axiom in Estes' theory is provided by an experiment by Schoeffler [1954]. Subjects were confronted with a panel of 24 light bulbs and conditioned to move a lever in one direction when eight particular lamps were illuminated and to move it in the opposite direction when eight other lamps were turned on. The total stimulus situation was conceived as a set S partitioned into three disjunct subsets, S_1, S_2, and S_3, and it was assumed that after conditioning, all elements in S_1 were conditioned to response A_1, that all elements in S_2 were conditioned to response A_2, and that elements in S_3 were conditioned to neither. After being conditioned, the subjects were presented with patterns of lights containing some from each of the three subsets. It follows from Estes' theory that the probability of response A_1 on such a test trial will equal the number of elements conditioned to A_1 divided by the total number of elements present. By assuming that each illuminated light bulb contains the same number of elements, the response probabilities are readily predicted from the numbers of lights of each kind turned on. Using nine different patterns on different test trials, Schoeffler found excellent agreement between the predicted response probabilities and the frequencies of responses for groups of subjects.

The second major axiom in Estes' system concerns the change of state of stimulus elements when responses in fact occur. Following Guthrie [1935, 1940], he postulates that after a trial, stimuli sampled are conditioned to the response that occurred, whether or not they were previously conditioned to that response. This is the learning axiom. Again, a minor generalization was proposed by Bush and Mosteller [1951b, 1955]; they postulate that one subset of the sampled stimuli becomes conditioned to the response that occurred and another disjunct subset becomes de-conditioned to that response. This de-conditioning is assumed to occur because of the work or effort required in making the response.

Estes and Burke [1953] generalized the Estes model to describe the effects of varying the stimulus situation on behavioral measures. They introduce a probability θ_i that the ith stimulus element is sampled on a given trial. In the simpler model it was implicitly assumed that θ_i had a constant value θ for all elements and so θ was called the sampling ratio — the proportion of elements sampled on any trial. It was shown that θ was a measure of the rate of learning and so could be estimated from data. In the generalized model, few predictions could be made without assuming the form of the distribution of θ_i. As a result, Burke, Estes, and Hellyer [1954] simplified the general model by assuming that the stimulus population consisted of two subsets and that θ_i had a constant value θ_L in one subset and another constant value $\theta_{\bar{L}}$ in the other subset. The number of elements in subset S_L was varied experimentally and it was shown that the observed learning rates changed in the predicted direction. They further predicted correctly (within experimental error) the relation between the learning rates of three groups of subjects run with different numbers of elements in subset S_L.

Whereas Estes derives relations between response probabilities on adjacent trials from axioms about stimulus sampling and conditioning, Bush and Mosteller [1951a, 1953, 1955] postulate such a relation from the start. A linear relation is assumed. (Some readers may feel that linearity is a severe restriction, but whether or not it is depends upon where in the theory, linearity is introduced.) For two response classes with probabilities p and $1-p$, respectively, they write

$$p_{n+1} = a_i p_n + (1-a_i)\lambda_i \qquad (1)$$

where n refers to trial number and where a_i and λ_i are two parameters which depend upon the response actually made on trial n and upon the outcome on that trial. Several interpretations of the basic parameters and their combinations are discussed at length elsewhere (Bush and Mosteller [1955]). Briefly, $(1-a_i)$ is a rate parameter and λ_i is the asymptote which would be approached if equation (1) were appropriate for every trial beyond a given point in the process. When λ_i is O or 1, the quantity $(1-a_i)$ is equivalent to Estes' sampling ratio, θ_i. The parameter values for a given experiment have not been determined independently of the data from that experiment. Various procedures for estimating the parameters from data have been used. From numerous such estimates, it does not appear that any of the parameters are universal constants. Estimates in the range $0 \leq \theta \leq 0.2$ have been observed but values of θ near 0.05 are most common.

For more than two response classes, Bush and Mosteller introduce a probability vector $\vec{p}_n$ for trial n and postulate that

$$\vec{p}_{n+1} = T_i \vec{p}_n \qquad (2)$$

where T_i is a linear operator, a transition matrix. It was demonstrated by

Bush and Mosteller [1951b, 1955] that these linear operators could be derived from Estes' theory of stimulus sampling and conditioning.

Whether one prefers to start with Estes' stimulus theory or with the linear operator approach, a random walk process results. For the simple case of two response classes, there is a single behavioral variable p_n for trial n, and on each trial one of several events occurs. To each event corresponds a transition law which gives p_{n+1}. In many experimental applications, either two or four events seem adequate. If the ith event occurs on trial n, equation (1) above gives the transition law. The problem, then, mathematically speaking, is to specify which events occur on which trials. If the sequence of events is known precisely, a trivial computation problem results, but if only the event probabilities are known on each trial, a distribution of probabilities obtains. Properties of such distributions have been the main subjects of several mathematical studies.

In generalizing their model to an arbitrary number, r, of alternatives, Bush and Mosteller introduce a "combining classes" condition which leads to a major theorem of the theory(*). Suppose that r alternatives are considered in the model and that each is identified with a response class in an experiment. On a particular trial, let the probability vector for the response occurrences, be $\vec{p}$, and on the following trial let the corresponding vector be $S\vec{p}$, where S is a stochastic operator which describes the effect of the event which just occurred. Then suppose the experimenter treated two or more of the response classes in identical manner and so wished to combine them. This can be represented by applying a projection operator C to the probability vectors so as to obtain vectors $C\vec{p}$ and $CS\vec{p}$ on the two trials in question. The same projection operator C must be applied to S to obtain a stochastic operator CS in the reduced space. In these terms, the combining classes condition requires that

$$(CS)\,C\vec{p} = C\,(S\vec{p})\,. \tag{3}$$

This merely asserts that the same projected vector is obtained independently of the trial on which the projection is carried out. If this condition is imposed for *all* projection operators C, the theorem referred to can be proved. L. J. Savage first proved that all continuous stochastic operators S that satisfy (3) can be written

(*) A somewhat different generalization to r alternatives has been given by Detambel [1955].

$$S = aI + (1-a)\Lambda, \tag{4}$$

where a is a suitably chosen scalar, I is the identity matrix, and where Λ is a matrix each of whose columns is a fixed probability vector $\vec{\lambda}$, called the fixed point of the operator. G. L. Thompson later showed that the Savage theorem was true for *any* stochastic operator S. Before this theorem was known, Bush and Mosteller had shown only that *linear* stochastic operators satisfying (3) were of the form (4). Proof of the most general theorem is given by Bush, Mosteller, and Thompson [1954] (*), whereas arguments for the desirability of the combining classes condition are given by Bush and Mosteller [1955].

With a set of linear operators S_i of the form (4), several "trapping" theorems have been proved (Bush, Mosteller, and Thompson [1954]). These theorems concern the region within which a probability vector must lie after an arbitrarily long arbitrary sequence of applications of the operators. In addition, for certain special cases of the theory, some moments of trial-to-trial distributions of the probability vectors have been computed.

An important theorem for the asymptotic distribution of probabilities when $r = 2$ was first proved by Harris [1952]. Given the transition laws

$$p_{n+1} = a_1 p_n + (1-a_1)\lambda_1 \text{ with probability } p_n,$$
$$\tag{5}$$
$$p_{n+1} = a_2 p_n + (1-a_2)\lambda_2 \text{ with probability } 1-p_n.$$

Harris proved that a stable asymptotic distribution exists independent of p_0 except when $\lambda_1 = 1$ and $\lambda_2 = 0$. For this exception, one has two "absorbing barriers" in the limit; all probabilities are 1 or 0 in the limit and the proportion at 1 depends upon p_0.

The problem of two absorbing barriers just mentioned leads to an interesting functional equation (Harris, Bellman, and Shapiro [1952], Karlin [1953]). If $f(p_0, a_1, a_2)$ is the probability that a "particle" beginning at p_0 is absorbed in the limit at 1, then we have the equation

$$f(p_0, a_1, a_2) = p_0 f(a_1 p_0 + 1 - a_1, a_1, a_2) + (1-p_0)f(a_2 p_0, a_1, a_2). \tag{6}$$

Shapiro and Bellman first showed that this functional equation has no closed analytic solution, but they studied many properties of the equation.

(*) W. G. Madow showed that lemma 3 is incorrect but that the theorem is correct as stated.

Karlin later showed that the distribution of probabilities for this case of two absorbing barriers converges very slowly but that the mean converges geometrically.

When the transitions given by (5) occur with *fixed* probabilities π and $1 - \pi$, instead of with probabilities p_n and $1 - p_n$, a simpler problem results and has been essentially solved. In fact, when there are any number, t, of possible transitions of this form, occurring with fixed probabilities π_i, all moments of the distributions of p_n have been calculated (Bush and Mosteller [1955]).

An "ergodic theorem for single sequences" was stated by Bush and Mosteller [1955], but no formal proof was given. This theorem states that when the transitions occur with fixed probabilities or when the Harris ergodic theorem holds, a single sequence of probabilities p_n generates (with probability one) a distribution which in the limit is identical to the asymptotic distribution yielded by all possible sequences. This theorem was used in numerical computations of the approximate shape of asymptotic distributions.

Additional theorems about the general model and some special cases have been proved by Karlin [1953] and by Kemeny, DeLeeuw, Snell, and Thompson [1955]. As a result the mathematical properties of the model are rather well understood. On the other hand, the usefulness of the model for describing learning phenomena is not so well understood and so we now return to the problem of how this model and others have been applied to several psychological problems on the acquisition of habits.

Reward Training. In the conventional type of reward training experiment, an animal is reinforced for making one class of responses and is not reinforced for making all other responses. An example is a simple T-maze in which a hungry rat is given food after right-hand turns but is given nothing after left-hand turns. For a group of rats treated in this way, one obtains an acquisition curve (a "learning curve") that begins at about $p = 0.5$ and approaches $p = 1.00$ asymptotically. The early attempts at finding the correct "learning function," mentioned above, were concerned with such curves. These early investigators, as well as Hull, merely postulated the shape of this curve of proportion of correct responses *versus* trial number. The curve is readily derived from the stochastic models just described, but these models' predict much more about the sequences of right and left turns that obtain. In principle, all properties of the sequences are predicted by those models. Monte Carlo computations can be made to generate theoretical sequences corresponding to the experimental ones (Bush and Mosteller [1955]). Hence the stochastic models predict (correctly or incorrectly) all that can be known about the data recorded. There are most serious problems of goodness-of-fit, of course, that need careful study in each instance.

An illustration of the detailed predictions made by stochastic models is provided by an experiment on paradise fish reported by Bush and Wilson [1956]. The experiment was similar to T-maze experiments on rats; on each trial a fish chose one of two goal compartments. The "favorable" side led to reward more often than did the other side. Various sequential properties of the data were compared with results of Monte Carlo computations as shown in the following table:

Statistic	Fish		Monte Carlo	
	Mean	S.D.	Mean	S.D.
Number of choices of favorable side	81.3	48.0	87.6	48.2
Total number of runs	27.3	13.7	29.8	20.2
Runs of length 1	12.9	6.7	14.2	10.1
Runs of length 2	4.4	3.8	5.3	6.3
Runs of length 3	2.0	1.8	3.0	2.6
Runs of length 4	1.5	1.6	2.2	2.2
Runs of length 5	1.1	1.3	1.0	1.4

In applications of the stochastic models to experiments on reward training, Bush and Mosteller found it expedient to assume that the limit points in their operator for reward were 1 so that reward tended to increase the probability of the response just made to a limit of 1. They also found it convenient to assume that the operators corresponding to non-reward were identity operators. This latter assumption leads to difficulties in describing experimental extinction, as noted below.

Partial Reinforcement. In many learning experiments, particular responses are not rewarded 100 per cent of the time they occur (Jenkins and Stanley [1950]. In these partial reinforcement studies, usually one response class is rewarded most frequently, however. The stochastic models of Estes [1954] and of Bush and Mosteller [1955] are readily applied to such problems — whenever reward occurs, an appropriate operator is applied; when non-reward occurs, another operator is applied. Indeed, these models were designed to handle just such problems. Previous mathematical learning models did not attempt to handle partial reinforcement.

Rote Learning. In most rote-learning experiments, a person memorizes a list of symbols, nonsense syllables, or words *in order* (Hull *et al.* [1940]). On each trial the subject is shown the list and then given a recall test. This leads to complex problems in serial learning or the "chaining" of responses because the recall of one word often reminds the subject of the next word on the list. However, in an experiment by Bruner, Miller, and Zimmerman [1955], the order of the words being memorized was randomized on each trial. As a result, Miller and McGill [1952] assumed that the words were learned independently of one another. With this assumption they developed a model which very closely described the data. Formally, the model was very similar to the stochastic models for reward training discussed above. If recall occurs on trial n, the recall probability p_n changes to

$$p_{n+1} = a p_n + (1-a),$$ (7)

whereas if non-recall occurs, p_n does not change.

Avoidance Training. In several experiments on animal learning, an animal is taught to make a particular response in order to avoid pain. For example, Solomon and Wynne [1953] trained dogs to jump over a barrier in order to avoid an intense electric shock. The sequences of "shocks" and "avoidances" were analyzed by Bush and Mosteller [1955] by assuming linear transition laws, and limit points equal to unity. They found it required about 2.5 shock trials to have the same effect on the avoidance probabilities as a single avoidance trial. The same formal model was used as that for reward training. No other authors have presented mathematical models for avoidance training.

Time and Rate Problems. In a number of learning experiments, response time or rate of responding is the dependent variable. In experiments with simple straight runways by Graham and Gagné [1940] and by Weinstock [1954], a rat was placed in a starting box and ran down an alley to a goal box in which food was sometimes placed. The latency (time in starting box) and running time were recorded on each trial. Estes [1950] developed a model for this experiment by assuming that in each small increment of time the animal made one of two responses, a response which led to the goal or one that did not. This led to a latency distribution of form e^{-t}. Bush and Mosteller [1955] generalized the model in several ways, but the basic notion of a sequence of choices on each experimental trial was maintained. Hence, the basic framework of the stochastic models, the idea of choices among mutually exclusive alternatives, was applied to problems in which response time is the important measure of learning.

In "Skinner-box" experiments (Skinner [1938]), a rat is placed in a box containing a lever or bar and a food delivery mechanism, or a pigeon is placed in a box containing a key and a food tray, or a psychotic patient is placed in front of a panel containing a button and a cigarette delivery mechanism. When the rat presses the bar, the pigeon pecks the key, or the psychotic pushes the button, reward may result. The subject is free to respond as often as he chooses. The data consist of a time record of bar-presses, key-pecks, or button-pushes. Rate of such responding or cumulative responses versus time are plotted. Various kinds of partial reinforcement schedules have been used. In a rudimentary way, the stochastic models have been applied to describing the gross features of such data. There is a serious question, however, about whether or not a routine application of those models can account for the systematic variations in the curves obtained. For example, when "periodic" reinforcement is used (reward after fixed time intervals), Skinner finds that the rate of responding becomes highest just before reward and lowest just afterwards. This experimental finding, intuitively reasonable as it is, is not predicted by a simple application of the stochastic models. It has been suggested that the animals are learning a time discrimination; hence, this problem may be an instance of the discrimination problem discussed in Chapter 5.

3. EXPERIMENTAL EXTINCTION

WHEN A RESPONSE that has been previously rewarded many times is no longer rewarded, the strength of that response decreases and it is said that extinction takes place. For example, the rate of bar-pressing of a rat in a Skinner box reaches some high level in acquisition but rapidly decreases when reward is withheld (Skinner [1938]). Or, in a T-maze, the frequency of right-hand turns might decrease from nearly 1.0 at the end of acquisition to about 0.5 after prolonged extinction. The shapes of the extinction curves that result are usually exponential-like, but many irregularities are often observed.

Various theories of the extinction process have been proposed. One of the most common mechanisms stems from Thorndike's law of effect and is included in Hull's theory: it is assumed that each response occurrence without reward leads to "inhibition" without a compensatory change from the reinforcement and so a decrement in the response strength results (Hull [1943]). This inhibition is assumed to be related to the work or effort expended in making the response. Another mechanism, proposed by Guthrie [1935, 1940] and also included in the Hullian system, involves the learning of other responses. Guthrie's theory has a single principle — association — which leads to learning response r in acquisition and to learning other responses $\sim r$ in extinction, but the circumstances under which each occurs are left ambiguous in this theory. The inhibition mechanism suggests that a decrement in the strength of response r occurs when response r is made, whereas the re-learning mechanism implies that a decrement results when response $\sim r$ is made. The two effects could co-exist, of course.

A third mechanism of extinction was suggested by Skinner [1950]. He says that extinction results from an increasing "novelty" of the experimental situation. The stimuli associated with reward and the consumatory behavior are absent and so the animal's behavior pattern changes (e.g., its rate of bar-pressing decreases). This in turn leads to a still greater change in the stimuli observed and so the animal's behavior changes still more. This "feedback" mechanism can be described in terms of stimulus generalization and discrimination discussed below.

Perhaps the most well established and universally observed experimental fact about extinction is that it occurs more slowly after partial reinforcement than after continuous reinforcement (Jenkins and Stanley [1950]). There is additional evidence that an increase in the proportion of rewarded trials during acquisition increases the rate of extinction. This phenomenon is not satisfactorily explained by either the inhibition or re-learning mechanisms described above because neither makes any reference to the conditions under which acquisition took place. Skinner's "novelty" mechanism, on the other hand, was undoubtedly invented to handle this fact; the situation in extinction is more "novel" after continuous reinforcement than after partial reinforcement. Alternative explanations have been proposed by other psychologists. For example, Mowrer and Jones [1945] argued that the response rewarded during partial reinforcement in a Skinner box is not a single bar-press but the whole sequence of behavior that precedes a single reward. When a response is re-defined in this way, the extinction curves obtained after various reinforcement schedules become more similar to one another. Several objections to this proposal have been cited. One is a logical one — Mowrer and Jones implicitly define a response in terms of reinforcement and this circularity leads to trouble, especially when one defines reinforcement in terms of the behavior it produces. Most psychologists strive to give independent operational definitions to responses and reinforcements so that laws relating them can be found. Another objection to the Mowrer-Jones proposal is that the dependency of extinction on the preceding acquisition schedule is found experimentally, even when trials are widely spaced. For example, Weinstock [1954] found this effect in a runway experiment using one trial per day. It is a bit difficult for anyone to believe that food today reinforces the responses of the last several days. Although the Mowrer-Jones view may still have some appeal in thinking about Skinner-box experiments in which key pecks by pigeons, for example, occur as rapid as a hundred per minute, that proposal cannot be considered an adequate explanatory mechanism for the spaced-trial experiments. This point is discussed here in some detail because the Mowrer-Jones suggestion, if satisfactory, would lead to a rather simple application of the stochastic models discussed next.

In most of the detailed applications of the stochastic learning models to experimental problems, a principle of "event invariance" has been invoked. An environmental change such as reward coupled with the immediately preceding response has been identified with one class of events and nonreward of the same response identified with another event class. Associated with each type of event is an operator which is applied to the response probability. In analyzing the data from two-choice experiments, Bush and Mosteller [1955] found that the non-reward operators were nearly identity operators during acquisition but that for extinction those operators produced large decrements in the response probabilities. Later, Bush and Wilson [1956] found in analyzing their experiment on paradise fish that non-reward of a response during acquisition actually increased the probability of that response. Thus, there is conclusive evidence that the event-invariance principle is untenable; non-reward during partial reinforcement simply is different from non-reward in extinction. The stochastic models face a major challenge here. The event-invariance principle must be discarded, but without it the models have much less predictive power. A new principle needs to be found.

An hypothesis to restore parsimony to the stochastic model applications was made by F. W. Irwin (unpublished). He maintained that a two-choice situation such as the T-maze should be considered a three-choice problem; during a small time interval the rat turns right or turns left or does neither. It was suggested that non-reward increases the probability of doing neither but does not increase the probability of either turning response. If it is further assumed that non-turning has no effect on the probabilities, it can be shown that extinction following complete acquisition of one turning response would not increase the probability of the other turning response but would increase only the probability of non-turning.

A preliminary experiment to test the prediction derived from Irwin's proposal was carried out by E. H. Galanter (unpublished). He conditioned rats to turn left by continuous reinforcement. During extinction, only ten seconds were allowed for a choice; if neither turn was made within that time, the animal was removed from the maze. The data show that the frequency of left turns decreases rapidly, the frequency of non-turning increases equally rapidly, but the frequency of right-hand turns stays very near zero. A more complete experiment is needed.

Another unexploited proposal for extending the stochastic models to handle extinction arises from the phenomena of secondary reinforcement, discussed in Chapter 6. It could be argued that the stimulating situation in which a non-reward occurs acquires reinforcing properties by association, that these properties are maintained as long as reward sometimes is given, but that in extinction the reinforcing properties of non-reward are gradually lost. This notion is quite similar to Skinner's novelty mechanism described above, but it further suggests that the way to handle the problem with stochastic models is to introduce for non-reward an operator whose parameters change each time reward follows non-reward. But this mechanism, like the one of Mowrer and Jones, would have trouble with the spaced-trial experiments.

When acquisition and extinction are alternated repeatedly, it is usually found that both occur more and more rapidly. None of the mechanisms discussed above, except Skinner's novelty mechanism, appear to handle this phenomenon. This observation, as well as others made above, suggests that a formal model based upon Skinner's notion should be developed in order to describe adequately a rather broad range of experimental results. It seems to the writer that such an approach would cast the problems involved into the framevork of stimulus discrimination, to be discussed in Chapter 5, but that a major problem would be to identify the discriminative cues and to specify when they occur.

Related to problems in experimental extinction is the sometimes observed phenomenon of spontaneous recovery. If a bar-pressing response is extinguished and the animal is removed from the apparatus and then is returned sometime later, the initial rate of responding may be greater than it was when the animal was removed. This spontaneous recovery effect has been studied by Estes [1955a]. He proposed a generalization of his set-theoretic model as follows. There exists a total set S of stimuli, including those associated with putting the animal in the apparatus, which gets conditioned to the response. Only a subset of S is perceived by the animal each time it is placed in the experimental box, and only this subset gets de-conditioned during one extinction session. The next time the animal is put in the box, a new sample from S is drawn and this contains stimuli still associated with the response. As a result, an initial increase in rate of responding occurs. Estes' model then predicts that the amount of spontaneous recovery in Skinner-box experiments decreases exponentially with the number of extinction sessions.

4. GENERALIZATION

IF A PARTICULAR response R is completely conditioned to a stimulus situation S and then the organism is presented with a new stimulus S' which is "similar" to S, it is found that response R is partially conditioned to S'. In other words, after conditioning in S, R may occur with probability 1; when S' is presented, R may occur with some probability less than 1 but greater than its probability before conditioning in S. This phenomenon is called stimulus generalization; the conditioning in S "generalizes" to S'.

The analogous process occurs on the response side of the picture. Conditioning of R to S produces partial conditioning to S of a similar response R'. This is called response generalization or response induction. Both stimulus and response generalization occur in many experiments on the transfer of training. In this section the two generalization processes are discussed. Relatively few experiments in this area have been carried out but the more important ones are described briefly and the mathematical attempts to explain the results are summarized.

Stimulus Generalization. The classic experiment on stimulus generalization was done by Hovland [1937a, 1937b]. A few seconds after a tone was sounded, a human subject was given an electric shock. The electrical resistance of the skin changed when shock occurred (galvanic skin response, GSR), and after several trials the GSR occured when the tone was sounded. Then, tones of different pitches (different intensities in another experiment) were presented and the GSR measured. It was found that the mean GSR's decreased monotonically with increasing difference (in either direction) between the original pitch and the pitch of the test tone.

Other demonstrations of stimulus generalization include an experiment by Postman [1951] in which subjects were shown a list of nonsense syllables and then asked to identify these on a recognition sheet which contained some syllables that had been shown and many that had not. The new syllables on the test sheet had varying degrees of similarity to the ones previously seen. In some syllables only one letter was changed, in others two letters were changed, etc. The number of new syllables checked by a group of subjects decreased monotonically with the number of letters altered.

Another example of stimulus generalization is an experiment by Brush *et al.* [1952]. Pigeons were trained to peck an illuminated disc to obtain food by a partial reinforcement schedule. After this conditioning, the size of the light spot on the disc was changed and the rate of pecking for a short time interval was observed. It was found that the average pecking rate decreased monotonically with the change in size of the test spot of light.

The single fact that emerges from the studies of stimulus generalization is that if the test stimuli are ordered with respect to similiarity to the original stimulus used in conditioning, the measure of response strength is a decreasing monotone function of the stimulus difference. One exception occurs when difference in pitch is used as an index of dissimilarity: an increase in response strength occurs at the octave intervals. The explanation, of course, is that pitch difference is not an adequate definition of degree of dissimilarity in this case. Another exception sometimes arises when an increase in the intensity of a stimulus increases response strength, independently of generalization. For example, a very loud tone might produce a higher GSR than a softer tone to which conditioning occurred. An analogous anomaly might have arisen in the Postman experiment if meaningful words had been used in place of nonsense syllables. For example, suppose PLUMS were on the original list and PEARS and PLOWS were on the test list. One might expect PEARS to be checked more often than PLOWS, even though the latter has more letters in common with PLUMS. Hovland tried to circumvent this difficulty in his experiment by measuring stimulus differences independently in terms of "just noticeable differences" (j.n.d.'s) as judged by other subjects. This procedure is not adapted readily to sub-human subjects, unfortunately, but it has remained the only technique which is even partly satisfactory. The "common elements" approach used by Postman has serious limitations and the physical dimension measure used by Brush *et al.*, is useful only when a single stimulus attribute is varied. In short, an independent behavioral definition of degree of similarity is needed if one wishes to have a quantitative *law* of stimulus generalization.

The j.n.d. measure of stimulus difference was accepted by Hull [1943] in his behavior theory. His fifth "postulate" is that response strength (however measured) is a decreasing exponential function of the number of j.n.d.'s difference between the original and test stimuli. This postulate is an attempt to state an empirical law, but testing this law raises serious measurement problems.

The common elements approach was followed by Bush and Mosteller [1951b] in a proposed model for generalization. Following Estes, they represented the stimulus situations by sets of elements. Denoting the original set by S and the test set by S', they defined an index of similarity, η, of S' to S by the measure of the intersection divided by the measure of S'. Employing Estes' axiom about response probabilities (cf. Chapter 2), they then concluded that p', the response probability in S', was η times p, the response probability in S. However, they considered this relation to be only an operational definition of η, because they did not try to define operationally stimulus elements and their measures. This model is clearly sterile for it merely gives a formal definition of similarity. It does predict, however, that p'/p is independent of p, and such a prediction is testable. The data of Brush *et al.* [1952], although an unsatisfactory test, do not give much support to the prediction.

A mathematical theory of stimulus generalization is of little value unless it leads to a testable theorem. As pointed out above, the major problem is one of measurement. Nevertheless, a satisfactory mathematical behavior theory must face up to the problem unless its sphere of applicability is to be very restricted. The mechanism of stimulus generalization is an essential part of stimulus-response theory.

Response Generalization. If a fixed stimulus S evokes a response R as a result of conditioning, it is likely to evoke a similar response R', at least when R is no longer possible. An example is an experiment by Bekhterev [1932] in which a dog was conditioned to lift a foot when a stimulus occurred; when the foot used was tied down the dog lifted another foot. In a similar study, Kellogg [1939] found that a buzzer which elicited lifting the right hind foot also caused occasional lifts of the other feet, even though no foot movements were restricted. Although Kellogg's experiment can be interpreted in terms of incidental conditioning — lifting of a front foot may have been accidentally reinforced a few times — it has been argued that response generalization was involved.

No mathematical theories of learning have attempted to handle the problems of response generalization, even though they are important to the analysis of experiments on the transfer of training. The set-theoretic models of the Estes type have focussed mainly on the stimulus space. The response space is partitioned and probabilities are associated with each subset of responses. In most applications, only two such response classes are considered. Many stimulus elements can be conditioned to a given response, but only one response can be conditioned to a given stimulus element. Thus, these models attempt to describe conditioning between stimuli and responses by a function of S onto R. Models employing a function of R onto S or a one-to-one correspondence between S and R have not been explored, but perhaps should be.

5. DISCRIMINATION

THE REVERSE of generalization is called discrimination. If a response R occurs equally often when two stimuli S_1 and S_2 are initially presented, but if through conditioning R occurs more often to one, discrimination is said to have taken place. More generally, whenever differential responding is conditioned one often speaks of discrimination, but when the term is used this broadly it becomes of little use. Several different classes of experimental problems are described as discrimination and so these classes will be considered separately.

Single Stimulus Situation. When a rat learns to turn right rather than left in a simple T-maze, one can say that the animal learned to discriminate those cues associated with the right-hand side from those cues associated with the left. If the right and left alleys are painted different colors, the discrimination is easier and learning occurs more rapidly. In experiments of this type the total stimulus situation is the same on all trials, even though the stimuli perceived by the subject may vary from trial to trial. The experiment can be characterized by a single set S of stimuli, two classes of responses, R_1 and R_2, and two outcomes, O_1 and O_2, (e.g., food and no food). The conditional probabilities

$$\pi_{ij} = Pr\left\{O_i\ R_j\right\} \tag{8}$$

are ordinarily fixed by the experimenter. Such experiments are considered to be discrimination experiments by some psychologists but not by others. In any case, the stochastic models discussed in Chapter 2 are designed to handle such phenomena.

Two Stimulus Situations. Another type of experiment uses one set of stimuli on some trials and another set on other trials. Suppose that in a T-maze a red card is placed at the choice point on some trials and a white card on the remaining trials, and that the reward conditions are such that the rat learns to go right on "red" trials and to go left on "white" trials. We can characterize this class of experiments by two sets of stimuli, S_1 and S_2, two classes of responses, R_1 and R_2, and two possible outcomes, O_1 and O_2. The conditional probabilities

$$\pi_{ijk} = Pr\left\{O_i \middle| R_j, S_k\right\} \tag{9}$$

are determined by the experimenter and ordinarily $\pi_{ij1} \neq \pi_{ij2}$. The sequence of presentations of S_1 and S_2 is also determined by the experimenter; it may be an alternating sequence or may be a somewhat random one, but usually the two sets of stimuli occur equally often in a block of ten or twenty trials. This experiment could be considered two simple acquisition processes if it were assumed that the two sets of trials were independent. In this event, the response probabilities

$$p_{jk} = Pr\left\{R_j \middle| S_k\right\} \tag{10}$$

for $k = 1$ would be unaffected by what happened on trials on which S_2 was presented, and *vice versa*. If this assumption were valid, the order of S_1 and S_2 would not matter — the S_1 trials could be run one month and the S_2 trials the next. Clearly, this model is inadequate. The two sets of trials are not independent. What happens to the animal on an S_1 trial alters his response probabilities on a following S_2 trial. We can think of S_1 and S_2 as two intersecting sets. Conditioning of elements in the intersection occurs on both kinds of trials.

Experiments following the paradigm just described are not handled by a simple application of the stochastic models for acquisition. Bush and Mosteller [1951b] attempted to construct a model for such experiments by postulating that the measure of the intersection of S_1 and S_2 decreased during learning. They introduced a discrimination operator D which was applied to the measure of the intersection each time S_1 followed S_2, or *vice versa*. When to apply the operator D was the major conceptual difficulty in this model. In addition, it was assumed that a single operator Q_1 was applied to the response probabilities each time S_1 was presented and another single operator Q_2 was applied when S_2 was presented. This assumption greatly reduces the range of applicability of the model, but it is an assumption which is easily modified as follows:

Consider the two sets S_1 and S_2. Let their intersection be I and let T_k be the complement of I in S_k as shown below.

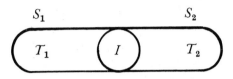

Assume that a single stimulus element x is perceived on a particular trial. Consider two responses R_1 and R_2, one and only one of which is made on each trial. Define

$$\begin{aligned}
\varphi_1 &= Pr\{R_1 | x \epsilon T_1\}, \\
\varphi_2 &= Pr\{R_1 | x \epsilon T_2\}, \\
\psi &= Pr\{R_1 | x \epsilon I\}, \\
\eta &= Pr\{x \epsilon I | x \epsilon S_1\} = Pr\{x \epsilon I | x \epsilon S_2\}.
\end{aligned} \tag{11}$$

We can then write,

$$\begin{aligned}
p_1 &= Pr\{R_1 | x \epsilon S_1\} = \eta \psi + (1 - \eta) \varphi_1, \\
p_2 &= Pr\{R_1 | x \epsilon S_2\} = \eta \psi + (1 - \eta) \psi_2.
\end{aligned} \tag{12}$$

These equations were developed by Bush and Mosteller [1951b] from somewhat different assumptions.

The four conditional probabilities, φ_1, φ_2, ψ, and η, change during discrimination learning. There are eight possible events which can change the probabilities, events corresponding to the eight triplets (S_k, R_j, O_i) and which can be identified experimentally. Each of these could be considered a pair of events, depending on whether $x \epsilon T_k$ or $x \epsilon I$; these cannot be separated behaviorally, except possibly by interviewing the subject or by making detailed observations of his perception. Thus, they will not be considered further. Operators Q_{kji} corresponding to the eight events can be specified and simplifications introduced by making some symmetry assumptions. For example, Q_{111} should have the same effect on φ_1 as does Q_{211} on φ_2. If outcome O_1 is identified with reward and outcome O_2 with non-reward, a reasonable set of transition laws between trials n and $n+1$ for $\varphi_{1,n}$, $\varphi_{2,n}$, and ψ_n are those shown below.

Note that only two parameters, a_1 and a_2, corresponding to the effects of reward and non-reward, respectively, are involved. These proposed laws do not specify how the conditional probability η changes; this is the problem of the discrimination operator D mentioned above. Whatever assumptions are made about the transition laws for η, the model leads to a rather complex stochastic process. This is true even when reward always follows R_1 in S_1 and R_2 in S_2 but never R_2 in S_1 nor R_1 in S_2, i.e., when only events (1,1,1), (1,2,2), (2,1,2), and (2,2,1) are possible.

Within the framework discussed, the problems in developing a satisfactory model include (1) specifying transition laws for φ_1, φ_2, and ψ, such as those given in the table below, (2) specifying transition laws for η, and (3) studying the mathematical properties of the stochastic process thereby defined.

k	j	i	$\varphi_{1,n+1}$	$\varphi_{2,n+1}$	ψ_{n+1}
1	1	1	$\varphi_{1,n} + a_1(1-\varphi_{1,n})$	$\varphi_{2,n}$	$\psi_n + a_1(1-\psi_n)$
1	1	2	$\varphi_{1,n} - a_2\varphi_{1,n}$	$\varphi_{2,n}$	$\psi_n - a_2\psi_n$
1	2	1	$\varphi_{1,n} - a_1\varphi_{1,n}$	$\varphi_{2,n}$	$\psi_n - a_1\psi_n$
1	2	2	$\varphi_{1,n} + a_2(1-\varphi_{1,n})$	$\varphi_{2,n}$	$\psi_n + a_2(1-\psi_n)$
2	1	1	$\varphi_{1,n}$	$\varphi_{2,n} + a_1(1-\varphi_{2,n})$	$\psi_n + a_1(1-\psi_n)$
2	1	2	$\varphi_{1,n}$	$\varphi_{2,n} - a_2\varphi_{2,n}$	$\psi_n - a_2\psi_n$
2	2	1	$\varphi_{1,n}$	$\varphi_{2,n} - a_1\varphi_{2,n}$	$\psi_n - a_1\psi_n$
2	2	2	$\varphi_{1,n}$	$\varphi_{2,n} + a_2(1-\varphi_{2,n})$	$\psi_n + a_2(1-\psi_n)$

Restle [1955] proposed a model which can be translated into the language being used here. He speaks of relevant and irrelevant cues and these can be considered elements in $T_1 \cup T_2$ and I, respectively. The "conditioning" process he postulates has to do with the transition laws for φ_1 and φ_2, and his "adaptation" process pertains to the changes in η. Restle asserts that an irrelevant cue cannot be "conditioned" and so he assumes that ψ does not change during learning. This model is now considered in more detail.

Let T_1 contain r cues and T_2 contain r cues (relevant cues) and let I contain i cues (irrelevant cues). Let "correct" responses be R_1 in S_1 and R_2 in S_2 and assume that these are always rewarded and that "incorrect" responses (R_2 in S_1 and R_1 in S_2) are never rewarded. Then the probability of a correct response is

$$p = p_1 = 1 - p_2. \tag{13}$$

A relevant cue is either "conditioned" to a correct response or not; let c be the probability that a relevant cue is conditioned. Assume with Restle that if the perceived cue is a conditioned relevant cue, a correct response will occur, whereas if it is a non-conditioned relevant cue, a correct response occurs with probability $1/2$. If x is a relevant cue, the probability of a correct response is

$$\varphi = \varphi_1 = 1 - \varphi_2 = c + \frac{1}{2}(1-c). \tag{14}$$

Irrelevant cues are either "adapted" or not. Restle assumes that an adapted cue is never perceived. Thus, if $x \in I$, it is not yet adapted; it is assumed that if x is an unadapted irrelevant cue, a correct response occurs with probability $1/2$ and so

$$\psi = \frac{1}{2}. \tag{15}$$

The probability that an irrelevant cue is adapted is a and so

$$\eta = \frac{i(1-a)}{i(1-a)+r}. \tag{16}$$

Implicitly, it is assumed here that all unadapted cues have the same probability of being perceived. Equations (12) above then lead to the result

$$p = \frac{rc + \frac{1}{2}r(1-c) + \frac{1}{2}i(1-a)}{r+i(1-a)}, \tag{17}$$

which is identical to Restle's equation (4) if one assumes that c is the same for all relevant cues and that a is the same for all irrelevant cues.

The transition laws assumed in Restle's model are that c and a increase by a constant percentage of their maximum possible increase each trial. His postulates are

$$c_{n+1} = c_n + \theta(1-c_n),$$

$$a_{n+1} = a_n + \theta(1-a_n), \tag{18}$$

and it is further assumed that

$$\theta = \frac{r}{r+i}.$$
(19)

The solutions of these difference equations, when used in equation (17), give p as an explicit function of n, the single parameter θ, and the initial values c_o and a_o which Restle takes to be zero. Thus a single probability variable, p, which of course changes with learning, describes the process. One does not obtain a distribution of probabilities on each trial, as is obtained in other stochastic learning models. The particular transition laws assumed by Restle are by no means necessary to his general approach, but they lead to major simplifications of the theory. One accomplishment of the model is that it predicts a relation among the rates of learning of three experiments. Let one experiment contain r_1 relevant cues, another contain r_2 relevant cues, and a third contain $r_1 + r_2$ relevant cues. Assume each of the three experiments contains i irrelevant cues. Then, Restle shows that the rate parameter for the third experiment is

$$\theta_3 = \frac{\theta_1 + \theta_2 - 2\,\theta_1\,\theta_2}{1 - \theta_1\,\theta_2},$$
(20)

where θ_1 and θ_2 are the corresponding rate parameters for the first two experiments. Restle [1955] discusses data which support this theorem.

Concept Attainment. Another class of experimental problems, called concept attainment, is closely related to those in discrimination (Bruner, Goodnow, and Austin [1956]). Pairs of stimulus cards are presented sequentially to a human subject, he is asked to indicate which card in each pair is "correct" — is an instance of the concept — and he is usually told whether or not he is in fact correct on each trial. Ordinarily one and only one card in each pair presented is correct. For example, consider three "attributes," position (L and R), color (B and W), and shape (S and T), each of which has one of two values as indicated in parentheses. Let each card in a pair contain one value of each attribute and the other card contain the complementary values. Then, the possible pairs of cards are (LBS, RWT), (LBT, RWS), (LWS, RBT), and (LWT, RBS). The concept may be L, in which case the left card (L) is always correct, or it may be W, in which case the white card (W) is always correct, etc. The possible one-attribute concepts are L, R, B, W, S, and T. However, the concept may have two attributes, e.g., it might be RT, in which case the right card with a triangle (T) is always correct. If the concept has two attributes, then only two of the four possible pairs of cards contain the concept. When RT is the concept it is contained only in the pairs (LBS, RWT) and (LWS, RBT). The concept may also contain three attributes. In general, if we have u attributes of which v are contained in the concept, the number of pairs of cards containing the concept is 2^{u-v}.

In Restle's terms, we can call the cues associated with attributes contained in the concept "relevant" and cues associated with the other attributes ("noisy" attributes) "irrelevant." However, the number of different stimulus sets (pairs of cards) presented in the sequence is $K = 2^{u-v}$. On each trial only two responses are possible and one and only one is a correct response. When $v = u-1$, Restle's model seems directly applicable. In his paper, Restle does not restrict his theory to two stimulus sets, although only two are involved in the applications he discusses. It might be reasonable to apply his model to any number of sets, to let r be a constant times v, and to let i be the same constant times ($u-v$). His parameter θ is then

$$\theta = \frac{v}{u}. \tag{21}$$

The writer's objection to such a model for concept attainment experiments is that Restle's transition axioms become less plausible as the number of different stimulus sets presented gets large. The approach is suggestive, however.

6. MOTIVATION

THE STUDY of motivation encompasses a large variety of psychological problems which may be conveniently classified as follows: (1) enumeration and genesis of biologically determined primary drives, (2) enumeration and determinants of secondary or acquired drives, (3) analysis of the processes by which secondary drives get established and maintained, and (4) determination of the relations between motivational variables and behavioral variables. Each of these classes of problems will be discussed briefly.

Primary Drives. Those drives possessed by an organism at birth are called primary. Lists of these drives most commonly include hunger, thirst, oxygen, sex, and pain avoidance. The strengths of the first two drives listed increase with increasing deprivation, and so the number of hours (or seconds) of deprivation is a common index of intensity of those drives. On the other hand, pain avoidance is a drive that is completely contingent upon the organism's environment. The strength of the sex drive is a complex thing, depending in part on length of deprivation and in part on environmental stimuli. In the female of lower species, it is periodic in time and is nearly independent of other factors.

From the point of view of behavior theory, the specification of primary drives and their strengths is merely a matter of measuring properties of organisms, of describing the state an organism is in at any particular moment. The problem is analogous to measuring the mass and density of a body in Newtonian mechanics. These are properties of the unit of study, properties which enter the theory as given quantities, but not properties predicted by the theory. The genesis of primary drives and the determinants of their strengths are problems for biology and physiological psychology.

In animal studies of learning, hunger and thirst are the most frequently used primary drives. Number of hours of deprivation is the most common index of drive strength, although percentage of normal body weight is more popular with experimenters using pigeons as subjects. Other indices proposed, if not actually used, include amount of effort expended to obtain food or water, the rate of consumption, and activity level.

Secondary Drives (Typology and Determinants). Drives which are acquired after birth as a result of the interaction of the organism with its environment are called secondary or acquired drives. Lists of such drives are lengthy but usually include dependency, social approval, and various modifications of primary drives such as "tastes" or "cravings" for particular kinds of foods and liquids. The enumeration of secondary drives of people has been a major problem in psychology. The most extensive studies are those of Murray [1938].

In addition to listing the numerous secondary drives, social scientists have been concerned with specifying the conditions under which secondary drives are acquired, i.e., with determining the environmental factors which lead to the development of a particular acquired drive. But this is a problem for social psychology, for sociology, or for social anthropology, not a problem for learning theory. So far, it has not been handled by formal theories.

Secondary Drives (Creation and Maintainance). The mechanism by which an acquired drive gets established and maintained has been considered a major problem in learning theory. According to most such theories, a child develops an acquired drive of dependency on its mother because she is the agent of satisfaction of the child's primary needs. Or, a person acquires a need for social approval because it was originally associated with reduction of hunger. The process by which an acquired drive is created has been studied both experimentally and theoretically in conditioning and learning terms.

Some confusion exists between the concepts of secondary drive and secondary reward. Sight of food may be a secondary reward to a hungry rat, or money may be a secondary reward to a thirsty alcoholic. On the other hand, a man's desire for money is usually considered to be a secondary drive. The existence of a secondary drive is inferred from behavior and the distinction between the two concepts is often one of degree. If a need becomes "functionally autonomous" (Allport [1937]), it is considered a well established secondary drive.

In experimental studies on animals, both concepts are often used in interpreting the data. For example, Bugelski [1938] trained two groups of rats to press a bar to obtain food. The experimental group heard a click from the food magazine with each bar press during extinction, whereas the control group did not. The main finding was that the experimental group extinguished more slowly. It was argued that the pairing of click and food resulted in the click becoming a secondary reward. On the other hand, one could say that temporarily the experimental rats had a secondary drive for the click, even though the strength of this drive apparently decreased during extinction. The distinction between secondary reward and secondary drive is mainly a semantic one in many such cases. Nevertheless, the phenomena exist and are important problems for behavior theory.

No mathematical learning theories have attempted to describe the process of drive acquisition or the process by which a neutral stimulus acquires reward properties. The mechanism involved seems akin to that involved in the classic experiments on Pavlovian conditioning, in which a dog begins to salivate to a tone that in the past preceded presentation of food. No mathematical theories have adequately described Pavlovian conditioning either. The problem seems to be one of stimulus-stimulus connections, whereas formal theories such as Estes' are concerned with stimulus-response connections.

In the framework of Bush and Mosteller, a neutral stimulus like a tone prior to Pavlovian conditioning is an outcome associated with an identity operator. After the tone has acquired reward properties, it is an outcome associated with operators that increase the probaility of the preceding response. Hence, the process of change in the stimulus properties is circumvented. This approach was followed by Bush and Wilson [1956] in analyzing a choice experiment on red paradise fish. It was postulated and confirmed that the sight of food without eating increased the probability of the response just made. The model developed for this experiment assumed the following transition laws.

Response	Outcome	p_{n+1}
Right turn	Food	$\alpha_1 p_n + (1 - \alpha_1)$
Right turn	Sight of food	$\alpha_2 p_n + (1 - \alpha_2)$
Left turn	Food	$\alpha_1 p_n$
Left turn	Sight of food	$\alpha_2 p_n$

Here, p_n is the probability of a right turn on trial n, and it was assumed that $\alpha_1 < \alpha_2$ because it was believed that the primary reward (food) would have a greater effect than the secondary reward (sight of food). Deductions from this model were found to be consistent with the data. No attempt was made, however, to describe the process by which sight of food became associated with the operators postulated. It was implicitly assumed that association took place during the preliminary training when the fish were trained to eat from an eye-dropper.

A possible model for the process by which neutral stimuli acquire reinforcing properties is suggested by Estes' theory. Consider a class of responses, R_c, that includes both consumatory responses and internal responses that occur just prior to and during this consumatory behavior. Assume that an occurrence of R_c constitutes an outcome which increases the probability of the overt motor response which preceded R_c. Next assume that whenever an element of R_c occurs it becomes connected or associated with whatever stimuli are present. Elements of R_c already will be associated with the goal object (such as food) but will become associated with the neutral stimuli paired with the goal object. The goal object is presented to evoke R_c and the non-conditioned stimuli become conditioned to R_c by the axioms given by Estes [1950]. Hence, by merely introducing a response class R_c and considering its elements to be outcomes of motor responses, the processes of Pavlovian conditioning and secondary drive acquisition could be made special cases of Estes' conditioning theory.

Motivational vs. Behavioral Variables. Problems that have concerned many experimental psychologists pertain to the relations between measures of motivation or drive strength and various measures of performance or speed of learning. How does the number of trials to a criterion of learning vary with hours of deprivation, for example? Or what is the effect on the rate of extinction of changing the drive strength just prior to extinction? A considerable amount of data on such problems has been accumulated.

The only theory of learning that explicitly introduces drive strength as a quantitative variable is Hull's. But Hull [1943] merely postulates how certain behavioral variables depend upon drive strength. These are *ad hoc* assumptions and are not derived from more primitive axioms. In the opinion of this writer such problems will probably always remain parametric questions in behavior theory proper.

7. PUNISHMENT

IN THE EARLY days of behavior theory, punishment was considered to be a negative reinforcement. Thorndike talked about "satisfiers" and "annoyers" and thought of these as being on a continuum: Reward increased the strength of an immediately preceding response, whereas punishment decreased it. Although this notion is still a part of most behavior theories, the main effect of punishment, according to modern formulations, is to "disrupt" behavior or produce "withdrawal reactions." If an organism is in a particular situation and is rewarded for making a particular response, the frequency of occurrence of that response increases. However, if the animal is punished for that response, the main effect is to cause withdrawal from the situation and thereby to decrease the opportunities for making the punished response. This effect places the problem of punishment on a different level from that of mere non-reinforcement.

Escape and Avoidance Experiments. The simplest demonstrations of the withdrawal effects of punishment are experiments on escape and avoidance. An animal is placed in an experimental situation such as a jumping stand and then exposed to a "noxious" stimulus such as electric shock. The animal learns to withdraw from this stimulus, by quickly jumping over a barrier, for example. If the withdrawal response occurs after the noxious stimulus is presented, "escape" takes place, whereas if the response precedes the stimulus, "avoidance" occurs.

Escape and avoidance experiments are easily treated as simple acquisition processes, as discussed in Chapter 2. The analogy with reward training is clear if we think of pain avoidance as a drive and both pain reduction and fear reduction as reinforcing. The noxious stimulus is parallel to food or water deprivation in reward training except that the pain avoidance drive is more quickly manipulated by the experimenter. The analysis of avoidance training data made by Bush and Mosteller [1955] is based essentially on such a conception of the effects of punishment.

Recovery from Punishment. In escape and avoidance experiments, the withdrawal response is the behavior that is studied and measured and it is under stimulus control by the experimenter. All other behavior is considered not-withdrawal although there have been studies of the "anxiety" reactions which precede withdrawal. In other experiments, however, an operationally defined overt response is punished; occurrences of that response rather than withdrawal responses are recorded. The classic study by Estes [1944] will serve as an example. Rats were conditioned to press a bar in a Skinner box by reward training. After the rate of bar pressing was high, strong shock was substituted for reward. As anyone would expect, the rate of bar pressing rapidly decreased when shock was introduced. The curious effect observed by Estes, though, was that the rate of responding increased again when shock was omitted but that extinction eventually occurred because the response was not rewarded. This temporary increase in rate during extinction is called "recovery" from punishment.

An attempt to describe recovery from punishment was made by Bush and Whiting [1953]. The animal was considered to be in one of two possible situations or states, S_1 and S_2. In situation S_1, the possible responses were R (e.g., bar pressing), W (withdrawal from S_1), and X (neither bar pressing nor withdrawal). In situation S_2, the animal could make response E (entering S_1) or Y (not entering S_1). The conditional probabilities of R, W, and X, given state S_1, were denoted by p_r, p_w, and $1-p_r-p_w$, respectively. Given state S_2, the conditional probabilities of E and Y were p_e and $1-p_e$, respectively. If the transition probabilities (between states), p_w and p_e, are constant, a simple two-state Markov chain results and the probability P_n that the organism is in state S_1 on trial n is readily computed. The frequency of response R is then proportional to $P_n p_r$.

The model just outlined can be applied to the Estes experiment if one is willing to let the probabilities p_r and p_w vary. Denoting the response probabilities in S_1 by the vector

$$\vec{p} = \begin{bmatrix} p_1 \\ p_2 \\ p_3 \end{bmatrix} \tag{22}$$

where 1, 2, and 3 correspond to R, W, and X, respectively, and the set of three outcomes by $\{O_i\}$ where O_1 is reward, O_2 is punishment, and O_3 is neither, we can define a set of stochastic operators. Then, if the ith outcome follows the jth response,

$$\vec{p}_{n+1} = T_{ij}\vec{p}_n \, . \tag{23}$$

Outcomes O_1 and O_2 follow only response R and so the allowed events are RO_1, RO_2, RO_3, WO_3, and XO_3. A plausible restriction is that identity operators are associated with WO_3 and XO_3. In extinction only O_3 follows R. An operator which can lead to the recovery effect is

$$T_{31} = \begin{bmatrix} \beta & 0 & 0 \\ 0 & a & 0 \\ 1-\beta & 1-a & 1 \end{bmatrix} \tag{24}$$

provided that $a < \beta$. This operator does not satisfy the combining-classes restriction described in Chapter 2. Bush and Whiting also assumed that the conditional probabilities, p_e and $1-p_e$, for state S_2 never change.

The non-Markovian process which results from the above postulates is complex and has not been studied except in a rudimentary way. Using the Monte Carlo method, Bush and Whiting [1953] showed that the model predicted a temporary increase in rate of responding during extinction, but no detailed analysis has been carried out.

Displacement. A phenomenon which is believed to arise from punishment is displacement. In the psychoanalytic literature, the term displacement is used in various ways, but most commonly it refers to behavioral modifications resulting from punishment or fear — a substitute form of activity that often is bizarre and apparently paradoxical. In learning theory terms, displacement has been considered a mechanism by which a response occurs more strongly in a stimulus situation somewhat similar to the one in which the response was punished than it does in either the original situation or one quite dissimilar.

N. E. Miller [1948] proposed a semi-mathematical model for describing displacement in stimulus-response terms. His main postulate was that approach tendencies generalize more than withdrawal tendencies. The model predicted the initial rise and eventual decline in response strength along a dissimilarity measure. Miller and his students have conducted several experiments to test this and other predictions of the model. Bush and Whiting [1953] objected to Miller's formulation, chiefly because of the ambiguous nature of the response strength measure involved and because of an axiom which says that the net response strength is the algebraic sum of the strengths of two or more conflicting responses. As a result, they attempted to modify the model using probability of responding as a measure of response strength. The set-theoretic model of generalization discussed in Chapter 4 was somewhat extended and combined with the two-state punishment model described above. It was concluded that the displacement effect could occur under some conditions and not under others but that it was a consequence of the increase in opportunities for responding to similar stimuli because of the decrement in the probability of withdrawal.

In summary, it is safe to say that the effects of punishment have not been adequately described by mathematical models. The initial attempts discussed may be suggestive but serious studies of the mathematical properties of the proposed models have not been made. Unfortunately, only a few experiments are available for testing future models for punishment; on the other hand, empirical studies often follow clear and precise theoretical formulations.

8. INTERACTION PROCESSES

THE BEHAVIOR of two or more persons in a face-to-face interaction situation has generally been considered the province of social psychology and sociology rather than of learning theory, but recent interest in small-group research and in stochastic learning models is beginning to cause a natural blend of these fields. For this reason, two applications of stochastic models to interaction problems are discussed here.

Imitation of one person by another is considered by Miller and Dollard [1941] to be a basic process in the socialization (rearing) of children. They demonstrated experimentally that imitation can be controlled by rewards and punishments, like other kinds of behavior; but, unlike many kinds of behavior, imitation is evoked by the stimulus of another person's behavior. Thus we have one of the simplest types of two-person interaction processes, even though many students of small-group research might consider it trivial or uninteresting. Several experiments on imitation have been reported; one by Shwartz [1953] was designed to facilitate analysis of the data with stochastic models. On each trial of her experiment, two children were asked to guess whether the experimenter was going to say "a" or "b." One child was told to be first on all trials; it was explained that this procedure was being used to save time. The experimenter confirmed the guess of the first child on eight out of every ten trials and denied it on the other two trials. The behavior of the second child was of major interest. It was found that the frequency of imitation increased during a sequence of trials when the first child was correct but appreciably decreased after the first child was wrong.

Their stochastic learning model was applied by Bush and Mosteller [1955] to the data obtained by Shwartz. It was assumed that the second child had a probability, p_n, of imitation on the nth trial and that this probability increased each time the experimenter confirmed the guess of the first child and decreased each time that guess was denied. The operators described in Chapter 2 were used, parameters were estimated from the data, and goodness-of-fit was measured. The results suggest that the particular assumptions made in the model are not entirely justified and that a better fit might have been obtained from somewhat different assumptions. However, the analysis does indicate that imitation problems can be handled mathematically in much the same manner as several other learning problems.

In an interaction situation, one person can influence the behavior of another person in many ways. He can be a stimulus or "model" as in imitation problems, but he can also be the agent of rewards and punishments — events which follow a response rather than precede it. The behavioral process can be a one-way interaction, as in Shwartz's imitation experiment, or it may be a two-way exchange of influence. Parsons [1951] introduced the concept of "support" into interaction theory, arguing that support of one person by another tends to "integrate" a group. Learning theorists probably would consider support to be simple reinforcement of certain kinds of behavior; but, whatever one's theoretical bias, he would agree that the actions of one individual are environmental events for another and can influence behavior accordingly. When such an interaction is mutual, a feed-back process occurs and the individual behavior patterns may reach a steady state.

In many real-life situations, a group is required to act as a unit and one can speak of various possible behaviors of the group. Following a suggestion by Estes for studying group decisions, Hays and Bush [1954] carried out a simple experiment in which a three-man group was asked to predict on each trial whether or not a light bulb would be illuminated. The light actually came on 75 per cent of the time. This prodecure was similar to the one introduced by Humphreys [1939] in studying individual subjects. The interaction process in the three-man groups was not systematically observed, but the group action was recorded on each trial. Two main models were proposed for analyzing the data. The first, called the "group-actor model," assumed that the group behaved like an individual organism and predicted that the asymptotic frequency of choices would be 0.75; this asymptote was deduced from the stochastic learning models and agrees with numerous experimental results on individual subjects. The second model for the three-man group behavior, called the "voting model," assumed that each individual behaved independently according to the learning model but that the group decision was made by "majority rule." Unfortunately, the data could not clearly choose one model over the other. However, it was indicated that, if the persons behaved independently, they learned more slowly than most individuals in other experiments.

The two models for group action were shown to be special limiting cases of a more general model which postulates that the first man to give an opinion behaves according to the learning model but that his behavior alters the probabilities of the other men according to a "support operator" which is introduced. In the same way the second man to react influences the third man. This more general model could not be tested by the data obtained in the group-action experiment, but recent studies by D. G. Hays were designed to test extensions of this model.

Several elaborate probability models for small-group behavior have been proposed by Bales [1953] but no serious investigation of their mathematical properties has been made. Flood [1954a, 1954b] has developed several mathematically complex models for interaction and for "game-learning-theory." A discussion of these models here would lead us too far afield from learning, however.

Interesting mathematical problems in random walk are suggested by interaction models. A simple example is the following. Let there be two persons and two responses available to each on every trial or step in the process. Associate with these responses probabilities p_n, $1-p_n$, p'_n, and $1-p'_n$. Assume that the response made by one person alters the other person's probabilities and that no other events are relevant. For one person's response probabilities there are two possible stochastic operators, but their probabilities of application are equal to the response probabilities of the other person. The state of the system on any trial can be represented by a point in the unit square and this point undergoes a random walk. If the operators have fixed points, the "particle" may be absorbed asymptotically or the process may have some special ergodic properties. The study of such random walks could be both mathematically and psychologically interesting.

9. OTHER PROBLEMS

THE EXPERIMENTAL phenomena described in the preceding Chapters by no means exhaust the list of problems in the psychology of learning. The problem areas discussed are only those in which at least a small start on mathematical theory has been made. Many other areas of learning have not been formalized but present challenges to future systematic mathematical theories. In this section, a few of these problems will be pointed out.

Higher mental processes have been subjected to extensive experimental study but no mathematical theories have attempted to handle the results. Since the early days of experimental psychology, problem solving has been an important topic of investigation and is often called "insightful learning." How does a person solve a novel mathematical problem? Conditioning alone cannot explain this because the response has never before occurred and, unless the person enjoys repetition, will probably never be made again. Most learning theorists would argue that stimulus and response generalization are involved — transfer of training from past experience with similar problems. Also involved are the processes of retention and forgetting which have received separate experimental investigation, but few formal theories to explain the data have been attempted. A number of psychologists have done research in an area called "thinking" and empirical results have been reported (Bruner, Goodnow, and Austin [1956]). It may turn out that problem solving and thinking are complex processes which can be handled theoretically by an integration of less complex processes.

Psychoanalytic mechanisms have been translated into stimulus-response terminology and this has led to many interesting experimental studies (Sears [1944]). The process of displacement was briefly discussed in Chapter 7. A closely related mechanism is that of projection — the process by which a person ascribes to another his own feelings or motives. Sears [1944] reports evidence to confirm Freud's conjecture that projection in fact occurs, but again no formal theories have tried to explain the results. Other Freudian mechanisms which have not been adequately studied include regression —

the re-occurrence of an early pattern of behavior when a present pattern is prevented or inhibited — and repression — the disappearance from conscious memory of unpleasant or traumatic experiences.

Conflict has been studied both experimentally and theoretically by Miller [1944] and others. An example of such studies concerns the behavior of rats in a maze containing a goal box which has been associated with food and punishment. Although Miller's formulation in terms of spacial gradients of approach and avoidance tendencies is provocative and ingenious, no mathematical models for the problem have been reported. Related to experiments on conflict are studies of experimental neurosis (in non-human subjects). A common procedure is to teach a discrimination between two stimuli by using reward and strong punishment and then to increase slowly the similarity of the stimuli until they can no longer by discriminated. The resulting behavior closely resembles what the psychiatrist calls neurosis in people.

Throughout this paper, no mention has been made of physiological theories or data, even though most psychologists agree that behavior theory and neurological theory must some day meet. The reason for the omission is that learning theories have not yet relied on physiological theories except in superficial ways. The approach most generally accepted is that learning theory is building a "thermodynamics" of behavior, but most investigators have faith that some day we will be able to derive the basic axioms of behavior theory from a more miscroscopic theory of the organism.

REFERENCES

Allport, G. W., *Personality: a psychological interpretation*. New York: Holt, 1937, pp. 191—207.

Bales, R. F., "The equilibrium problem in small groups." In T. Parsons, R. F. Bales, and E. A. Shils, *Working papers in the theory of action*. Glencoe, Illinois: The Free Press, 1953.

Bekhterev, V. M., *General principles of human reflexology*. New York: International, 1932, p. 216.

Bruner, J. S., Goodnow, J. J., and Austin, G. A., *A study of thinking*. New York: Wiley, 1956.

—,   Miller, G. A., and Zimmerman, C., "Discriminative skill and discriminative matching in perceptual recognition." *J. exp. Psychol.*, 1955, *49*, 187—192.

Brunswik, E., "Probability as a determiner of rat behavior." *J. exp. Psychol.*, 1939, *25*, 175—197.

Brush, F. R., Bush, R. R., Jenkins, W. O., John, W. F., and Whiting, J. W. M., "Stimulus generalization after extinction and punishment: an experimental study of displacement." *J. abnorm. soc. Psychol.*, 1952, *47*, 633—640.

Bugelski, R., "Extinction with and without sub-goal reinforcement." *J. comp. Psychol.*, 1938, *26*, 121—134.

Burke, C. J., Estes, W. K., and Hellyer, S., "Rate of verbal conditioning in relation to stimulus variability." *J. exp. Psychol.*, 1954, *48*, 153—161.

Bush, R. R., and Mosteller, F., "A mathematical model for simple learning." *Psychol. Rev.*, 1951a, *58*, 313—323.

—, and Mosteller, F. "A model for stimulus generalization and discrimination." *Psychol. Rev.*, 1951b, *58*, 413—423.

—, and Mosteller, F. "A stochastic model with applications to learning." *Annals of math. Stat.*, 1953, *24*, 559—585.

—, and Mosteller, F., *Stochastic models for learning*. New York: Wiley, 1955.

—, Mosteller, F., and Thompson, G. L., "A formal structure for multiple-choice situations." In R. M. Thrall, C. H. Coombs, and R. L. Davis (Eds.), *Decision Processes*. New York: Wiley, 1954.

—, and Whiting, J. W. M., "On the theory of psychoanalytic displacement." *J. abnorm. soc. Psychol.*, 1953, *48*, 261—272.

—, and Wilson, T. R., "Two-choice behavior of paradise fish." *J. exp. Psychol.*, 1956, *51*, 315—322.

Deese, J., *The psychology of learning*. New York: McGraw-Hill, 1952.

Detambel, M. H., "A test of a model for multiple-choice behavior." *J. exp. Psychol.*, 1955, *49*, 97—104.

Estes, W. K., "An experimental study of punishment." *Psychol. Monogr.*, 1914, *57*, No. 3 (Whole No. 263).

—, "Toward a statistical theory of learning." *Psychol. Rev.*, 1950, *57*, 94—107.

—, "Individual behavior in uncertain situations: an interpretation in terms of statistical association theory." In R. M. Thrall, C. H. Coombs, and R. L. Davis (Eds.), *Decision processes*. New York: Wiley, 1954.

—, "Statistical theory of spontaneous recovery and regression." *Psychol. Rev.*, 1955a, *62*, 145—154.

—, "Statistical theory of distributional phenomena in learning." *Psychol. Rev.*, 1955b, *62*, 369—377.

—, and Burke, C. J., "A theory of stimulus variability in learning." *Psychol. Rev.*, 1953, *60*, 276—286.

—, and Burke, C. J., "Application of a statistical model to simple discrimination learning in human subjects." *J. exp. Psychol.*, 1955, *50*, 81—88.

—, and Straughan, J. H., "Analysis of a verbal conditioning situation in terms of statistical learning theory." *J. exp. Psychol.*, 1954, *47*, 225—234.

Ettlinger, H. J., "A curve of growth designed to represent the learning process." *J. exp. Psychol.*, 1926, *9*, 409—414.

Flood, M. M., "Game-learning theory and some decision-making experiments." In R. M. Thrall, C. H. Coombs, and R. L. Davis (Eds.), *Decision processes*. New York: Wiley, 1954a.

—, "A stochastic model for social interaction." *Trans. N. Y. Acad. Sci.*, 1954b, *16*, 202—205.

Goodnow, J. J., and Postman, L., "Probability learning in a problem-solving situation." *J. exp. Psychol.*, 1955, *49*, 16—22.

Graham, C. H., and Gagné, R. M., "The acquisition, extinction, and spontaneous recovery of a conditioned operant response." *J. exp. Psychol.*, 1940, *26*, 251—280.

Gulliksen, H., "A rational equation of the learning curve based on Thorndike's law of effect." *J. gen. Psychol.*, 1934, *11*, 395—434.

—, and Wolfle, D. L., "A theory of learning and transfer: I." *Psychometrika*, 1938, *3*, 127—149.

Guthrie, E. R., *The psychology of learning*. New York: Harper, 1935.

—, "Association and the law of effect." *Psychol. Rev.*, 1940, *47*, 127—148.

Harris, T. E., Abstract: *Annals of math. Stat.*, 1952, *23*, 141.

—, Bellman, R., and Shapiro, H. N., *Studies in functional equations occurring in decision processes*. Research Memorandum RM-878, RAND Corporation, Santa Monica, Calif., July 1, 1952.

Hays, D. G., and Bush, R. R., "A study of group action." *Amer. sociological Rev.*, 1954, *19*, 693—701.

Hilgard, E. R., and Marquis, D. G., *Conditioning and learning*. New York: D. Appleton-Century, 1940.

Hovland, C. I., "The generalization of conditioned responses: I." *J. gen. Psychol.*, 1937a, *17*, 125—148.

—, "The generalization of conditioned responses: II." *J. genet. Psychol.*, 1937b, *51*, 279—291.

Hull, C. L., *Principles of behavior*. New York: Appleton-Century-Crofts, 1943.

—, Hovland, C. I., Ross, R. T., Hall, M., Perkins, D. T., and Ritch, F. B., *Mathematico-deductive theory of rote learning*. New Haven: Yale University Press, 1940.

Humphreys, L. G., "Acquisition and extinction of verbal expectations in a situation analogous to conditioning." *J. exp. Psychol.*, 1939, *25*, 294—301.

Jenkins, W. O., and Stanley, J. C., "Jr. Partial reinforcement: a review and critique." *Psychol. Bull.*, 1950, *47*, 193—234.

Karlin, S., "Some random walks arising in learning models I." *Pacific J. of Math.*, 1953, *3*, 725—756.

Kellogg, W. N., "Positive and negative conditioning, without contraction of the essential muscles during the period of training." *Psychol. Bull.*, 1939, *36*, 575.

Kemeny, J. G., DeLeeuw, K., Snell, J. L., and Thompson, G. L., Progress Report Number 1, Dartmouth Mathematics Project, Dartmouth College, March, 1955.

Lauer, D. W., and Estes, W. K., "Successive acquisitions and extinctions of a jumping habit in relation to schedule of reinforcement." *J. comp. physiol. Psychol.*, 1955, *48*, 8—13.

Miller, G. A., and Frick, F. C., "Statistical behavioristics and sequences of responses." *Psychol. Rev.*, 1949, *56*, 311—324.

—, and McGill, W. J., "A statistical description of verbal learning." *Psychometrika*, 1952, *17*, 369—396.

Miller, N. E., "Experimental studies of conflict." In J. McV. Hunt (Ed.), *Personality and the behavior disorders*. New York: Ronald, 1944, pp. 431—465.

Miller, N. E., "Theory and experiment relating psychoanalytic displacement to stimulus-response generalization." *J. abnorm. soc. Psychol.*, 1948, *43*, 155—178.

—, and Dollard, J., *Social learning and imitation*. New Haven: Yale University Press, 1941.

Mowrer, O. H., and Jones, H., "Habit strength as a function of the pattern of reinforcement." *J. exp. Psychol.*, 1945, *35*, 293—310.

Murray, H. A., *Explorations in personality*. New York: Oxford, 1938, Chapter II.

Parsons, T., *The social system*. Glencoe, Illinois: The Free Press, 1951, pp. 299—301.

Postman, L., "The generalization gradient in recognition memory." *J. exp. Psychol.*, 1951, *42*, 231—235.

Rashevsky, N., *The mathematical biology of social behavior*. Chicago: University of Chicago Press, 1951.

Restle, F., "A theory of discrimination learning." *Psychol. Rev.*, 1955, *62*, 11—19.

Schoeffler, M. S., "Probability of a response to compounds of discriminated stimuli." *J. exp. Psychol.*, 1954, *48*, 323—329.

Sears, R. R., "Experimental analysis of psychoanalytic phenomena." In J. McV. Hunt (Ed.), *Personality and the behavior disorders*. New York: Ronald, 1944, pp. 306—332.

Shwartz, N., *An experimental study of imitation: the effects of reward and age*. Senior honors thesis, Radcliffe College, 1953.

Skinner, B. F., *The behavior of organisms*. New York: Appleton-Century-Crofts, 1938.

—, "Are theories of learning necessary?" *Psychol. Rev.*, 1950, *57*, 193—216.

Solomon, R. L., and Wynne, L. C., "Traumatic avoidance learning: acquisition in normal dogs." *Psychol. Monogr.*, 1953, *67*, No. 4 (Whole No. 354).

Spence, K. W., "Theoretical interpretations of learning." In S. S. Stevens (Ed.), *Handbook of experimental psychology*. New York: Wiley, 1951.

Thurstone, L. L., "The learning curve equation." *Psychol. Monogr.*, 1919, *26*, 1—51.

—, "The learning function." *J. gen. Psychol.*, 1930, *3*, 469—491.

Weinstock, S., "Resistance to extinction of a running response following partial reinforcement under widely spaced trials." *J. comp. physiol. Psychol.*, 1954, *47*, 318—322.

PART THREE

Quasi-Linear Operator Models
in the Study of Manual Tracking

By J. C. R. LICKLIDER

BOLT BERANEK AND NEWMAN INC., CAMBRIDGE,

MASSACHUSETTS

Contents

1. INTRODUCTION

MANUAL TRACKING is not an area of research in which mathematical models have led to conspicuously great accomplishments. Nor are quasi-linear models basically appropriate for detailed representation of human behavior. Yet the role played by quasi-linear models in the study of manual tracking is important, both as a practical matter in connection with the design of man-machine systems and as a part of behavioral theory.

The practical importance is due to the fact that human operators, as people have come to be called in several branches of engineering psychology, are extremely useful components in fire-control, missile-guidance, and other aiming and steering systems. In these systems, they interact with electrical and mechanical components. It is essential for designers to know about the relevant features of human behavior in terms that are compatible with those in which the characteristics of the "hardware" components are described. These terms usually involve linear models.

The theoretical importance stems from the fact that linear models are in a more advanced state of development than are nonlinear models. The concept of quasi-linearity permits, or assumes the legitimacy of, taking over much of the highly developed linear theory and using it in the study of behavior that is obviously not linear in a rigorous sense. This is at least an interesting strategy — to use available structures with modification and addition, rather than to withdraw from construction of models in order to devise new structures.(*) It is perhaps especially effective when even the gross features of the behavior are complex and therefore likely to require, for the basis of a successful model, a highly developed mathematical structure. This is the case in manual tracking, as it appears to be in most of psychology.

The study of manual tracking gives us an opportunity to make a comparative examination of models, for there has been much interest also in discontinuous and nonlinear models of the human operator. We can compare the accomplishments. It turns out that quasi-linear models do relatively well.

(*) The distinction made here between structure and model is the one advanced by Bush and Mosteller: A structure is a developed apparatus, usually mathematical, that is capable of serving as a model. A model is the structure plus the identifications that relate its parts to parts of the process it is used to represent.

2. MANUAL TRACKING

BROADLY DEFINED, tracking is trying to effect some degree of match between controlled objects or quantities and target objects or quantities. It is "trying" because the operator is said to be engaged in tracking even though he is having no success. Various kinds of match are of interest in connection with various targets and followers. A machine-gun operator tries to maximize his "time-on-target." A person tracking an object to determine statistical parameters of its course may try to minimize some average, such as the mean square, of the error over an interval of time. The driver of a car tries to stay on the road, or perhaps in his lane — to minimize the probability of exceeding tolerance limits.

Compensatory and Pursuit Tracking. By far the greatest part of the research on tracking has been concerned with one rather special case, compensatory tracking without influence of follower upon target. This fact greatly facilitates our study, for the conditions correspond directly to those of the operation of a servomechanism, which are relatively simple and thoroughly analyzed. In compensatory tracking, the operator sees only a representation of the error, the discrepancy between the follower and the target. His effort to match follower to target is therefore an effort to nullify the error. Compensatory tracking is thus quite different from the other main category, pursuit tracking, in which representations of target and follower are displayed separately. The automobile driver sees both his car and the road ahead of it. He sees their relative position, also, of course, but much of his behavior involves information about the target and information about the follower, separately. The compensatory tracker is not given the separated data — nor is he given the preview of the target course. He sees only the difference between the target and follower variables.

Because the compensatory tracker is deprived of some of the information presented to the pursuit tracker, he usually tracks less accurately.(*) A rather direct path to the improvement of man-machine servo systems, therefore, is wherever possible to substitute pursuit for compensatory track-

---

(*) Actually, he is not in a rigorous sense deprived of it. He has the control in his hand and therefore has available to his somesthetic and/or kinesthetic sense a description of his response. If he could use this information effectively — if he could add his response to the error to recreate the target course — he would be in as favorable a position as a pursuit tracker without preview of the target course. The fact is, however, that he cannot take full advantage of the theoretical possibility. It is tacitly assumed in most discussions of compensatory tracking that he takes no advantage of it at all.

ing. Surprisingly, this path has been used very little. Compensatory tracking has been the object of detailed study, much of it with the aim of achieving improvements in performance that could readily be achieved by simply ceasing to withhold from the operator information that is in principle readily available. Insofar as our study of models is concerned, however, the concentration on compensatory tracking is helpful. Compensatory tracking is definitely more amenable to modeling.

Compensatory Systems. Figure 1 *A* is a block diagram of a simple compensatory tracking set-up. Its main features are the target or system input signal *X*, the human operator *H. O.*, his output *R*, which is also the system output *Y*, and a subtractor in which the system output is subtracted from the system input to produce the error *E*. *E* is displayed as the stimulus *S* to *H. O.* This diagram includes all the absolutely essential features, but compensatory tracking situations are rarely so simple. In a very important class of them, however, all the components external to the human operator are linear networks. If they are linear, several external networks can be lumped together for convenience of representation, and the over-all system then reduces to reasonable proportions.

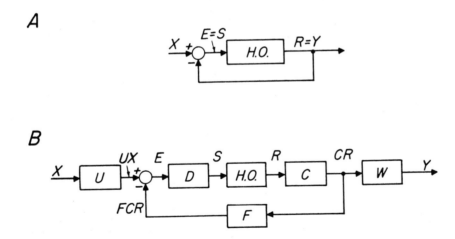

Fig. 1. *A.* Block diagram of simplest compensatory tracking system. *B.* Block diagram of generalized compensatory tracking system. The variables are: *X*, target or system input signal; *E*, error; *S*, stimulus; *R*, response; and *Y*, follower or system output signal. The operators are: *U*, input network; *D*, display; *H.O.*, human operator; *C*, control; *W*, output network; and *F*, feedback network. The circle is a subtractor or differential.

A generalized set-up including linear networks external to the human operator is represented in Fig. 1 *B*. The networks are *U* and *W*, external to the feedback loop, and *D*, *C*, and *F*, within the loop. We may call them all "*external* dynamics," since they are external to the human operator upon whom our attention will be focused. *D* includes both the display and dynamic components associated with it.(*) *C* includes both the control and dynamic components associated with it. *F* includes everything in the feedback path. In the generalized set-up, there are more signals among which to distinguish then there are in the simple set-up. The loop input *UX* may now be distinguishable from the system input *X*, the stimulus *S* from the error *E*, and the system output *Y* from the loop output *CR* and from the human operator's output *R*. The signal fed back to the subtractor is now *FCR* instead of *R = Y*. We shall not have occasion to make all these distinctions at one time, but it may be helpful to see the general form of the system at the outset.

In many practical tracking situations, the target may move in a space of two or three dimensions, or there may be several targets. Much of the specifically applied research on tracking has dealt with multidimensional signals. But this work has not contributed very much to the development of models. With only two or three exceptions, the more basic research that has contributed has dealt with a single dimension of movement. We shall therefore not have much opportunity to concern ourselves with such matters as coupling between vertical and horizontal modes, but even so the problem will be complex enough.

With this delimitation of the main field to one-dimensional compensatory tracking by a system consisting of a man plus linear networks, we may turn to examine the concept of quasi-linearity.

3. QUASI-LINEAR MODELS

Linearity. In order to discuss quasi-linearity it is necessary to start with linearity. A number of variations of the concept, linearity, are in widespread use. Here we shall mean by linear that the superposition principle applies. This restricts us to systems described by linear differential equations. In

---

(*) The sense in which "dynamic" is used here is an extension or generalization from situations in which an input force or forcing function causes an output motion or response. The "dynamics" are not the forces but the system or network or operation or rule relating output response to input force — or, more generally, output signal to input signal.

order to make superposition operationally meaningful, we shall add a further qualification. We shall speak of linear, time-invariant systems, requiring that the inherent properties of the systems be invariant with time. This further qualification corresponds to the assumption that the coefficients of the linear differential equation are constant. A system is linear and time-invariant by our definition, then, if it permits joint stimulus and response superposition: When applied separately, stimulus *a* leads to response *A*, and stimulus *b* leads to response *B*. When the two stimuli are applied together (i.e., stimulus *a*+*b*), the response is the sum of the individual responses (i.e., response *A*+*B*). Requiring that the parameters be constant makes it possible, in our measurements, to apply the stimuli one after the other to an actual network. If we wish to see the responses separately, we must wait for the response to the first to die out, of course, before we apply the second. Abiding by that restriction, we can perform the test of applying first *a*, then *b*, and then *a*+*b*, checking to make sure that the response to the sum is the sum of the separate responses.

Several of the consequences of the assumption of time-invariant linearity are not rigorously applicable to human beings. Human beings change their modes of reaction as they pass from one situation to another. Even within a homogeneous situation, their characteristics "drift." They may have thresholds — we are less sure of that now than we once were — that make them wholly insensitive to very small or very weak signals, and they certainly have overload limits that keep them from responding proportionally when the signals become very large or very intense. Human beings appear, in the fine, to respond discontinuously, and perhaps their time scales are quantized. They do not give identical responses to identical stimuli. In all these ways, they differ from purely linear systems. And, of course, what we know of the nervous system invalidates any detailed picture of the human mechanism as a network of linear components.

All this inconstancy and nonlinearity may seem — and has seemed to many — to suggest that we should pass by the realm of linear models in our search for a representation of the human operator. But there seem to be good reasons for examining that realm carefully before going on to more complex ones. First, the assumption of linearity leads to mathematical tractability. Second, it opens up the wealth of structures and models of classical mechanics and modern electronics. Third, it facilitates communication with designers and engineers, most of whom have had more experience with linear than with nonlinear models. Fourth, it may be appropriate in the gross even though it is not appropriate in the fine. Fifth, some parts of human behavior develop under influences that force or favor linearization. And, sixth, although all the apparently damaging deviations from linearity are encountered in engineering, they have not precluded successful use of linear models in that field.

Quasi-Linearity. The variation with time of parameters of an otherwise linear system causes trouble if the periods of variation are comparable to those of stimulation or response. However, if on infrequent occasions the parameters change suddenly and then remain fixed — if switches are not thrown so often that the behavior never has a chance to settle down — it is entirely possible to make good use of linear models. It is necessary only to change models when the system parameters are altered and to determine the initial conditions of the new regime from the terminal conditions of the old one. At the other extreme, if the parameters of the system drift slowly enough, it is usually possible to make good use of a linear model. The parameters of the model have to vary, but they can be changed stepwise, being allowed to remain constant throughout the interval during which a given temporal segment of stimulation contributes to the response. We must incorporate corresponding tolerance for variation of parameters into our concept of quasi-linearity.

Overload limits cause difficulty only if they are exceeded. It is often good human engineering to make the human overload limits coincide with those of other components of the system. When that is done, the commonplace engineering procedure is applicable: a linear model is used with the stipulation that the overload limits must not be exceeded. Actually, the overload "limits" are more likely to be zones, and the choice of operating limits must therefore depend upon the precision with which the model must represent the system.

The deviations from linearity produced by amplitude (threshold) and time-base discontinuities may be handled readily if they are fine enough. If their scale is small relative to the scale of the signal, they produce effects quite similar to weak noise. The "threshold" for visual misalignment (about 5 seconds of arc), for example, plays only a minor, statistical role if the displayed error dot moves through 10 or 15 degrees. On the other hand, the possibility that the time base of human perception is quantized into "moments" of about 0.1-second duration (Stroud [1954]), and the possibility that response is inherently discontinuous (Craik [1947]; Hick [1948]) with reaction delay and adjustment duration about 0.2 second each, are reasons for concern. They are within the spectrum of the behavior under study. We can only tell ourselves that perceptual quanta and refractory periods have not been clearly demonstrated in continuous tracking — and hope that they will not cause too much trouble.

In order to handle variations from trial to trial with the same target signal, and to make a place for the fine-grained deviations from linearity mentioned in the preceding paragraphs, we introduce noise generators into our models. By "noise" we shall mean any part of a signal not linearly correlated with the target motion. Noise will therefore include both truly random, unrelatable components and components related in a nonlinear (but not in a linear) way to the input signal. There is nothing to prevent our attempting to discover nonlinear relations, but the quasi-linear approach rests on the assumption that the part of the output not linearly related to the input is not likely to be readily usable, anyway, and that it may therefore be lumped together with random noise.

To summarize this discussion, we may define a quasi-linear system.(*) It is one the determinate behavior of which may be described with sufficient approximation by a linear differential equation with coefficients whose variation with time is subject to restriction. The restriction is that their variations must be either rapid or slow in relation to the range of periods of the target signal and in relation to the memory spans of the system in its various states. By determinate behavior we mean output that can be related to input by definite rules. The part of this determinate behavior not accounted for by a linear relation must be small—just how small to be judged in relation to the specific problem under study. The question of tolerance for indeterminate behavior, i.e., for random noise, is left open. Usually that tolerance will be related to the tolerance for deviations from linearity.

A quasi-linear model is, then, either (1) a linear differential equation (or mathematical equivalent) with time-varying coefficients of the kind just described, plus additive terms consisting of random variables, or (2) a describable, physical, quasi-linear system used as a model for another system.

We shall make use of the time-varying property principally in order to adjust the model to accomodate changes in the parameters of the input signal or of the external dynamics.(†) The model will be constant between

---

(*) "Quasi-linear" is sometimes used in other senses than the one to be given. We shall use it in this chapter only in the sense of this definition, but in other contexts it is likely to mean something else.

(†) A system with characteristics that change in response to changes of the input is usually considered non-linear. The idea here is to make a special place for systems that adjust to the input parameters now and again, but hold constant in between adjustments, or which change so slowly that their characteristics may be treated as constant over reasonably long intervals.

such changes — except perhaps for other adjustments of a similar kind to account for learning or fatique and boredom. The linear part of the model will then define (for the interval between changes) a transfer characteristic, a function that will completely specify the linear part of the behavior of the human operator. The random part plus the nonlinear part, taken in relation to the linear, will determine a signal-to-noise ratio, i.e., a fractionation of response variance between signal and noise. The basic problems are (1) to determine the degree to which a quasi-linear model is capable of representing the human operator and (2) to relate the various transfer functions and noise characteristics that correspond to the various states of the model to parameters of the input signal and of the external dynamics.

4. TIME-DOMAIN AND FREQUENCY-DOMAIN REPRESENTATIONS(*)

IT IS HELPFUL in studying the behavior of linear servosystems to think in terms of signals and operators. The signals are seen most simply as real, single-valued functions of time. The position of the target in one spatial dimension is such a function. So is the velocity of the horizontal motion of a joy stick control, or the force exerted upon it by the human operator. This representation of the signals as waveforms (time functions) is sometimes called representation in the time domain. The cathode-ray oscilloscope gives one an almost ideal view of the time-domain picture (though it usually represents time as a spatial dimension).

Differential Equations. The actions of the linear components upon the signals may be described by linear integro-differential equations. But this mode of description leads in all but the simplest problems to long and tedious calculations that often obscure the picture and inhibit insight. The fact is that elementary textbooks on servomechanisms that restrict themselves to the use of integro-differential equations are more difficult than more advanced textbooks that use transform theory. The best approach may well be analagous to the one often mentioned in connection with the teach-

(*) This section is an introduction to several techniques of signal analysis that are widely used in electrical and mechanical engineering. They are described here because (1) they are not as well known in the behavioral sciences and (2) they are essential tools for work involving quasi-linear models. There are so many possible references that it seems best to give none in the text. For more extensive treatment of the techniques and for lists of references, see Gardner and Barnes [1942], Guillemin [1953], Truxal [1955], Chestnut and Mayer [1951], and James, Nichols, and Phillips [1947].

ing of swimming. In any event, although we shall not attempt anything very advanced, we shall not spend much time on differential equations. In fact, we shall consider only one simple problem with the aim of examining the passage from differential equations to impulse-response and frequency-response functions.

Let us consider the response of a very elementary (model) servomechanism to a rather unrealistic target motion, a sudden step-like displacement from $x = 0$ to $x = 1$ at time $t = 0$. The model is shown in Fig. 2 A and again in Fig. 2 B. The servomechanism consists of a subtractor, to the positive input of which the input signal is applied, an amplifier with gain k, a time integrator with scale-factor unity, and a direct feedback path to the negative input of the subtractor.

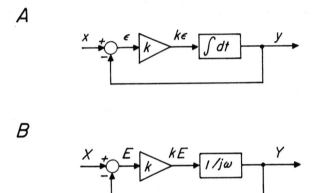

Fig. 2. Block diagrams of simple, illustrative servomechanism. *A.* Variables and operators identified by time-domain symbols. *B.* Variables and operators identified by frequency-domain symbols.

The amplifier operates on the error ϵ to produce $k\epsilon$. The integrator converts $k\epsilon$ into $y = k\int \epsilon \, dt$. (There was no input before $t = 0$, and we may assume that the integrator was empty at that time.) The integrator output y is subtracted from the input, which is $x = 1$ for $t > 0$. The error is therefore $\epsilon = 1 - k\int \epsilon \, dt$. Differentiating both sides yields the equation:

$$\frac{d\epsilon(t)}{dt} = -k\epsilon(t) . \tag{1}$$

This tells us that, after the step is applied, the error decreases at a rate proportional to its size, i.e., exponentially. The error size at $t = 0$ is of course $\epsilon(0) = 1$, since the output of the integrator cannot change instantly.

The error as a function of time is therefore $\epsilon(t) = e^{-kt}$. The loop output then has to be $x(t) - \epsilon(t)$, or $1 - e^{-kt}$. As time goes on, the output approaches closer and closer to the input. The rate of approach is determined by the gain k.

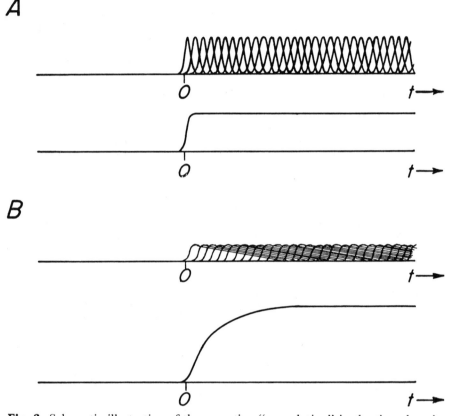

Fig. 3. Schematic illustration of the operation "convolution" in the time domain. The impulses in the top line add together to form the approximation to a step waveform in the second line. The step waveform is the input to a linear network. To find the resulting output, we first determine the response of the network to a single input impulse, then construct (third line) a series of similar responses, one corresponding to each of the impulses in the first line. The sum of the response waves of line three is shown in line four. It is the output that would develop in response to the sum of the impulses in line one, and therefore also the output corresponding to the step waveform of line two. This way of forming the output . . . by adding together a series of suitably time-delayed and amplitude-weighted impulse responses . . . is the idea underlying the convolution (or superposition) integral. In this illustration, the amplitude weights for times $t < 0$ are zero and those for times $t \geq 0$ are unity. To approximate other input waves, other weightings are of course required.

Waveforms, Impulse Responses, and Convolution Integrals. Analyzing the behavior of the simple system in that way makes some appeal to imagery involving waveforms. It is often helpful in more complex problems to go further in that direction. The procedure is to think, first, of the response of the system to an elementary input wave. This may be the step function we have just used, but it is perhaps more natural to use a single spike or pulse, a delta pulse $\delta(t)$. This is defined as being zero at all times except in the vicinity of $t=0$. In a narrow interval about $t=0$, the area under $\delta(t)$ is unity. The time integral of $\delta(t)$ is therefore essentially the unit step.

Inasmuch as we know the response to the step, we may save ourselves the trouble of working out the impulse response (response to the delta pulse) by simply differentiating our step solution. That gives us $h(t) = d(1-e^{-kt})/dt = ke^{-kt}$. The function $h(t)$ is the time-domain characteristic called the impulse response of the servo. Knowing it, we may find the response to an arbitrary input by using the convolution integral, to which we now turn.

The idea behind convolution is very simple. Inasmuch as the system is linear, we add outputs when we add inputs. Think of the target signal, therefore, as a dense succession of delta pulses, properly adjusted in height. In our example, they are adjusted to equal height, as shown in Fig. 3A, and their sum is the step. The approximation to the true input grows better if the pulses are made narrower and denser. In Fig. 3B, the declining exponential responses to the individual pulses are shown, together with their sum, which approximates the function $1-e^{-kt}$. Again, the approximation improves as the pulse density is increased. The convolution integral assumes passage to the limit and therefore exact representation of the output. The integral may be expressed in either of two equivalent ways. Following the schema of Fig. 3, we displace the h's by the various intervals τ, multiply them by the amplitudes of the input at the corresponding instants in the past, and have

$$y(t) = \int_{-\infty}^{\infty} x(\tau) h(t-\tau) d\tau. \tag{2a}$$

Alternatively, we may think of $h(\tau)$ as a weighting function or memory function that specifies the strength (and sign) of the trace remaining from unit excitation τ seconds past. This formulation leads, by a path that the reader may wish to trace out, to

$$y(t) = \int_{-\infty}^{\infty} x(t-\tau) h(\tau) d\tau . \tag{2b}$$

The two integrals are equivalent if $x(t) h(-t) \to 0$ as $t \to \infty$ and as $t \to -\infty$.

It is evident that the impulse response and the convolution integral provide a general method of working with linear systems. It is equally evident, however, that they lead to complicated expressions, for every time a signal passes through a network, a convolution must be performed. It is even worse if, as is often the case, we must work with a complicated input signal and if we must determine the characteristics of a device by comparing the output with the input. To find the impulse-response function of a device we would have to perform the inverse of convolution, which is a rather forbidding operation.

Nevertheless, our examination of the convolution technique focuses our attention on the impulse response. This wave gives us a good display of several facts about the component or system it characterizes. Of particular importance is the fact that it is a picture of the memory span of the network. We can learn from it at once, for example, how far apart excitations must be spaced if their responses are not to tread on one another's heels.

Still we should like a technique that would make it easier to see what happens to the signals as they are operated upon by the networks — and to find the network characteristics if we are given the outputs that correspond to specified inputs.

Spectra and Frequency-Response Characteristics. In order to achieve that ease of operation, we must transform the problem into the frequency domain. Several variations of the basic transformation technique are in widespread use. We shall examine only two of them. Mathematically, they involve integral transformations. Actually, however, the servo expert is familiar with all the common transform pairs and resorts to printed tables instead of calculations when his mental tables fail.

The key to the Fourier transformation lies in what we shall call an elementary oscillation, $e^{j\omega t}$. The e is a constant, the base of natural logarithms; $j = \sqrt{-1}$; ω is the angular frequency (number of radians per second); and t is time. (*) The quantity $e^{j\omega t}$ is defined by an infinite series. All that need concern us here about the series is that it is the sum of the

(*) Inasmuch as i is used so often in electrical engineering for input and for current, $\sqrt{-1}$ is given the symbol j.

two series that define $\cos \omega t$ and $j \sin \omega t$. That fact gives us the fundamental relations

$$e^{j\omega t} = \cos \omega t + j \sin \omega t \tag{3a}$$

and

$$e^{-j\omega t} = \cos \omega t - j \sin \omega t. \tag{3b}$$

Since $\cos \omega t$ and $\sin \omega t$ are the cosine and sine waves familiar from the study of simple harmonic motion, it appears that $e^{j\omega t}$ and $e^{-j\omega t}$ are "simple complex" oscillations. They are simple in the sense of harmonic analysis but complex in the sense that they are part real and part imaginary. They are represented graphically as rotating vectors (counter-clockwise and clock-wise, respectively) of unit length. The vectors rotate through ω radians per second. Since there are 2π radians in a complete cycle, the cyclic frequency is $\omega/2\pi$ cycles per second.

The elementary oscillation $e^{j\omega t}$ has two properties that are both beautiful and useful:

First, the set of functions formed by giving ω all the values from 0 to ∞ is an orthogonal set. That is, the time integral of the product of any member by the complex conjugate (*) of any other member is zero. That is practically the same as saying that each nember is (linearly) uncorrelated with every other member. It is important because, when it comes to synthesizing a complex oscillation, each elementary component contributes its part and no other, thus making possible an orderly procedure and providing as-surance that subsequent analysis will find precisely the pattern used in the synthesis, not some equivalent alternative.

Second, $e^{j\omega t}$ is invariant under linear transformations. Linear transfor-mations applied to $|A|e^{j(\omega t + \theta)}$ merely change the amplitude $|A|$ or shift the phase θ. For this reason, it is often convenient to use a complex coefficient, as in $Ae^{j\omega t}$, in which

$$A = a + j\beta = |A|e^{j\theta} \tag{4a}$$

Since

$$|A|e^{j\theta}e^{j\omega t} = |A|e^{j(\omega t + \theta)} \tag{4b}$$

that incorporates both steady features into the coefficient A and lets $e^{j\omega t}$ carry the invariant oscillation. The amplitude is then

$$|A| = (A^* A)^{\frac{1}{2}} = [(a - j\beta)(a + j\beta)]^{\frac{1}{2}} = (a^2 + \beta^2)^{\frac{1}{2}} \tag{4c}$$

(*) The complex conjugate of $e^{j\omega t} = \cos \omega t + j \sin \omega t$ is $e^{-j\omega t} = \cos \omega t - j \sin \omega t$.

and the phase angle is

$$\theta = \tan^{-1}\left(\frac{\beta}{\alpha}\right). \tag{4d}$$

In the frequency-domain representation of a signal, the important quantities are the complex coefficients. If we are given a waveform (the time-domain representation) and wish to find its spectrum (the frequency-domain representation) we break the former up into component sinusoids and find their complex coefficients or their amplitudes and phase angles. Because of their orthogonality, any physically measurable time function is the sum of just one (usually infinite) set of sinusoids. Their complex coefficients or their amplitudes and phase angles, in association with their frequencies, therefore specify the time function uniquely. The spectrum is the complex function relating the complex coefficients, or the pair of real functions relating the amplitudes and phase angles, to the frequencies.

The method of isolating the component sinusoids (Fourier analysis) is based on the orthogonality of the set of oscillations of $e^{j\omega t}$, $0 < \omega < \infty$. If, for example, we multiply the function $f(t) = F_1 \cos \omega_1 t + F_2 \sin \omega_2 t$ successively by one after another of the $e^{j\omega t}$ (formed by giving ω all possible values) and average each product over all time, we find that the result is always zero except in the instances when $\omega = \pm \omega_1$ and $\omega = \pm \omega_2$. From the values of the averages in those instances, we can determine directly the amplitudes and phase angles of the components of frequencies ω_1 and ω_2. Thus, with the aid of averaging(*) over time, each $e^{-j\omega t}$ selects out its partner $e^{j\omega t}$ and exposes its complex coefficient. The concept of negative frequency ($\omega < 0$) is therefore quite convenient. Negative frequency corresponds to clockwise rotation of the vector $e^{j\omega t}$ whereas positive frequency corresponds to counter-clockwise rotation. Zero frequency of course corresponds to no rotation, since $e^0 = 1$.

We may consolidate the foregoing discussion by saying that the spectrum of a signal is the Fourier transform of its waveform, and the waveform is the inverse Fourier transform of its spectrum:

$$F(j\omega) = \int_{-\infty}^{\infty} f(t) e^{-j\omega t} dt, \tag{5a}$$

(*) If the time function is of finite duration, as is the case in practical problems, we should integrate over time instead of averaging. That has an additional advantage of avoiding a minor mathematical difficulty that need not concern us here.

$$f(t) = \frac{1}{2\pi} \int\limits_{-\infty}^{\infty} F(j\omega)\, e^{t\omega j}\, d\omega \;. \tag{5b}$$

Similarly, the frequency-response function of a network is the Fourier transform of its impulse response, and the impulse-response function is the inverse Fourier transform of its frequency response:

$$H(j\omega) = \int\limits_{-\infty}^{\infty} h(t)\, e^{-j\omega t}\, dt \;, \tag{6a}$$

$$h(t) = \frac{1}{2\pi} \int\limits_{-\infty}^{\infty} H(j\omega)\, e^{j\omega t}\, d\omega \;. \tag{6b}$$

Thus the impulse response is to a network what the waveform is to a signal, and the frequency response is to a network what the spectrum is to a signal. Evidently, the distinction between signal and network is mathematically unnecessary. It makes no difference whether the signal passes through the network or the network passes through the signal. Therefore two cascaded networks may be combined by treating one as signal and the other as network.

Our dissatisfaction with the time domain stemmed from the difficulty of making convolutions and, particularly, deconvolutions. How does the transformation to the frequency domain facilitate our analysis? The answer is that the frequency-domain operation corresponding to convolution is multiplication, and that the inverse is division. If we work in the frequency domain, therefore, we can pass signals through networks by multiplying spectra by frequency-response functions, and we can combine cascaded networks into a more inclusive network by multiplying together the separate frequency responses. Given input and output spectra, we can find the frequency-response characteristic by dividing the latter by the former. The only prices we pay for the convenience are making the transformations and working with complex quantities instead of real ones.

It may be helpful, at this point, to go back to our simple servo problem with our new tools. In Fig. 2*B*, the servo diagram is shown with frequency-domain symbols substituted for the time-domain symbols of Fig. 2*A*.

We find the response of the servo to the step by doing three things: transforming the input signal to the frequency domain, transforming the network operation to the frequency domain, and solving the simple algebraic equation that then describes the system.

We ascertain, first, that the Fourier transform of the step waveform is $1/j\omega$. It will be worthwhile to see why this is so. We start with the definition of the step as $x = 0$ for $t < 0$ and $x = 1$ for $t \geq 0$. The Fourier transformation is then

$$X(j\omega) = \int_{-\infty}^{0} (0) e^{-j\omega t} dt + \int_{0}^{\infty} (1) e^{-j\omega t} dt. \tag{7a}$$

That simplifies to

$$X(j\omega) = \left[-\frac{1}{j\omega} e^{-j\omega t} \right]_{0}^{\infty} \tag{7b}$$

and, therefore, to

$$X(j\omega) = 0 - \left(-\frac{1}{j\omega} \right) = \frac{1}{j\omega}. \tag{7c}$$

Second, we transform the operation of time integration, $\int(\quad) dt$, into division by $j\omega$. It will be worthwhile to examine this transformation also. The key again lies in $e^{j\omega t}$ and in the notion that the waveform $f(t)$ is the linear superposition of a set of sinusoids $F(j\omega) e^{j\omega t}(*)$. The integral of $f(t)$ — let us call it $g(t)$ — is the sum of the integrals of the sinusoidal components. Each integrated component has the form $F(j\omega)(e^{j\omega t}/j\omega)$. Since this is the same as $[F(j\omega)/j\omega] e^{j\omega t}$, and since the spectrum is the set of complex coefficients arranged as a function of frequency, it is evident that time integration divides the spectrum by $j\omega$.

Third, in order to find the servo output we set down

$$E = X - Y = X - \frac{kE}{j\omega}. \tag{8a}$$

It simplifies to

$$E + \frac{kE}{j\omega} = E \left(1 + \frac{k}{j\omega} \right) = X = \frac{1}{j\omega} \tag{8b}$$

and then to

$$E = \frac{1}{j\omega \left(1 + \dfrac{k}{j\omega} \right)} = \frac{1}{j\omega + k} \tag{8c}$$

(*) For the sake of simplicity, we shall neglect the coefficient $1/(2\pi)$ associated with the inverse transform.

Finally,

$$Y = \frac{k}{j\omega(j\omega + k)} \tag{8d}$$

The result given by (8d) is very useful. It tells us that the response falls off with increasing frequency, dropping as $-j/\omega$ when ω is much smaller than k and as $-k/\omega^2$ when ω is much larger than k. The negative imaginary coefficient in the case of small ω and the negative real coefficient in the case of large ω tell us that the very low-frequency components are in sine phase (they all rise across the zero axis, changing from negative to positive values, at the same time) and that the very high-frequency components are in inverted cosine phase (they all have their minimum values at the same time). Evidently, there is a transition as ω passes k in magnitude. We see, therefore, that not only the over-all gain but also the dynamic behavior is controlled by k. We saw this in another way when, in the time domain, we found that the error declined exponentially at a rate governed by k.

If we wish to supplement the frequency-domain analysis by examining the response waveform, we may perform the inverse Fourier transformation or, more simply, enter a table of Fourier transform pairs with $k/[j\omega(j\omega + k)]$. The inverse transform is of course our familiar $1 - e^{-kt}$.

Laplace Transforms and Transfer Functions. The Laplace transformation is closely related to the Fourier transformation. The form of it called the one-sided Laplace transform (which is the only one we shall consider here) brings the initial conditions of the system into the picture in a direct and convenient way by having things start happening at time $t = 0$, whereas the Fourier transformation in principle supposes that the system has been operating throughout all time. (One may handle the problem with the Fourier transformation by assuming zero input until the desired starting instant, but the appropriate machinery is built into the one-sided Laplace transformation.) The Laplace transformation leads directly to an appreciation of the structure of the system in terms that have more physical significance than the infinitely extended oscillations that are the elements of Fourier analysis. And, the Laplace transformation leads to a true understanding of such methods as Heaviside's operational calculus, which was long used in practical work with the justification that it gave correct answers, but with little rationale.

The key to the Laplace transformation is the oscillation $e^{(\sigma + j\omega)t}$. Both σ and ω are real. If we let p be the complex quantity $p = \sigma + j\omega$, our

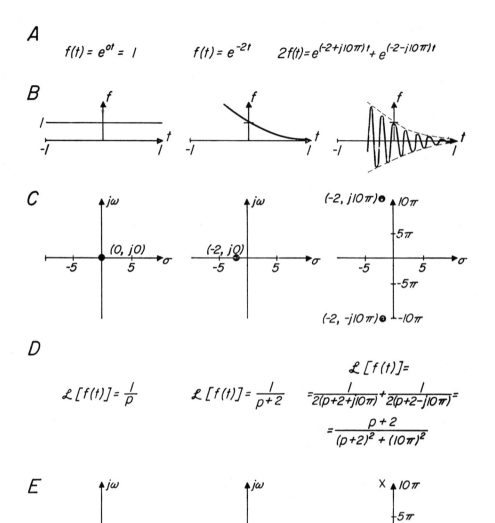

Fig. 4. Alternative representations (*A* through *E*) of three simple signals: a constant or d–c wave, a declining exponential, and an exponentially declining oscillation. *A*, the signals are defined symboilcally in exponential form. *B*, they are shown as functions of time. *C*, their frequencies are represented in the complex plane. *D*, their Laplace transforms are given in symbols. And, *E*, the poles and zeros of the Laplace transforms are shown in the complex plane.

elementary wave is e^{pt}. Since e^{pt} has the same form as $e^{j\omega t}$, the complex p is in a very useful sense a complex frequency.

The interpretation of $e^{pt} = e^{(\sigma + j\omega)t}$ is made clear by noting that $e^{(\sigma + j\omega)t} = e^{\sigma t} e^{j\omega t}$. Thus e^{pt} with complex p is $e^{j\omega t}$ with a time-varying coefficient. We call the coefficient a growth coefficient because it controls the rate of growth of the oscillations. If σ is positive, the coefficient $e^{\sigma t}$ (the amplitude of the oscillations) increases exponentially with time. If σ is negative, the coefficient $e^{\sigma t}$ decreases exponentially with time. If σ is zero, $e^{\sigma t} = 1$, and $e^{pt} = e^{j\omega t}$, our constant amplitude elementary oscillation of the Fourier transformation.

We may say that the Laplace transformation makes an analysis of the same general kind as Fourier analysis, but with differences. They are (1) that the building blocks are in general exponentially growing or decaying oscillations instead of constant amplitude sinusoids and (2) that the process is assumed (when we use the one-sided transform) to start in a specified initial state at $t = 0$ rather than to have run throughout the past. Because growing exponentials may cause trouble by increasing beyond finite bounds, the Laplace transform is defined only for a restricted range of values of σ, but our study will not go far enough for that to concern us greatly.

The Laplace transform of a time function seems to have no generally accepted name comparable to spectrum. It would be convenient for us to have one, but this is not the place to invent terms. We shall say, in full, "the Laplace transform of the waveform."

The Laplace transform of a waveform is

$$F(p) = \int_0^\infty f(t) e^{-pt} dt. \tag{9a}$$

The Laplace transform of an impulse-response function is a transfer function,

$$H(p) = \int_0^\infty h(t) e^{-pt} dt. \tag{9b}$$

Whenever we decide to let the σ be zero in $p = \sigma + j\omega$, the Laplace transform of a function that is zero for $t < 0$ reduces to the Fourier transform. We therefore avoid using a new symbol by designating the Laplace transform of $f(t)$ as $F(p)$, the Fourier transform of $f(t)$ as $F(j\omega)$. This will cause no trouble at all when we are dealing with the transfer and frequency-response functions of physically realizable systems. A physically realizable system cannot respond before it is excited. Its impulse response is therefore zero for $t < 0$. It may be necessary to use some caution, however, in dealing with waveforms, which are not thus constrained.

We may consolidate these introductory remarks about Laplace transformations by looking again at $p = \sigma + j\omega$ and at $F(p)$ and $H(p)$. It is convenient to represent p as a vector quantity in a complex plane, the p-plane. The three signals specified by the equations of Fig. 4A are represented as time functions in Fig. 4B. Their complex frequencies are represented in the three p-planes of Fig. 4C. The first signal is a constant, 1, a fixed position, for example, or a unit direct current. Its angular frequency is zero, and it neither grows nor decays. Its complex frequency is therefore zero, and it is represented by the point $(0, j0)$ in the p-plane plot of Fig. 4C. The second signal, the declining exponential, is damped but does not oscillate. Its complex frequency is $(-2, j0)$, as shown in the p-plane plot. The third signal, the exponentially damped oscillation, declines at the same rate as the second, but it oscillates, also. The cyclic frequency of oscillation is 5 cycles per second, and the angular frequency is 10π radians per second. Note, however, that the waveform is a real function, whereas $e^{(-2 + j10\pi)t}$ has both real and imaginary parts. There must therefore be two complex frequencies, so related that their imaginary parts cancel each other. That is why the signal $f(t)$ is given as $(1/2)[e^{(-2 + j10\pi)t} + e^{(-2 - j10\pi)t}]$. The two complex frequencies represented in the third p-plane of Fig. 4C are conjugate. Their real parts are equal and their imaginary parts are opposite.

The Laplace transforms of the three signals are given in Fig. 4D. Since the value of $f(t)$ prior to time $t = 0$ is irrelevant to the Laplace transformation, the constant signal has the same transform, $1/p$, as the step waveform in our illustrative servo problem. The damping of the second signal adds a constant to the denominator of the transform. The Laplace transform of the third signal is more complicated. The numerator and the first part of the denominator give it a close resemblance to $1/(p+2)$, but the angular frequency enters the denominator in such a way as to predominate over the damping.

If one tries to visualize a Laplace transform, he has to visualize a complex function of a complex argument. In general, the picture resembles two mountain ranges (one real, one imaginary) rising above the p-plane. Fortunately for those who prefer simpler pictures, the essence of the Laplace transform — of a function that belongs to a broad class that includes the ones with which we shall deal — resides in a plot of its poles and zeros.

The poles are the complex frequencies at which the transform is infinite. The zeros are the complex frequencies at which it vanishes. The first signal has a pole at the origin, the second a pole at $(-2, j0)$, the third a pair of poles at $(-2, +j10\pi)$ and $(-2, -j10\pi)$. Thus the poles correspond to the complex frequencies determined by inspection of the waveforms. The third signal has a zero at $(-2, j0)$, since the numerator of the transform is zero when $p = -2$. The significance of this null point is not immediately evident from inspection of the waveform.

If we blank out the parts of the three signals corresponding to $t < 0$, the signals could be the responses of networks to delta-impulse excitations at $t = 0$. Let us suppose that to be the case. The Laplace transforms are then the transfer characteristics of the networks. We recall at once that $1/p$ in the frequency domain corresponds to integration in the time domain, and that the unit step is the time integral of the unit impulse. We note that integration puts a pole at the origin of the complex plane.

The second impulse-response suggests that the network makes an approximate integration. The delta pulse is stretched out in time, but the resulting "step" dies out. It is as though the delta pulse were a sudden squirt of water from a faucet into a bucket, and as though, instead of being a perfect integrator, the bucket had a leak. The level of the water rises stepwise when the faucet is opened momentarily, but it then declines at a rate proportional to its height. Thus the -2 in the exponent of e^{-2t} and in $1/(p+2) = 1/[p-(-2)]$ corresponds to the leak in a leaky integrator. It makes the impulse response die out, and it moves the pole off the origin.

The third network "rings" when impulsive excitation is applied. Oscillations are excited, but they die out as time goes on. The frequency of oscillation is the natural frequency (10π) of the network — or natural *frequencies* $(\pm 10\pi)$, since there must be a conjugate pair to let the network yield real outputs in response to real inputs. The oscillations die out at a rate governed by the negative growth coefficient -2 (damping coefficient 2).

We may ask, now, what the response of a leaky integrator (*cf.* second network) would be to a unit step (*cf.* first signal). The Laplace transform of the output would be $(1/p)[1/(p+2)] = 1/p(p+2)$. This we recognize as, except for a constant factor, a particular case of $k/p(p+k)$, which was the step response of our simple servo.

But what if the network defined by the third impulse response $[h(t) = f(t), t \geq 0;\ h(t) = 0,\ t < 0]$ of Fig. 4 is connected in tandem with the simple servo? The step response of the over-all system is then

$$\frac{1}{p} \cdot \frac{1}{p+2} \cdot \frac{p+2}{(p+2)^2 + (10\pi)^2} , \qquad (10a)$$

which simplifies to

$$\frac{1}{p[(p+2)^2+(10\pi)^2]} \cdot \qquad \text{(10b)}$$

At very high frequency, the p's in the denominator make the response very small. The natural oscillations at $p = -2 \pm j10\pi$ are excited but weakly. At very low frequency, however, the value of (10b) is large. At zero frequency, it is infinite, and the response waveform therefore is similar to the step input in that it (eventually) reaches and maintains a steady value.

Correlation Functions and Power Spectra. We should examine one more set of conceptual tools before turning to problems concerned directly with manual tracking. This set of tools is useful when we cannot specify the signals (e.g., target movements) exactly — when all we know are certain of their characteristics.

Actually, we are often interested not in a particular target signal but in a class of target signals that have certain characteristics in common. The paths followed by similar aircraft taking continuous but separate and un-planned evasive actions are likely to constitute such a class. They are all constrained by the same inertias, acceleration limits, etc., but their motions are not coordinated, one with another. Knowing where a plane is now, one can predict with some accuracy where it will be three seconds later, but he makes the prediction largely on the basis of his knowledge of the average behavior of many similar aircraft seen under similar circumstances, not by recognizing a maneuver and extrapolating. It is of course to the evader's advantage to make no identifiable maneuvers.

When we are dealing with signals of the type suggested, one of our first questions is: what is the covariation between the signal quantity at one instant and the signal quantity τ seconds later? We might ask this about the speed of an aircraft, or its angle of bank, or some other parameter. If the statistics of the signals are homogeneous over the set of similar signals and constant over time, we may make either a single pair of observations on each of the signals or many pairs of observations on one of them. Either way, we find an average value of the product $f(t)$ and $f(t+\tau)$. We may be interested in various values of τ. The function relating the average product $\varphi(\tau)$ to the interval τ is called the unnormalized autocorrelation function. When the observations are made continuously on one time function $f(t)$,

$$\varphi_{ff}(\tau) = \frac{1}{2T} \int_{-T}^{T} f(t)f(t+\tau)\,dt. \tag{11}$$

We may idealize this equation by taking the limit of the right-hand expression as $T \to \infty$.(*)

The autocorrelation function displays several characteristic of the signal. If the autocorrelation function is periodic, so is the signal — in the same fundamental period. If the autocorrelation falls off and approaches zero as τ increases, the signal has no steady and no periodic component. On the other hand, if $f(t)$ has a periodic component that is buried in aperiodic noise, the periodic component will make itself evident in $\varphi_{ff}(\tau)$ for large τ. This is true because the noise component of $\varphi_{ff}(\tau)$ dies out and the periodic component does not. (The autocorrelation function of the sum of two mutually uncorrelated time functions is the sum of the autocorrelation functions of the two time functions.) If $f(t)$ has a steady (d-c) component, it shows up, just as the periodic oscillation does, in $\varphi_{ff}(\tau)$ for large τ.

The autocorrelation function does not tell us anything about the phases of the Fourier components of the signal. All the signals with the same amplitude-*vs*-frequency characteristics have identical autocorrelation functions, regardless of their phase-*vs*-frequency patterns. If the autocorrelation function is the same for all the signals of a set (e.g., the angles of bank of our evasive airplanes), we know that their amplitude-*vs*-frequency characteristics are the same, also.

A convenient way of describing the amplitude-*vs*-frequency characteristic is to give the square of the amplitude (i.e., $|F(j\omega)|^2$) as a function of frequency. This is the power spectrum.(†) It is $\Phi_{ff}(j\omega) = |F(j\omega)|^2 = F(j\omega)F^{\star}(j\omega)$, where $F^{\star}$ is the conjugate of the ordinary spectrum F.(**) The power spectrum is the Fourier transform of the autocorrelation function,

(*) In our discussion of spectra, we tacitly assumed that the signals were of finite energy. If we want to think of them as infinitely enduring and not as dying out at least in the distant past and distant future, we must change the integrals to averages, as we have done here, because the integrals would in general exceed all bounds. We deal with power instead of energy. Only the units and not the forms of functions are changed by the shift.

(†) If the spectrum consists of line components, the power spectrum is the appropriate function. If the spectrum is a continuous distribution over frequency, the power-density spectrum is the appropriate function. The distinction is similar to the one between distributions of probability and distributions of probability density.

(**) As mentioned earlier, the complex conjugate of $F(j\omega)$ is $F(-j\omega)$. In general, if $F = \alpha + j\beta$, its conjugate is $F^{\star} = \alpha - j\beta$.

$$\Phi_{ff}(j\omega) = \int_{-\infty}^{\infty} \varphi_{ff}(\tau)\, e^{-j\omega\tau}\, d\tau \; , \qquad (12a)\,(*)$$

and the autocorrelation function is the inverse Fourier transform of the power spectrum,

$$\varphi_{ff}(\tau) = \frac{1}{2\pi} \int_{-\infty}^{\infty} \Phi_{ff}(j\omega)\, e^{j\omega\tau}\, d\omega \; . \qquad (12b)\,(*)$$

When we work with target signals about which we know only amplitude characteristics, we have to be content with the descriptions provided by the functions just presented. The autocorrelation constitutes a statistical abstraction of the waveform, and the power spectrum is the corresponding abstraction of the ordinary spectrum. There are of course other levels of abstraction, but this is conceptually the simplest, and it is the one that is currently of greatest engineering importance.

We must now consider the problem of discovering the characteristics of a network through which a random signal — of the kind we have been discussing — is passing. Can we determine the characteristics from the autocorrelation functions or power spectra of the input and output signals? The answer is no. From autocorrelation functions or power spectra we can calculate the amplitude-*vs*-frequency characteristic, but we can determine nothing about phase. We need something more.

The "something more" is a cross-correlation function or a cross-power spectrum. They are analogous to autocorrelation functions and power spectra, respectively, but they constitute relations between two functions rather than relations within one function. The cross-correlation function relating $f(t)$ to $g(t)$ is(†)

$$\varphi_{fg}(\tau) = \frac{1}{2T} \int_{-T}^{T} f(t)\, g(t+\tau)\, dt \; . \qquad (13a)$$

(*) Because the autocorrelation function has even symmetry, $\varphi_{ff}(\tau) = \varphi_{ff}(-\tau)$, the complex $e^{-j\omega t}$ and $e^{j\omega t}$ can be replaced by the real $\cos\omega t$ in (12a) and (12b). We have used the complex form to emphasize the similarity with the Fourier transforms, discussed earlier.

(†) If, instead of $g(t)$, $f(t)$ is advanced along the *t*-scale, $\varphi_{fg}(\tau)$ is turned around the other way on the τ scale.

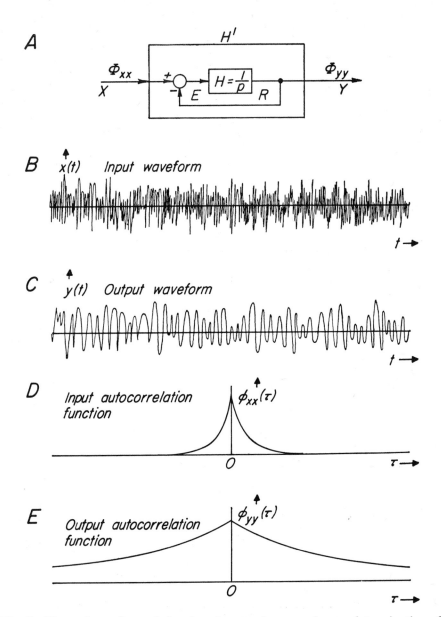

Fig. 5. Illustrations of correlational and spectral approaches to determination of the transfer function of a linear network. At *A*, the "black box" is shown with its cover off. *B* is the input waveform. *C* is the corresponding output waveform. With an autocorrelator, we determine *D* from *B* and *E* from *C*. With a cross-correlator, we determine *F* from *B* and *C* together. Since *D* dies out fairly rapidly as τ increases, *F* is a fair approximation of the impulse response of the network. To find the true impulse response, which is a declining exponential, we would have to "deconvolve" *F* against *D*. Alternatively, in the frequency domain, we use a power-spectrum analyzer to determine *G* and *H* from *B* and *C*, respectively.

[195]

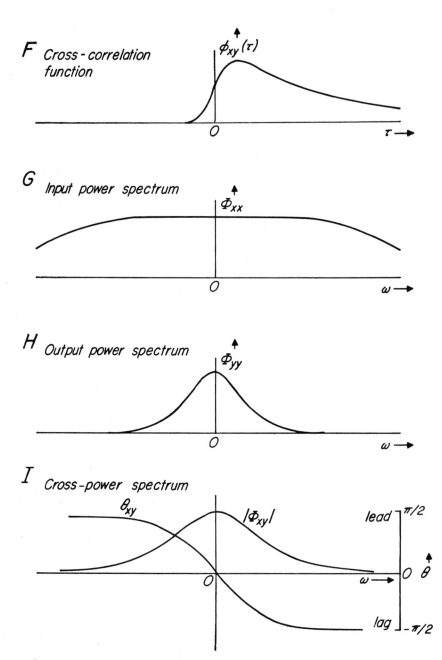

F *Cross - correlation function* $\phi_{xy}(\tau)$ $\tau \longrightarrow$

G *Input power spectrum* $|\Phi_{xx}$ $\omega \longrightarrow$

H *Output power spectrum* Φ_{yy} $\omega \longrightarrow$

I *Cross-power spectrum* θ_{xy} $|\Phi_{xy}|$ lead $\pi/2$ $\omega \longrightarrow$ $O\ \theta$ lag $-\pi/2$

and a cross-power-spectrum analyzer to determine I from B and C togethers The magnitude of the frequency-response function is the ratio of the magnitudes of I and G, which obviously is nearly the same as the magnitude of I. The phase shift of the frequency response functions is exactly the phase shift of I.

The cross-power spectrum is

$$\Phi_{fg}(j\omega) = F^{\star}(j\omega) G(j\omega) = \int_{-\infty}^{\infty} \varphi_{fg}(\tau) e^{-j\omega\tau} d\tau, \tag{13b}$$

where $F(j\omega)$ and $G(j\omega)$ are the Fourier transforms of $f(t)$ and $g(t)$, respectively, and $F^{\star}$ is the conjugate of F.

Working with these functions puts us back into a position to find out all about the network through which the signal passes. The input-output cross-correlation function is related to the input autocorrelation function by the network's impulse response:

$$\varphi_{fg}(\tau) = \int_{-\infty}^{\infty} \varphi_{ff}(\tau - \sigma) h(\sigma) d\sigma . \tag{14a}$$

More conveniently, the input-output cross-power spectrum is related to the input power spectrum by the network's frequency-response function:

$$\Phi_{fg}(j\omega) = \Phi_{ff}(j\omega) H(j\omega) . \tag{14b}$$

The latter expression leads to a simple way of finding $H(j\omega)$:

$$H(j\omega) = \frac{\Phi_{fg}(j\omega)}{\Phi_{ff}(j\omega)} . \tag{14c}$$

An elementary application of the correlational and power-spectral techniques is illustrated in Fig. 5. Suppose that our problem is to investigate the behavior of the (assumed) linear component H' represented schematically at A. We cannot open the box to see that actually it contains the simple servo that we have already examined. Nor can we disturb the system in which it is operating by disconnecting the component for tests with simple signals. We can only record the signals at its input and output. They turn out to be too complicated, as shown by the illustrative samples in B and C, to represent analytically, but they appear to be statistically stationary. We have to give up hope of finding the complete spectra $X(j\omega)$ and $Y(j\omega)$. Still, we wish to know the characteristic of the component.

We might elect to employ time-domain operations. We would then determine, with the aid of a correlator, the autocorrelation functions of the input and output signals (Fig. 5, D and E). The autocorrelation functions will be based on sample segments of the signals, of course, but we use a long enough averaging time for the autocorrelations to stabilize. We find that the input autocorrelation dies out rapidly. This tells us that samples of the input signal spaced only a short interval apart are linearly independent of one another, and that any marked autocorrelation observed in the output is due largely to the network and not to the input signal. If we were not interested in the phase characteristics of the network, we might think of deconvolving $\varphi_{yy}(\tau)$ by $\varphi_{xx}(\tau)$ and transforming the result to find the magnitude $|H'(j\omega)|$ of the frequency-response characteristic. More probably we would transform first and complete the solution in the frequency domain.

But let us suppose that we need to know the phase characteristic. Then we have to connect a cross-correlator to the input and output terminals and find the cross-correlation function shown in Fig. 5F. We note that, except for a rounding of the corners, it is approximated for $\tau > 0$ by the exponential $e^{-\alpha\tau}$. We therefore ask ourselves what might have rounded the corners. The rounding could well be due to the input autocorrelation function $\varphi_{xx}(\tau)$. If $\varphi_{xx}(\tau)$ were an ideal delta pulse, falling immediately to zero for $\tau > 0$, the cross-correlation function $\varphi_{xy}(\tau)$ would be identical with the impulse response $h'(\tau)$ of our component. But because $\varphi_{xx}(\tau)$ is spread out a little, we have to take into account the effect of its convolution (14a) with $h'(\tau)$. If we proceed intuitively, we are likely to regard that explanation of the rounding of the corners of $\varphi_{xy}(\tau)$ as sufficient, to say that $h'(\tau) = e^{-\alpha\tau}$. From that, one versed in the art could conclude that our component is the equivalent of a simple low-pass filter with one pole at $(-a, j0)$, i.e., with the transfer function $1/(p+a)$. That is the correct solution, but we may suspect that the intuition was somewhat aided by fore-knowledge.

If we wish to solve the problem more formally, we are likely to be diverted from the time domain by the difficulty of deconvolution. We therefore either (1) transform $\varphi_{xx}(\tau)$ to $\Phi_{xx}(j\omega)$ and $\varphi_{xy}(\tau)$ to $\Phi_{xy}(j\omega)$ or determine the input power spectrum and the cross-power spectrum (Fig. 5, *G* and *I*) directly with appropriate analyzing equipment. It is then necessary only to divide $\Phi_{xy}(j\omega)$ by $\Phi_{xx}(j\omega)$ to find $H'(j\omega)$. This step is not shown in Fig. 5 because it is obvious from the frequency-domain plots that the effect of $\Phi_{xx}(j\omega)$ is very small.

In order to obtain an analytic representation in the frequency domain, it is necessary to approximate $H'(j\omega)$ — or the magnitude $|H'|$ and the phase θ — by simple pole-and-zero characteristics. This requires either familiarity or persistance. It turns out that $H' = 1/(a+j\omega)$ fits adequately, and this leads us to the same conclusions as finding that $h'(\tau) = e^{-\alpha\tau}$.

Note, however, that we could never discover with this approach (or any other analysis based upon inputs and outputs) that there is a servo in the box — or anything else about the specific composition of the internal network.

The array of techniques discussed in the foregoing sections is only a part of the highly developed apparatus associated with linear network theory. It will be sufficient, however, for our purpose, which is now to examine efforts to determine the characteristics of the human operator in manual tracking tasks. In making that examination, we shall introduce and use two or three displays of relations that we have not thus far discussed, but we shall need no additional basic concepts.

5. TIME-DOMAIN ANALYSIS WITH STEP WAVEFORMS

SEVERAL EXPERIMENTAL STUDIES, most of them not aimed directly at determining the frequency-response or the transfer function of the human operator, are interesting in connection with the development of the concept of quasi-linearity. They point up difficulties that would be encountered if a linear, time-invariant model were adopted without the several qualifications we have encompassed within the concept of quasi-linearity. The experiments will be described in an order related to the conceptual progression, not in chronological order. The discussion should therefore not be permitted to develop the impression that a rigorously linear and time-invariant model of the human operator was accepted widely at first but progressively discredited by a succession of experiments. Actually, most of the qualifications we have applied to linearity and time invariance in order to arrive at quasi-linearity were made at least tacitly by Tustin in connection with his work during World War II.

In our discussion of conceptual tools, we examined the response of a linear network to a unit impulse and to a unit step. The impulse might well have been,(*) and the step actually was, the stimulus waveform used in some of the first experimental studies of human tracking response characteristics. These studies were, in part, deliberate tests of the linearity and time invariance of the human operator.

On the whole, the results of the studies were interpreted as leading to the rejection of models with those properties and as favoring models in

(*) Testing a well-trained human operator with delta-pulse inputs would at once remove from consideration the too-rigorous interpretation of linearity and time invariance, A good operator would not respond to it at all, for it would be gone before he could react, and any response on his part would add to the discrepancy between input and output.

which the response characteristics changed, discontinuously, from time to time. The difference between that interpretation and the one we are using here is not great, for we are allowing for some switching of characteristics in our notion of quasi-linearity. The main point of divergence concerns the validity of the extrapolation from discrete tracking tasks to continuous tracking tasks. Even on that point, the only real difference is in readiness to discard the hypothesis of roughly continuous operation and to accept the hypothesis that an intermittency with a period of 0.4 to 0.6 second is an essential characteristic of human data processing. The approach we shall take, here, is that the assumption of such medium-grained intermittency leads to very interesting models and useful working hypotheses, but that — since one may use several models and hypotheses concurrently — we should be slow to reject the notion that in temporally homogeneous tasks the human operator may behave in an approximately linear way over intervals that are long in comparison with, say, 0.1 second.

Phillips' Analysis of Aided Tracking. One of the first analyses of a servo system with a human operator was made at the M. I.T. Radiation Laboratory during World War II. This work concerned ground control of fire against aircraft and the design of rate-aiding controls. They are especially useful in tracking targets that tend to move with constant velocity. A displacement of the control can correct an error in position and an error in velocity at the same time. Once the error and its time derivative are reduced to zero, the follower follows a truly constant-velocity target without further adjustment on the part of the operator. The transfer function of a rate-aiding control has the form $C = (1 + \tau p)/p$. Since $(1 + \tau p)/p$ may be broken up into two terms $1/p$ and τ, a rate-aiding control is in effect a displacement-to-displacement control with gain τ "aided" by a parallel displacement-to-velocity (i.e., time integrating) auxilliary $1/p$.

In order to determine the optimal value of τ, Phillips (1947) adopted a model for the human operator and proceeded to optimize the aiding and the operator parameters jointly. The model of the human operator he adopted was the transfer function $pH(p) = k(1 + Tp)e^{-Lp}$. This is a linear operator, of course, but he expected that its parameters would change to meet changing conditions, and he realized that there was a haphazard remnant of human behavior for which it would not account.

As a criterion, Phillips adopted the minimization of mean-squared error — largely because of its mathematical tractability. As a target motion, he chose a course characterized by constant velocity within each of a number of intervals and abrupt changes of velocity at the ends of intervals. The target-position waveform was, that is to say, a series of concatenated ramps, and its time derivative was a series of steps. Both the amplitudes of the steps and the intervals between them were random under constraints imposed by specified distribution functions.

The time-delay transform e^{-Lp} is usually difficult to handle in calculations of the kind required in the optimization. Phillips therefore replaced it by the factor $(1 + pL/3)^{-3}$. This is a cascade of three simple lags of the form $1/(1 + L'p)$. It provides an approximation to time delay L.

In the solution of the optimization problem, the best value for the time constants τ of the aiding unit and T of the human operator depended upon the reaction time L of the human operator. To get working values, Phillips assumed that $L = 0.5$ second. This made the optimal τ and T both 0.9 second.

Phillips referred to experiments by his co-worker Sobczyk [1943]. In these experiments, the operators had not been able to introduce much derivative control. Their time constants had been small. Phillips therefore determined the optimal aiding time constant for $L = 0.5$ and $T = 0$. It turned out to be 2.5 second.

In Phillips' analysis, we see an example of engineering need for a model of the human operator that is compatible with linear models of hardware components. We see that there was considerable tolerance for roughness of approximation. The thing conspicuously lacking was a set of well-defined parameters for a quasi-linear model of the human operator. On the basis of current data, we should say that, for a well-engineered tracking set-up, 0.5 second is probably too large for L and that 0 second is too small for T. Nevertheless, the analysis contributed to an understanding of the operation of the system under study. With better data, it might have done more.

Vince's Experiment. Carrying through a series of experiments begun before his untimely death by Craik [1947, 1948], Vince [1948] examined responses in a pursuit task to pairs of step inputs. The two steps of a pair were displacements in opposite directions. The interval between them was varied systematically. Instead of using techniques of the kind we have discussed, Vince measured the reaction times (delays between steps in the stimulus and beginnings of corresponding responses), the durations of movements, and the errors at the ends of movements. She found that, when the two steps of a pair were widely separated, the reaction time was about 0.25 second and the movement time about 0.20 second, and that the response amplitude usually came within 25 per cent of matching the amplitude of the stimulus step. However, when the second step of the pair came within 0.5 second after the first, the second response of a pair was delayed beyond its normal reaction time. This she interpreted as evidence of discontinuity in the human operator. She identified the phenomenon with Telford's psychological refractory phase. Telford [1931] had observed that, in the interval immediately following one auditory stimulation, the response to a second auditory stimulus was abnormally delayed. This finding has been confirmed by more recent experiments of Hick [1948] and Marill [1953]. The idea that the human operator processes signals in a fundamentally discontinuous way, that he accepts a segment of input and selects an appropriate response program for it, meanwhile being refractory to additional inputs, set off a series of experiments with paired step waveforms.

Repetitions of Vince's Experiment. Ellson and Hill [1948] repeated Vince's study with minor modifications. They changed the target motion from vertical to horizontal, altered the display somewhat, and used a different kind of handle as a control. Insofar as an idealized description of the target waveform is concerned, however, their experiment was quite similar to Vince's. It is noteworthy, therefore, that their results and conclusions were quite different. They found that, when the second step followed the first after a short interval, the second response started before the first was completed. There appeared to be some abnormal delay, but — since it came as a continuation of the initial response — it was difficult to decide when the return movement began. In brief, however, the response to the pair was rather nearly equal to the sum of the responses to the same steps presented separately. This result is of course entirely in line with linearity and time invariance.

In a related study, Ellson, Hill, and Craig [1949] made similar tracking tests with pairs of steps of various amplitudes. They found the same result insofar as refractoriness is concerned: the response to a pair was essentially the sum of the responses to the individual steps. However, there was a different manifestation of nonlinearity or of time variation. Responses to small steps were too big, responses to large steps were too small. This phenomenon had been noted earlier by Searle and Taylor [1948]. They called it the "range effect." Craig [1949] interpreted it in terms of two stimulus components: the present step, and a weighted average of past steps.

It does not appear that Vince learned of the studies of Ellson and his co-workers, for she made no reference to them in her second paper, but she, too, repeated her experiment. In the repetition [1950]. she found some instances in which the second response occurred during the reaction time or during the movement time of the first, but they were in the minority. She concluded that the human operator tends to respond discontinuously, that the psychological refractory state, while not absolute, is nevertheless a basic characteristic of the operator.

Possible Resolution of Difference between Vince's and Ellson's Results. Pondering the discrepancy between Vince's results and those of Ellson and his colleagues leads to the idea that the details of the presentation of the step displacements might be very important. The reason for thinking so is that the step displacement is displayed to a system, the retina and its projection, that is essentially a manifold of interacting channels. Interactions are strong among neighboring channels but weak among distant ones. If a dot is moved about slowly in the visual field, the excitatory processes at various levels in the nervous system no doubt move through functionally (though perhaps not always spatially) continuous paths. A reaction mediated by such a process, which we may identify with the process underlying the perception of movement, may be roughly linear. On the other hand, if the dot is removed suddenly from one location and, at the same time, another dot is presented in another (distant) location, as would be the case with a large ideal step displacement, then we have a very different problem. The visual process can no longer depend upon a succession of local interactions to shift the excitation through the intervening neural tissue. The displaced dot is essentially a new stimulus, and to connect the response mechanism to it may even require a rudimentary search for the new location. It is obvious that, if the display surface were very large and if the step displacement were truly instantaneous, the reaction would involve search.

The possibility is, therefore, that Vince's steps were more sudden than Ellson's, or that the line marking the jump was thinner or less clearly visible. If the operators in Vince's tests saw enough to tell in which direction the target jumped, but not to let them follow it visually all the way to its destination, they had to search momentarily for it after each presentation. In the first experiment, this would have caused little or no delay (because the steps were always of the same amplitude and the search was therefore confined to a highly restricted area) *except in those trials in which the dot jumped again before it was seen in its new position*. In those trials, the first momentary search would have to be abandoned, and the operator would have to look back to the baseline before he could pick up the target again. This, it seems, could easily account for the difference between the observed results.

The conception of the visual system as a manifold of channels characterized by predominately local interaction has a bearing on the question: for what kinds of signal might we expect the human operator to be reasonably linear and constant? Intuitively, we should not except him to be time-invariant if he is called upon during some intervals merely to be quiescent and during others to engage in search. Those requirements, alternating, would almost surely call forth intermittent behavior. Demonstrating that they do call forth intermittent behavior does not provide a good basis for concluding that the human operator responds nonlinearly or discontinuously in continuous, statistically homogeneous tasks.

Variation in Size of Response Ensemble as a Possible Explanation for the Psychological Refractory Phase. In a particularly interesting paper, Hick [1948] gave a possible explanation of the refractory phase that is relevant to the present discussion. He pointed out that, in an experiment such as Vince's, the response to the first step of a pair may be selected from a small ensemble of ready responses — in the experiment with steps of constant amplitude, from a set of only two (up, down). If the second response is delayed until the first is completed, it also may be chosen from a small ensemble — perhaps even from a set with only one member. However, if the second response is begun while the first is in progress, it must be selected from a much larger ensemble. The operator must select the one that will take the follower back to the baseline. On the basis of his own observations [1951, 1952], Hick knew that reaction time depends markedly upon the size of the response ensemble — in the case of equiprobable responses, he found it to be approximately $0.27 \log_e (n+1)$, where n is the number of responses — and concluded that either of the two strategies open to the operator would cause delay in the second response. The operator could wait and then make a simple reaction, or he could start at once to make the slower choice of the appropriate response from among many. Presumably he would do whichever led to the better performance.

Hick did not pursue this interpretation of tracking in terms of information theory, for he [1948] and Bates [1947] found that the refractory phase appeared also in tasks that involved only such response selections as the pressing of a key. But the stimuli in all these tasks were discrete. We must conclude, therefore, that the explanation of refractory phase in terms of the size of the response ensemble does not require that the human operator respond intermittently in tracking a target the statistical parameters of which are homogeneous over time. Under those circumstances, the size of the ensemble is constant.

Opening the Loop. An approach closely related to that of Craik, Vince, and Hick, involving analysis and step inputs, was made by Searle and Taylor [1948], Taylor and Birmingham [1948], and Searle [1951] at the Naval Research Laboratory. They worked with isolated steps as well as with steps spaced at intervals in time.

To facilitate examination of the responses, they recorded not only the position, but also the velocity, the acceleration, and the jerk (third time derivative) of the joystick control as functions of time. Since the joystick approximated a pure inertia, acceleration was approximately proportional to the force applied to the control. It was continuous throughout an operator's response to a step, first increasing to a positive peak, then reversing and falling to a negative (braking) peak before returning to zero.

Taylor [1949] mentioned briefly an important observation made with a technique similar to the ones used by Tustin [1947, 1952] and Raggazini [1948]. During a test in which steps were presented at irregular intervals, the feedback loop was opened. A loop is "opened" by breaking the feedback path at any point. The operator saw the stimulus step, but his follower did not follow. Instead of responding with an indefinitely continued movement as a simple, continuous servo would do, the operator made the same response as he made on other occassions on which the loop was closed.

As Craik [1948] pointed out, it is difficult to evaluate the contribution of kinesthetic feedback in the situation just described. Clearly, if kinesthetic feedback were immediate, and if the operator could exchange information between his visual and kinesthetic modalities quickly and effectively, the response could be controlled as well by kinesthesis as by vision, and the loop would not in fact have been opened. The discussion therefore has to fall back upon the argument that the reaction time is the fundamental obstacle in the way of continuous operation, that the operator must see the result of the last response before making the next one. This makes it difficult to extend to continuous tracking tasks the conclusion that the human operator responds intermittently. As we shall see, the status of reaction time in continuous tracking is not clear.

The Step Response as a Characteristic of the Human Operator.
In none of the studies we have mentioned was the step response of the

human operator used as a characteristic function. Instead, it was used to support an argument leading to the conclusion that he is nonlinear or time-varying. The alternative approach would be to use the assumption of linearity and time invariance as a working hypothesis, and to analyze the step response with the aim of learning something from it that will be useful in understanding the behavior of the human operator in continuous tracking situations.

That approach was taken by Mayne [1951]. He based his analysis upon the notion that the human operator is in some ways comparable to a system consisting of a navigator and an autopilot. Under any one adjustment, the autopilot is approximately a linear system. It functions in a closed loop, the characteristics of which are readily measurable. However, the navigator sometimes changes the heading adjustment. This change alters the loop characteristic. The over-all system is therefore discontinuous.

Mayne's conception is essentially similar to the conception of quasi-linearity we have discussed. The main qualification implicit in his formulation is that the dynamics of the autopilot remain constant; only the heading parameter is changed. If something comparable is true of the human operator, one might hope to obtain the basic transfer characteristic through measurements with step inputs.

Thinking of the operator's response mechanism as consisting of higher centers (the navigator), charged mainly with computation and prediction, and lower centers (the autopilot), responsible for carrying out the response movements, Mayne associated reaction time with the former, movement time with the latter. In order to find the step response of the linear operator, therefore, he simply recorded a pursuit response to a step, neglected the quiescent reaction-time interval, and arbitrarily set $t = 0$ at the beginning of the response movement.

In order to determine whether or not the step response would characterize the behavior of the operator in continuous tracking, Mayne and his co-worker, Payne, (1) found an analytic function that closely approximated the step response, (2) determined its Fourier transform and, from it, the frequency-response characteristic of the operator, (3) set up the corresponding linear network on an analogue computer, and (4) had both the network and the human operator track a signal synthesized by superposing three sinusoids.

At the time Mayne's study was published, the procedure just described had been followed with only one operator, and in fact with only one particular step response. (A second operator's step response was analyzed, but not simulated.) The fact that the computer's and the operator's responses to the superposed sinusoids were rather similar, therefore, is little more than suggestive. However, the work is continuing. If the step response thus determined turns out to be truly descriptive of the operator's response characteristic under a variety of conditions, it will greatly simplify the problem of representing the human operator. As we shall see as we discuss other recent work, however, things are probably not so simple.

One further application of the step response is of interest. It differs from Mayne's principally in that it involves a different assumption about the invariance of the operator's response characteristic. Whereas Mayne considered both the form and the frequency-selective parameters of the operator to be invariant, Elkind [1956] considered only the form to be invariant from one tracking situation to another. He used step responses only incidentally, to check the form of the closed-loop transfer characteristic of his pursuit-tracking model. The coefficients were left to vary from one tracking task to another. Closed-loop transfer characteristics of the form

$$H'(j\omega) = \frac{k}{(1 + Tp)} e^{-Lp} \tag{15}$$

were consistent with both the step responses and responses to noise-like target courses.

6. FREQUENCY ANALYSIS WITH SINUSOIDAL TEST SIGNALS

Ellson and Gray's Experiment. One of the first experiments conducted after World War II by Ellson and his co-workers [1948] tested the too-rigorous interpretation of constant linearity with a method borrowed directly from the electronics laboratory. Sinusoidal inputs were applied to the (human) device under test in a pursuit tracking set-up, and measurements were made of input-to-output gain and phase shift at each of a number of frequencies. Two different amplitudes of the input signal and two degrees of control sensitivity were tested.

In the results, there was some departure from linear proportionality of response when the input amplitude and control sensitivity were changed. The phase shift varied greatly from test to test, even with the same subject under the same normal conditions. But the main evidence of nonlinearity was the fact that, trying to track 3- or 4-cps targets, the operators often drifted not only out of phase but off frequency. Whenever they did so, their response frequency was a little higher than the stimulus frequency. Evidently, they estimated the amplitude and the phase or frequency through separate processes, for they continued to produce responses of approximately the correct amplitude even when they were responding at the wrong angular rate.

Noble, Fitts, and Warren's Experiment. A recent experiment, by Noble, Fitts, and Warren [1955], is in some respects quite similar to the one just described. The task was again a pursuit task, and the target signals were again sinusoids of various frequencies. Time-on-target and mean-squared error were determined for each frequency. The former decreased and the latter increased, of course, with increasing frequency. Stimulus-response desynchronization appeared in the tests with the higher frequencies, though the subjects in this experiment sometimes underestimated the stimulus frequency. The results are interpreted as favoring a basically intermittent model with the capacity to predict.

Sinusoidal and Step Tests in Relation to Quasi-Linearity. Taken solely as refutations of the assumption of time-invariant linearity, these frequency-response experiments are comparable to the step-response experiments described in the first part of the last section. They are effective in destroying the obviously-too-rigorous interpretation, but they do not go far toward restricting the domain within which quasi-linear models may be applicable. Indeed, we might take 3 or 4 cps as an upper limit for the target spectra for which we would expect linear response, but there is a question even about that. It stems from the fact that, when they were responding off frequency, the operators were making greater mean-square, mean-absolute, and peak errors than those they would have made if they had stopped responding. It is by no means evident that highly trained operators, working with knowledge of results, would behave in the obviously nonlinear way observed in the tests.

The main point to be made about the relation of these experiments to quasi-linear models, however, is that they did not test the models in the domain within which the models are intended to operate. The steps in the step-displacement signals were spaced, on the average, at such intervals that a quasi-linear model would spend most of its time switching from one mode to another. The sinusoids presented a problem best solved by learning the oft-repeated form of the stimulus motion and reproducing it at constant level and in proper phase under the guidance of separate feedbacks for amplitude and phase. In fact, if he were regarded as a pair of regulators (devices designed to maintain constant output), one for amplitude and one for phase, the human operator might turn out to be reasonably linear while "tracking" a given sinusoid.

Walston and Warren's Study. Despite what we have just said about probing the human operator with sinusoidal test signals, it is of interest to consider a recent study of Walston and Warren [1954] in which specific linear models were subjected to sinusoidal test. Walston and Warren made a few observations also with a noiselike target movement, but we shall consider now only their tests with sinusoidal target movement.

Two tracking set-ups were used, one compensatory and one pursuit, as shown schematically in Fig. 6. In each case, the display and control were so simplified that they introduced no dynamics other than the scale factors of the transductions from voltage to displacement and from displacement to voltage. Various values of each scale factor were employed in the series of tests.

At the outset, Walston and Warren adopted a model of the human operator for each of the two tracking situations. For the compensatory system they selected, apparently independently, a model that several previous investigators had used. As indicated in Fig. 6, the compensatory model has the linear part

$$H_c = \frac{R}{S} = \left(c_1 + \frac{c_2}{p}\right)e^{-Lp}.\tag{16}$$

Translated into time-domain language, this expression says that the response displacement $r(t)$ is proportional to the value, L seconds earlier, of the weighted sum of the stimulus error displacement $s(t)$ and its time integral $\int s(t)\,dt$. L is identified with reaction time, but its value is to be adjusted to be appropriate to the particular tracking situation. Actually, the operators learned the 0.5-cps sinusoid so well that, when it was used as the target signal, L turned out to be very close to zero. This simplified the linear part of the operator to $c_1 + c_2/p$, an amplifier in parallel with an integrator.

The rationale for the choice of this operator was discussed by Tustin [1947], Phillips [1947], and others. It is perhaps simpler to describe if we think in terms of the velocity dr/dt with which the tracker moves his control. We may suppose that he moves it rapidly to neutralize a big error, slowly in response to a small one. This gives us $dr/dt = c_2 s(t)$. We may suppose at the same time, however, that the tracker tends to displace his control in proportion to the error displacement. That gives us $r(t) = c_1 s(t)$ or $dr/dt = c_1 ds/dt$. Adding the two tendencies together yields

$$\frac{dr}{dt} = c_1 \frac{ds}{dt} + c_2 s(t) . \tag{17a}$$

That is the differential form of

$$r(t) = c_1 s(t) + c_2 \int s(t)\, dt , \tag{17b}$$

which, in the frequency domain, is expression (16) without the factor e^{-Lp}. That factor corresponds to the time delay L, since a delayed elementary oscillation $e^{p(t-L)}$ is simply e^{-Lp} times the same oscillation undelayed, i.e., $e^{-Lp} e^{pt}$.

Walston and Warren's pursuit model is closely related to the compensatory model just described. The amplifier part of the operator looks at the target displacement (instead of the error displacement), while the integrator part of the operator looks at the error displacement. The rationale of this arrangement was discussed earlier by North [1952], who spoke of division of attention between target and error.

In both compensatory and pursuit models, nonlinearities and fluctuations are lumped into a noise component that is added at the output. Walston and Warren assume this noise to have a uniform power-density spectrum $N^2(j\omega) = k$. This does not mean, however, that the noise component of Y has a uniform power-density spectrum, for the noise circulates repeatedly through the loop and has the loop's characteristics impressed upon it. In Fig. 6, the pursuit noise N' is distinguished from the compensatory noise N only to indicate that it may have a different level. Both noises are assumed to be uniform over frequency.

Walston and Warren used their empirical tests to determine the parameters of the models just described. They determined the autocorrelation function of the error $\epsilon(t)$ and the mean-squared value of the noise $n(t)$. They then compared the empirically determined values with values predicted from the model. Making the predictions proved to be mathematically very difficult, since the models led to transcendental equations and to infinite numbers of poles and zeros. (That is not at all unreasonable. A neural mechanism may be more nearly like a distributed electrical network than like an electrical network with a finite number of lumped parameters and therefore a finite number of poles and zeros.) It was necessary, therefore, for Walston and Warren to make theoretical approximations.

The main difficulty, however, stemmed from the variability of the experimental results. The parameters of the model that best described the

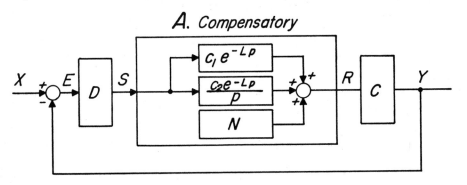

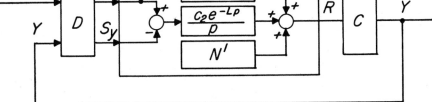

Fig. 6. Block diagrams illustrating Walston and Warren's models of the human operator. In the compensatory model (A), both the amplifier and time-delay component c_1e^{-Lp} and the integrator and time-delay component $(c_2e^{-Lp})/p$ look at the error signal. In the pursuit model (B), the former looks at the target and the latter at the error. L is the same for both components of a model, but not for both models. [After Walston and Warren (1954)]

data varied rather widely from subject to subject. They are shown in Table 1. The parameters c_1 and c_2 have been multiplied by the (dimensionless, scalar) display scale factor D, apparently in order to facilitate comparisons at the point in the system corresponding to the operator's response.(*) All

(*) The way the noise was handled is not entirely clear. Evidently, the noise values refer to a point at the output of the control but ahead of an external "control-sensitivity" amplifier.   *Continued next page.*

the values in Table 1 were derived with the aid of the assumption that $L = 0$ in both the compensatory and the pursuit tests.

Table 1.

Parameters of Walston and Warren's Operators Tracking a 0.5-cps Sinusoid

Op.	$c_1 D$ rad/in Pursuit	Compen.	$c_2 D$ rad/in sec Pursuit	Compen.	N^2 (volts)^2/rad Pursuit	Compen.
A	1.07		28.4		89*	
B	0.19		5.1		5	
C	0.035	0.71	2.7	4.1	31	43*
D	2.72	0.35	51.5	31.1	162	441
E	1.90	0.018	34.2	7.0	166	39
F	2.86		55.6		222	
G		0.018		6.2		35

(*) Divide noise values in table by 10^4.

In two of the three instances in which data were obtained with the same subject in both pursuit and compensatory tasks, the amplifier gain c_1 and the integrator scale factor c_2 are higher in pursuit. In two of the three cases, the noise has a higher level in compensatory. This is in the direction indicated by other studies. In general, strong noise is associated with high gain.

Walston and Warren used their model to determine "performance factors" for the individual subjects and to analyze various possibilities for improving performance that would be open to an operator who was able to select optimal parameters for his behavior. The thing that concerns us more directly in the present discussion, however, is the degree to which the linear model fits the empirical data. Because the analysis required to answer that question depends heavily upon assumptions and because, even so, it is quite complicated, we shall simply quote Walston and Warren's conclusion:

"We have assumed that the operator performs as a linear mechanism over the range of scale factors used for a given input. It may be true that he is not linear over the entire range. However, the linear approximation yields acceptable results so that the extra work involved in attempting to determine the nature of the nonlinearity does not seem to be justified at this stage of the analysis." ([1954], p. 85).

The conversion factor of the control was 6.45 volts per radian. The noise values should therefore be divided by $(6.45 \text{v/rad})^2$ if they are to be related to the operator's gain parameters. This would put them into the form $(N')^2/\text{rad}^2$ of handle variance per radian per second of frequency.

Inasmuch as Warren participated also in the conclusion that the results of his experiment with Noble and Fitts [1955] were best fit by an intermittent operator model, we should probably summarize the tests with sinusoids as follows: (1) a linear model accounts for a satisfactorily large fraction of the overall variance in the tracking of low-frequency sinusoidal motion. (2) The human tracker adopts an approach quite different from that of a simple, linear network when he is called upon to follow rapid sinusoidal oscillations.

7. FREQUENCY ANALYSIS WITH SIGNALS CONSISTING OF SUPERPOSED SINUSOIDS

As WE HAVE just seen, the approaches most widely used in the study of linear systems do not lead to clear analyses of quasi-linear systems. If the transfer characteristic changes when the input parameters change, one cannot determine, through tests with simple signals, the transfer characteristics that describe the behavior set off by complicated signals. This was understood by the electrical engineers who, during and after World War II, became interested in the human operators of their servo systems. They were careful to work, therefore, with reasonably realistic test signals.

Synthetic Target Signals. "Realistic" implies a reference to actual situations. The actual situations may be those in which a particular control system is to be used, or they may be the vague and general class of real-life situations in which human operators operate. In neither case are the target signals likely to be sinusoidal. Step displacements are more often encountered but are by no means typical. More and more, experimenters have turned toward a random, gaussian process(*) as their source (actual or conceptual) of target signals. The rationale for this choice is that such a process, a sequence of random decisions made in infinitely rapid succession, is the epitome at the same time of homogeneity and simplicity and of irregularity and complication. The parameters are few and simple. The part not specified by the parameters is entirely indeterminate. The gaussian process therefore makes signals that suit the experimenter who has to control them,

(*) A "gaussian process" is a generator of time functions, of which we can consider an infinitude simultaneously, so that there is a distribution of probability density for each instantaneous value. The process is defined by the property that the joint distribution of the values at any N instants is an N-dimensional normal distribution.

the theoretician who has to handle them mathematically, and the operator who has to learn their learnable characteristics.

To serve as a reasonable signal for tracking, however, a gaussian process has to be constrained. Without constraint, its power-density spectrum extends to infinite frequency. Although the outputs of commercial "random noise generators" are limited in frequency by the restricted bandwidths of electronic amplifiers, they produce such wide-band noise that, if it is transduced into target displacement, only a microscopic part of it is within the scope of the human operator. The procedure, therefore, is to pass the random noise through a filter, usually a low-pass filter, thereby applying a constraint of roughly the same kind as is inherent in the inertia of physical bodies. The result, the "filtered random noise," is still easy to specify, since its parameters are those of the gaussian process (mean and variance) and those of the filter (poles and zeros). Actually, it is even a little simpler than that, for the phase pattern of the gaussian signal is random, and the phase characteristic of the filter is therefore irrelevant.

One model of the gaussian process involves adding together an infinitude of sinusoidal oscillations. Their individual amplitudes are all the same, and, of course, very small. The frequencies are spaced with uniform density along the frequency scale. Their phases are selected at random. Mathematically, if only the low-frequency part of the noise is considered, this leads to the same result as starting with an infinitude of delta pulses and positioning them at random along the time scale.

Therefore, instead of working with resistance noise or ionization noise, which constitute very close approaches to the mathematical ideal, one can stimulate a band-limited gaussian process by superposing a number of sinusoids.

Disappointingly, the number of sinusoids superposed to produce the target signals for tracking experiments has usually been only three or four. This seems hardly enough, either to produce a close visual approximation to random noise or to permit detailed analysis in frequency. But three or four sinusoids do produce irregular waveform and considerations of cost and complexity of apparatus have tended to hold the number down.

Tustin's Experiments. Tustin [1947] used three superposed sinusoids, the first, third, and sixth harmonics of a very low fundamental, e.g., 0.018 cps. The tracking set-up simulated that used in the fire-control system of a tank. The operator twisted a lightly spring-loaded spade grip, the angular position $r(t)$ of which controlled the angle $y(t)$ of the gun sight through a dynamic network. In most of Tustin's tests, velocity of the gun and sight was proportional to the handle displacement. That is, in terms of Fig. 1B, $V = D = W = F = 1$, and $C = k/p$. The target signal $x(t)$, the operator's response $r(t)$, and the error signal $\epsilon(t)$ were recorded.

Tustin was well aware, as we have noted, of the amplitude nonlinearities, temporal discontinuities, and haphazard fluctuations that complicate the human operator's response. His aim, therefore, was to examine the possibility of determining an "approximate linear law" that would describe the main part of the operator's behavior. Because the output of a linear, time-invariant operator would consist only of components at the three input frequencies, the presence of response components at other frequencies was clear evidence of some departure from constant linearity. However, Tustin was interested in seeing how much of the response could be accounted for by the best linear model.

The basic limitations of his method are direct results of (1) his use of so few signal components and (2) his selecting them in harmonic relation. With only three components he could determine only three points on a frequency-response curve in any one test. There were response components at other frequencies, it is true, but although they circulated through the loop, there was no way, independent of *ad hoc* assumptions, to use them in determining the operator transfer characteristics.

The harmonic relation among the components led to a more basic difficulty. Tustin could not be sure that the response component at 3ω was not nonlinear response to the fundamental component at ω, and that response at 6ω was not nonlinear response to ω or 3ω. In retrospect, it would seem that anharmonic target motion would have been a better choice.

Some of Tustin's results are shown in Fig. 7. The quantity plotted is $j\omega H(j\omega) = j\omega R/E$. Tustin elected to plot handle velocity, rather than handle displacement, because it figured more directly in the rationale of the model and because it separated the points more widely. The plots have been reoriented to make the axis of reals horizontal, and the individual vectors shown by Tustin have been removed in favor of the "vector locus" curves. The latter are not well determined by the few points, but they do serve to tie the parts of the display together. The frequencies of the target components are marked by dots and labeled in *tenths* of radians. The nature of the control dynamics and the designation of the subjects is indicated by the code explained in the legend.

The question is, what can one tell from Fig. 7 about the "approximate linear law" of the operator. Clearly, there are variations among the plots.

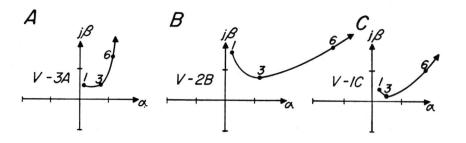

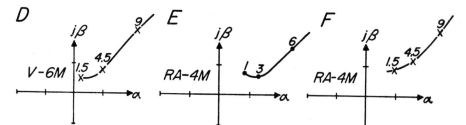

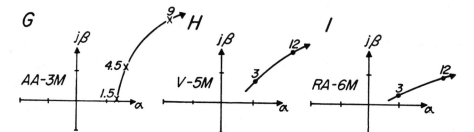

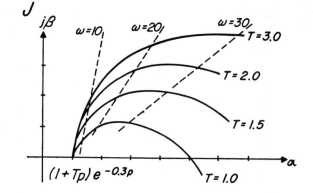

Fig. 7. Illustrations of Tustin's transfer functions. In A through M, each plot is of $pH = pR/E = \alpha + j\beta$, in which $H = R/E$ is the open loop characteristic relating handle displacement to error displacement in compensatory tracking. Plots A through I show experimental human operator characteristics. J through M show how the four specified model transfer functions look when plotted in the same way.

[216]

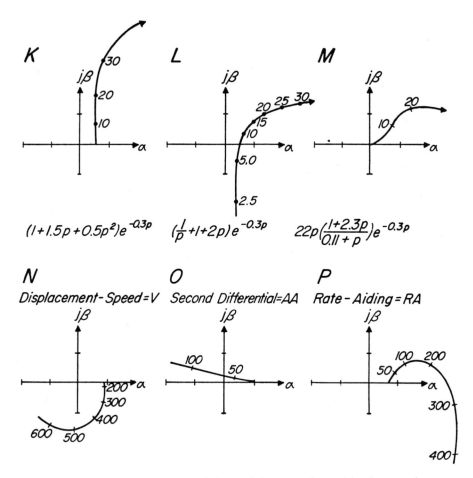

K

30 20 10 $j\beta$ α

$(1+1.5p+0.5p^2)e^{-0.3p}$

L

$j\beta$ 20 25 30 15 10 5.0 2.5 α

$(\frac{1}{p}+1+2p)e^{-0.3p}$

M

$j\beta$ 20 10 α

$22p\left(\frac{1+2.3p}{0.11+p}\right)e^{-0.3p}$

N

Displacement-Speed=V

$j\beta$ 200 300 400 500 600 α

O

Second Differential=AA

$j\beta$ 100 50 α

P

Rate-Aiding=RA

$j\beta$ 100 200 50 300 400 α

N, O, and P are characteristics of three of the controls used in the experiments. The key to the designations in plots A through I is: V (velocity) = displacement-to-speed control, RA = rate-aiding control, AA (acceleration aiding) = second differential control, $3A$ = average of three runs with subject A, $2B$ = average of two runs with subject B, $6M$ = average of six runs with several subjects. [After Tustin (1947)].

In each of the plots *A* through *F*, however, there is a suggestion of concavity. And, at any rate, all the curves lie in the same quadrant, and the magnitudes increase and the phases are relatively retarded at the higher frequencies. In order to interpret the diagrams, we must note that taking the handle velocity as the response variable would produce, for an ideal amplifier, a vertical plot along the positive imaginary axis. The plot would, in fact, be a plot of $j\omega$ for various values of ω. Since phase or time delay corresponds to clockwise rotation (and advance to counter-clockwise rotation) in the diagram, we see that the handle velocity leads the error displacement, but not as much as it would if the operator were an ideal amplifier. At first thought, we might attribute the difference to human reaction time, but second thought tells us that 0.3 second corresponds only to about 11 degrees at 0.6 radian, the highest frequency in plots *A*, *B*, and *C*. There is obviously another source of lag.

The magnitude of the operator increases with increasing frequency (as it should, since it includes the arbitrarily introduced differentiation), but the magnitude at the lowest frequency is usually rather great. This fact, taken together with the phase lag, suggests that time integration and the operator $1/p$ may play a role in the model. The inclusion of $1/p$ would precisely neutralize the choice of handle velocity as the response variable and leave us only the problem of explaining the phase advance from the axis of reals into the first quadrant.

The use of phase-advance networks is a standard technique in servo engineering. Whenever there is a lag to be overcome, networks are introduced to make the output depend upon time derivatives of the input. I the human operator has to overcome a reaction time, one may expect to find phase-advance networks. The simplest such network, short of a pure differentiator, is one with the characteristic $1 + Tp$. This is a quasi-differentiator, the inverse of the leaky integrator we discussed earlier in the chapter.

Following the line of reasoning just outlined, Tustin put together the reaction time e^{-Lp}, the integration $1/p$, the phase advance $1 + Tp$, and the gain k to form the trial operator

$$H(p) = \frac{R}{E} = \frac{k\,(1 + Tp)}{p}\,e^{-Lp} \tag{18a}$$

or

$$pH(p) = \frac{pR}{E} = k\,(1 + Tp)\,e^{-Lp}. \tag{18b}$$

This we recognize as the linear part of the compensatory model we discussed in connection with the study of Walston and Warren [1954].

Tustin's plot of (18b) is shown in Fig. 7J. To the extent that the data agree with the model, the experimental loci should have the same shape as the theoretical ones. Since the test frequencies fall at the low-frequency ends of the theoretical curves, the requirement is merely that the experimental loci run upward and curve slightly to the right. But in six instances the point corresponding to the lowest test frequency falls off that path.

The problem is therefore to decide whether to change the model or to tolerate the deviation of the test results from the model. Tustin considered possible changes. He noted that it would not help much to add further derivative or integral components in parallel with the trial operator, for they would produce characteristics of the types shown at K and L in Fig. 7. The most likely possibility, Tustin thought, was to change the conception of the response from pR to $(1+\tau p)R$, with τ quite large. That would be a small compromise back in the direction of taking the handle displacement as the response variable. It would lead to a model of the form

$$\frac{(1+\tau p)R}{E} = k\,(1+Tp)\,e^{-Lp}, \tag{19a}$$

$$H(p) = \frac{R}{E} = k\left(\frac{1+Tp}{1+\tau p}\right)e^{-Lp}, \tag{19b}$$

$$pH(p) = \frac{pR}{E} = kp\left(\frac{1+Tp}{1+\tau p}\right)e^{-Lp}. \tag{19c}$$

The new factor $p/(1+\tau p)$ introduces a phase advance at low frequencies, since it is approximately equal to p when p is very small. At high frequencies, on the other hand, it is approximately constant with the value $1/\tau$, which is also quite small. The low gain of this series addition to the model is compensated for by choosing $k \gg 1$.

A characteristic curve for a model of the modified form is shown at M in Fig. 7. It is evidently some improvement, but not very much. Because he thought the excess gain at low frequency might possibly be either a spurious effect due to the learning of the grossest feature of the target course or an unexplained result of nonlinearity — and thus perhaps something best not accounted for in the model — Tustin went back to the simpler model,

$k(1+Tp)e^{-Lp}$, in his analysis of the relative merits of various control dynamics.

The dynamics of the controls Tustin used in his tests are shown at N, O, and P in Fig. 7. He called them, respectively, displacement-speed, second differential, and rate-aiding controls. The quantity plotted is the frequency-domain equivalent of sight velocity divided by handle displacement. In the symbols of Fig. 1, with $W=1$, the quantity plotted is $pC = pY/R$. The thing to note is that, within the range of target frequencies, all those controls respond essentially the same way. This makes one wonder why they were used, but it probably accounts for the degree of similarity seen in the human operator characteristics determined with the different controls.

The final question about Tustin's results, of course, is to what extent the linear model accounted for the actual behavior of the human operator. Instead of determining a signal-to-noise ratio or partitioning the response variance to find out, Tustin calculated the responses of the model to some of the test signals and compared the model's responses with the responses of his subjects. That permitted only a qualitative answer. To judge from his published examples, one would call the fit fairly good but by no means perfect. There is no way to tell by eye, of course, how much of the discrepancy was due to nonlinearity and temporal variations and how much to random fluctuations.

Raggazini's Experiment. In a paper presented at a meeting but apparently never published, Raggazini [1948] described experiments in compensatory tracking in which the loop around the operator was opened for short intervals, during which the operator continued to respond. In his discussion of tracking, Fitts [1951] says that the results led Raggazini to use the transfer function $H = (pa + b + c/p)e^{-Lp}$ with the parameter a quite small. Raggazini's choice was thus only slightly different from Tustin's.

Russell's Experiments. Russell's [1951] work is described in a thesis. Russell viewed the human operator in the tracking situation as a quasi-linear device in essentially the sense we have described. As Tustin had done, he studied only compensatory tracking, but he explored a variety of questions and techniques. Most of the experiments were made with a set-up in which a spot on a cathode-ray tube was displaced horizontally by the difference between two voltages. One voltage was the target signal, four sinusoids in superposition. The other was the feedback signal, derived from a potentiometer connected to a handwheel.

Russell's method of analysis was in principle presisely the same as Tustin's. It involved examining, in the error signal, the components at each of the four input frequencies and measuring the magnitudes of the parts that were in phase and in quadrature (i.e., 90 degrees out of phase) with the input. That, of course, is equivalent to measuring amplitudes and phases in the error relative to corresponding amplitudes and phases in the input.

In about half of Russell's tests, the tracking set-up was a simple servo without external dynamics. Nyquist plots(*) of some of the results obtained with that set-up are shown in Fig. 8. This figure gives us a good idea of the variability from operator to operator. It indicates, also, that the transfer characteristic changes when the spectrum of the input signal is altered. The eleven solid curves are $R(p)/E(p)$ vector loci for Russell's medium-speed target signal. The lowermost (dashed) curve is for one subject tracking a low-speed signal. The uppermost (dotted) is for another tracking a high-speed signal. Note that Russell's low-speed signal is about as fast as Tustin's fastest.

In interpreting Fig. 8 it is important to bear in mind that Russell took the handwheel displacement as the operator's output, and that the plot is in the R/E plane. This is a different presentation from Tustin's (Fig. 7). Tustin's plots were in the plane of pR/E, and his datum points therefore correspond to Russell's multiplied by p. From one point of view, it would be best to convert all the graphs to one form, but, from another, there appears to be some point in following through the steps of interpretation that become almost automatic for servo engineers who use linear models frequently. For example: Inasmuch as we are dealing with Fourier frequency, $p = jw$. We have seen that multiplying by jw multiplies the vector magnitude by the value of the frequency and rotates the vector angle 90° counterclockwise. This transformation brings Russell's plots into some degree of conformity with Tustin's.

One of the main results of Russell's experiments is a strong suggestion that the human operator does not have one of the properties involved in the definition of a true servo-mechanism. The desirability of including this particular property in the definition, it should be said, is not universally accepted, but it does serve to highlight an important feature of servo response. It is that, given sufficient time and not subjected to any external load, the closed-loop system will bring its output to equal a steady input

(*) A Nyquist plot may be described either as the ratio of the output spectrum to the error spectrum, plotted in the complex plane with frequency a parameter, or as a plot of open-loop frequency response magnitude and phase shift in polar co-ordinates, again with frequency a parameter.

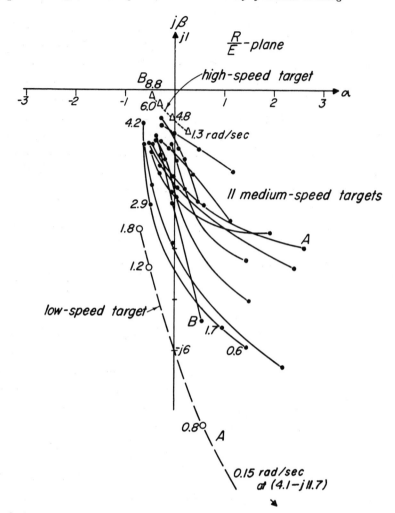

Fig. 8. Nyquist plots of human operator transfer functions obtained by Russell. The quantity plotted is $H = R/E = \alpha + j\beta$. Curves are shown for several subjects, of whom two (A and B) are identified to permit comparison of runs with different target spectra. Each of the three targets consisted of four superposed sinusoids. Their frequencies are indicated, in radians per second, in the figure. [After Russell (1951)]

exactly, without deviation or error. In order to meet the definition just suggested, it is necessary for a closed-loop(*) system to include a time integrator. This makes the output position depend upon the past positions

(*) A "closed-loop" system is a system that includes feedback. "Closed-loop" characteristics of the system are characteristics relating output to input, measured with the feedback operative. "Open-loop" characteristics are characteristics relating output to error or, equivalently, relating output to input with feedback path broken.

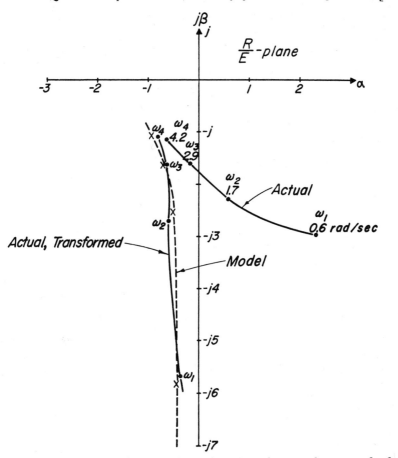

Fig. 9. Illustrations of the effect of attenuation upon the open-loop transfer function. The operator's actual open-loop function curves off to the right as frequency decreases. That is not at all characteristic of an integrator, the transfer function of which would follow the negative imaginary axis. An explanation is to assume that the operator includes an integrator, but that its effect is modified by attenuation. The attenuation must be applied to the closed-loop response, for example in the way illustrated in Fig. 10. The actual transfer function is consistent with the hypothesis that the operator's basic transfer function is the one labeled "Actual, Transformed," which corresponds closely to the "Model" that includes a true integrator. The basic operator is then regarded as being within a loop, the closed-loop response of which is seen as the open-loop response of the actual operator. [After Russell (1951)]

as well as upon the present position of the error. The Nyquist plot of an operator consisting of a single integrator would follow the negative imaginary axis in Fig. 8.

Russell noted that his characteristic curves appeared to be heading out in the direction of the positive real axis, rather than proceeding along the negative imaginary axis. In fact, in the case Russell treated, extrapolation of the transfer characteristic of the closed-loop system indicated that the ratio of steady-state output to steady-state input magnitude would be approximately 0.84. This meant that the characteristic would have to be multiplied by 1.18 in order to bring the zero-frequency value to unity and thus to make it consistent with the assumption that it includes an integration. Doing this brought the Nyquist plot into close conformity (see Fig. 9) with the plot representing the transfer characteristic

$$H(p) = \frac{3.7\,(1 + 0.28\,p)}{p}\,e^{-0.38p}\,. \tag{20a}$$

Putting (20a) into the form used by Tustin and Phillips, we have

$$pH(p) = 3.7\,(1 + 0.28\,p)\,e^{-0.38p}. \tag{20b}$$

This is for Russell's medium-speed target signal. There is a little more than three times as much weight given to position error as to velocity error in determining the velocity response.

The observation just described led Russell to introduce an additional factor into his model, one not present in the models discussed thus far. This additional factor is the factor of attenuation. Russell's model does the things

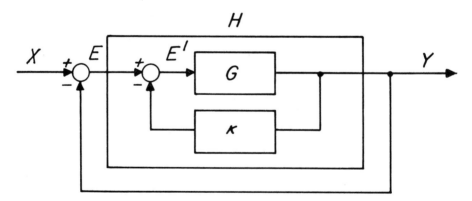

Fig. 10. Schematic diagram of a servo-within-a-servo. H is the transfer function of the box that includes G and k. H is therefore the open-loop characteristic of the external servo. Even if G is a true integrator in the time domain, the negative feedback through k will keep H from corresponding to true integration. H will be a "leaky integrator," of the type we have discussed. [After Russell (1951)]

prescribed by the other models and then attenuates the resulting signal by a specified factor. The attenuation is not just a reduction in the value of k, the gain of the open-loop operator, for this would not bring the response to unity at zero-frequency. It must be a reduction in the gain of the closed loop.

Russell postulated that the attenuation is introduced by proprioceptive feedback as shown in Fig. 10. The reasoning behind this idea is as follows. Proprioceptive feedback obviously holds down the magnitudes of movements. In diseases that destroy proprioception, for example, movements are exaggerated. Therefore, in simple servo analogy, the feedback is negative. For the present purpose, it suffices to consider it a simple amplifier with gain k. If we call the forward operator within the human operator G, we have

$$Y = GE' \tag{21a}$$

and

$$E' = E - kY. \tag{21b}$$

Combining those relations with

$$H = Y/E \tag{21c}$$

leads to

$$H = \frac{G}{1 + kG}. \tag{21d}$$

This is the very useful relation between the open-loop transfer function $G(p)$ and the closed-loop transfer function $H(p)$. But note that, with respect to the external servo of which H is the forward component, $H(p)$ is an open-loop, not a closed-loop, transfer function. It relates Y to E, not to X. If we call the closed-loop transfer function of the external loop $H'(p)$,

$$H' = \frac{H}{1 + H} = \frac{\dfrac{G}{(1 + kG)}}{1 + \dfrac{G}{(1 + kG)}} = \frac{G}{1 + (1 + k)G}. \tag{21e}$$

Going back to the data of Russell's experiment, we see that, if we make $k = 0.18$,

$$H = \frac{G}{1 + 1.18G}. \tag{21f}$$

Therefore, if $|G| \to \infty$ as the frequency goes to zero, as must be the case if the loop includes an integration,

$$\left| H(0) \right| = \lim_{\omega \to 0} \left| \frac{G}{1 + 1.18G} \right| , \qquad (21\text{g})$$

which, as Russell intended, is

$$|H(0)| = 0.84 . \qquad (21\text{h})$$

Russell pointed out that the introduction of attenuation makes good sense from the point of view of prediction theory. If an operator with a reaction time is to minimize his mean-squared error while tracking a randomly fluctuating target, he must attenuate the signal. The proper amount of attenuation is related to the regression of the target fluctuation, during the reaction-time interval, toward its long-term mean.

Russell tested the hypothesis that the attenuation was introduced by the operator's reliance upon feedback of information concerning his output, i.e., the position of the handwheel. Russell decreased the gain of the tracking control to such an extent that the subject had to turn the handwheel farther than he could while holding it in a fixed grip. Releasing the hand-wheel and regripping it lost for him the information about its absolute position. It turned out, as predicted, that, in the tests with low- and medium-speed targets, the attenuation almost disappeared when this was done. The deprivation of proprioception was of course not perfect. There was still attenuation in the tests with the high-speed target. Russell gave parameters for one of his subjects who took tests at all three target speeds. The values of the parameters are shown in Table 2. This set of parameters indicates that, as the target signal spectrum is shifted up the frequency scale, the operator reduces his reaction time, decreases the loop gain, gives less weight to the derivative of the error, and attenuates his output. From an engineering point of view, all these things are reasonable.

In two cases, Russell determined the spectrum of the noise introduced by the tracker. This showed that the noise was of somewhat higher frequency than the signal. Russell pointed out that the noise may play the role of the "informative feedback" discussed by Wiener [1948]. Deviating from linearity to make his responses suddenly, the operator may introduce into the loop testing signals that he does not confuse with the target signal because they fall outside its frequency band. The operator may use these components to ascertain the over-all gain and perhaps other parameters of the loop.

A considerable part of Russell's work was concerned with aided tracking. He examined the effects caused by introducing into the loop circuits designed to compensate for its undesirable characteristics, or, in some instances, to exaggerate them.

Table 2.

Parameters for one subject with three different target spectra

	Low speed	Medium speed	High speed
Reaction time	0.48	0.26	0.26
Loop gain	3.6	3.4	1.8
Derivative time constant. . .	0.40	0.18	0.22
Attenuation factor	1.03	1.06	1.40

Russell performed a number of experiments with a simple low-pass resistance-capacitance filter [transfer function of form $1/(1 + Tp)$] introduced within the loop at a point following the operator. When the time constant of this filter was less than 0.05 second, there was little or no effect upon the transfer characteristic of the over-all closed loop. As the time constant of the filter was increased, the over-all transfer characteristic changed, but the change was mainly in gain and not in shape. This implies that the operator developed a dynamic factor in his own open-loop transfer characteristic that cancelled the dynamic factor introduced by the filter. The cost of modifying his transfer characteristic appeared in the form of the reduced gain and, also, increased noise.

No case appeared, in Russell's experiments, in which insertion of a simple lag within the loop improved the tracker's performance. This fact suggests that the filter's suppression of noise was overcome by the operator's intensification of his exploratory signals. He had to make strong signals in order to get them through the filter. In addition, they were probably less useful to him after they had been distorted by passage through the filter.

Russell explored a number of interesting points in his experiments on effects of external dynamics. In terms of Fig. 1, the external dynamic components were D, C, and F. The outcomes are largely suggestions, rather than conclusions, because the number of runs was small, but the suggestions appear to be worth following up. Some of them will be described in the following paragraphs.

Introducing an integration within the loop at a point following the operator $(C = 1/p)$ improved the low-frequency part of the performance at the expense of increasing the noise in the high-frequency part. With a low-speed target signal, the tracker introduced lead control of the form $1 + Tp$

in order to maintain system stability. Even with a medium-speed target, the operator managed to introduce enough lead compensation to keep the system stable. In tests with external dynamics of the type used in aided-tracking or rate-aiding systems, the filter inserted into the loop had a transfer characteristic of the form $(1 + Tp)/p$. When the time constant was greater than 2.5 seconds, the tracker did not change his own open-loop characteristic appreciably to compensate for the introduction of the integral control. The over-all transfer characteristic was therefore corrected in approximately the same way it is in the case of an ordinary servomechanism. It turned out to make little difference whether the compensation was introduced ahead of the operator (at D, to affect the error signal) or at a point following the operator (at C, to affect his output). When the time constant was shorter than 2.5 seconds, the tracker introduced compensation to maintain over-all system stability. The noise level in the output signal was higher with rate aiding than without. Similar results were obtained in tests with resistance-capacitance networks that approximated rate-aiding circuits.

Russell described a way, which he found very effective, to remove part of the operator's noise from the system without producing adverse effects. This was to place a simple lag network [lowpass resistance-capacitance filter with transfer function $1/(1 + \tau p)$] in the circuit following the operator and to compensate for its effects by placing a lead network [high-pass resistance-capacitance filter with transfer function $(1 + \tau p)/(10 + \tau p)$] at a point ahead of the operator. The effect of the two networks in cascade was equivalent to inserting only the very small lag $1/(10 + \tau p)$ into the system. As mentioned earlier, a very small lag has no appreciable effect on the operator's performance. The full value of the low-pass filter following the operator was therefore obtained. It filtered out the operator's high-frequency noise, yet the lead network kept it from disrupting the loop dynamics. Of course, such a system could function efficiently only with low-frequency target signals. To handle high-frequency signals, it would have to have help from an external network that would emphasize the highs and thereby remagnify the noise.

An even better system was one that used the external dynamics employed in aided-tracking systems, but divided the external network into two parts. The phase-advancing part $1 + Tp$ was introduced into the circuit ahead of the operator, and the phase-retarding part $1/p$ was introduced into the part of the circuit following the operator. The high-frequency performance of the system was left unaltered, and the low-frequency performance was substantially improved. The noise component of the error was reduced about 10 decibels. The best low-speed run made in Russell's series of experiments was made with this system.

It is evident from this discussion of the work of Tustin and Russell that quasi-linear models permit quantitative examination of questions that would be extremely difficult to approach with less well developed techniques. We still have with us, however, the problem of the degrees of fit of the various linear models that, taken together, constitute the linear part of the quasi-linear human operator. Russell's data give us the first direct quantitative evidence on that problem.

Russell analyzed the error and the output signals of one test into four components at the target frequencies and a fifth component, the remainder. This breakdown is given, in terms of variance (i.e., a quantity proportional to the square of the signal magnitude) in Table 3. From the table we find that the noise component of the output, which includes both random fluctuations and the effects of nonlinearity in the operator, is about 3.5 per cent of the total output power, or about 10 per cent of the root-mean-square voltage. This is to say that the quasi-linear model accounts for about 96.5 per cent of the total response variance. The figure refers, of course, only to one medium-speed test, but it is sufficient to indicate that the preponderant part of the tracker's behavior falls within the scope of a quasi-linear model.

Another way to look at the problem is to partition the error. What part is due to time delay or phase shift and to over-response at one frequency and under-response at another?

Table 3.

Analysis into variance components
of input, error, and output in one of Russell's tests

Component	Input(*)	Error(*)	Output(*)
$\omega_1 = 0.6$	6084	230	5329
$\omega_2 = 1.7$	2704	565	2304
$\omega_3 = 2.9$	841	402	676
$\omega_4 = 4.2$	400	384	361
Noise	0	316	316
TOTAL	10029	1897	8986

(*) In hundredths-of-an-inch, squared.

Table 3 indicates that these linear sources of error account for about five-sixths of the total error variance. Only one sixth is attributable to non-linearity plus random fluctuations.

8. FREQUENCY ANALYSIS WITH RANDOM TEST SIGNALS

THE EXPERIMENTS that remain to be described were made with test signals closely approximating filtered random noise. The methods of analysis involved correlation functions and power spectra. They make it possible to separate the part of the tracker's output that is linearly related to his input from the part that is not, even though the two parts cover the same interval of frequency. The possibility of examining the behavior of the operator all along the frequency scale is therefore the main advantage of these methods.

The main disadvantage of the methods is that they are very time-consuming and expensive. This is in large part not an essential, intrinsic property of the principles of analysis, but one that stems from unreliability of the complex electronic equipment used in the analyses. Recently, it has seemed that the problem of processing data has been largely solved, and that solid results are at hand. In the earlier stages of the studies with random test signals, however, the returns in the form of actual data were obtained through disproportionate effort.

Krendel's Experiments. In a series of studies aimed at determining the frequency-response characteristics of an aircraft pilot flying a jet simulator, Krendel and his co-workers at the Franklin Institute tried out a number of correlational and power-spectral techniques. The more recent of the studies at the Franklin Institute have been roughly parallel and concurrent with experiments by Elkind, who has used similar techniques in the study of tracking in a more highly idealized situation.

The history of Krendel's preliminary experiments is of methodological interest. In his first reports [1951, 1952], Krendel attempted to determine the amplitude-*vs*-frequency characteristic of the human operator in a simple, compensatory system (not the simulator) from measurements of input and output autocorrelation functions. He had the autocorrelation functions $\varphi_{xx}(\tau)$ and $\varphi_{yy}(\tau)$ transformed into power-density spectra $\Phi_{xx}(j\omega)$ and $\Phi_{yy}(j\omega)$, and he determined the closed-loop amplitude-*vs*-frequency characteristic $|H(j\omega)|$ from

$$\left| H(j\omega) \right|^2 = \frac{\Phi_{yy}(j\omega)}{\Phi_{xx}(j\omega)} \tag{22}$$

If the operator were linear, time-invariant, and noiseless, that procedure would be straightforward. But if the operator introduces noise(*), as of

(*) We might distinguish, here, between the noise₁ used as a synthetic target signal and the noise₂ introduced by the operator. The latter is defined as being uncorrelated with the former.

course to some extent he must, the method just described leads to an uncertain result. If the noise is the predominate part of the output, then the ratio of the two power-density spectra depends more upon the power spectrum of the noise than upon the response of the linear part of the operator to the input. If there is only a little noise, the ratio of the power-density spectra approximates the frequency-response characteristic of the linear part of the operator. But the power-spectrum approach tells us nothing about the amount of noise introduced by the operator. We are left in the unfortunate state of not knowing what it is we have found.

In order to have a guiding model for his experimental work, Krendel [1954] adopted a hypothesis that is at first sight somewhat simpler than Phillips' and Tustin's. Krendel looked first at the closed loop, rather than at the open loop. He took the joystick displacement as the operator's output. He related it to the target (input) displacement simply by a gain factor $|G|$, less than unity, and a time delay, e^{-Lp}. The closed-loop gain of Krendel's best linear approximator, expressed as a relation between output displacement and input displacement, therefore, is

$$\frac{R}{X} = |G| e^{-Lp} . \tag{23a}$$

The question is, how would Krendel's operator look with the loop opened. The open-loop expression is

$$H = \frac{R}{E} = \frac{|G| e^{-Lp}}{(1 - |G| e^{Lp})} . \tag{23b}$$

That is equal to

$$H = \frac{R}{E} = |G| e^{-Lp} + |G|^2 e^{-2Lp} + |G|^3 e^{-3Lp} + \cdots \tag{23c}$$

$|G|$ is a function of frequency in Krendel's model. It is always less than unity but not so small that its second and third powers are negligible. Therefore, the several delay terms call for a reverberating reaction on the part of the open-loop operator. The hypothetical model would respond after a reaction time, and then again after another reaction time, and then again after another, and so on. It would echo itself. It would stutter.

It is possible, of course, that the human operator is so flexible that he adjusts himself to the requirements of the loop, even though to do so he must react in the way just outlined. In a pursuit set-up, it is quite possible

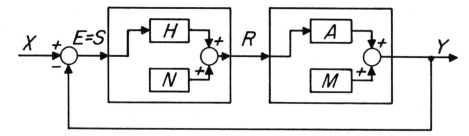

Fig. 11. Schematic diagram of Krendel's test situation. The human operator is represented as a linear network H plus a noise source N. The control dynamics are the dynamics of an aircraft simulator, which itself has a linear part A and a noisy part M. Actually, the simulator has two characteristics, one for the aileron channel and one for the elevator channel. They are dissimilar.

for him to make such an adjustment if the target motion is very slow. He simply sets himself the rask of following the path of its motion and remaining a fixed interval behind it. But servo analysis of the pursuit task is complicated. And it certainly seems as though it would be very difficult to follow the input path with fixed delay in a compensatory set-up, for the operator never sees the input path. We can make only the tentative reaction, therefore, that, on analysis, Krendel's model seems more complicated than models in which the *open*-loop transfer function is assumed to have a simple form.

Because Krendel's model implies repetitive reaction on the part of the human operator, it is somewhat disconcerting to find that the frequency-response characteristics obtained in the simple tracking task were in agreement with the model. It is in fact something of a relief that the operator characteristics determined in the simulator were not.

In the experiments with the simulator, which represented an F-80 jet airplane, Krendel [1954] used the method we discussed in the section on cross-power spectra. In addition to the power-density spectra of input, output, and error, he determined the cross-power-density spectra that related those quantities to one another. The necessity of employing information corresponding to that provided by cross-power-density spectra had been pointed out in a memorandum by Huggins [1949]. The particular procedure used by Krendel was one suggested by Tukey. We need not be concerned with the detailed procedure, but the underlying idea is important to our understanding of quasi-linear models. Let us discuss it briefly here. It will come into the picture again in connection with Elkind's work.

The variables of interest are indicated in Fig. 11, a schematic diagram of the tracking set-up. The human operator is considered there to be a linear operator plus a noise source. The aircraft is thought of in the same way, except that the aircraft noise or perturbation is of course different from that inherent in the human operator, and the airplane dynamics are not only different, but known. The main difference between this set-up and the simpler ones we have been discussing, of course, is the introduction of a quasi-linear component external to the operator. The aircraft lies in between the human response R and the system output Y. However, the departure of the aircraft dynamics from time-invariant linearity did not play an essential part in Krendel's study. We may therefore think of the aircraft as a form of control dynamics. It thus corresponds to C in Fig. 1.

A basic assumption is that the input disturbance $x(t)$, the human operator's noise $n(t)$, and the aircraft's perturbation $m(t)$ are all linearly uncorrelated. This is reasonable if the only deviations from linearity are random noises. It is an approximation of unknown closeness if nonlinearities are lumped in with the noises, for the nonlinear action of one part of the over-all system probably depends upon disturbances arising in others.

The response characteristic in which we are most interested is the one, H, relating R to E. For an engineering study of the system, we would wish to know also the statistical characteristics of N, but Krendel did not determine signal-to-noise rations. To find the characteristic H of the human operator, we need the power-density spectrum of $\epsilon(t)$ and the cross-power-density spectrum relating $r(t)$ to $\epsilon(t)$. The cross-power-density spectrum is related to the spectra of $\epsilon(t)$ and $r(t)$ in a simple way. Its amplitude part is the product of their amplitude parts, and its phase part is the difference between their phase parts. In the complex notation,

$$\Phi_{\varepsilon r}(j\omega) = E^*(j\omega)R(j\omega) = |E||R|\,e^{j(\theta_\varepsilon - \theta_r)}. \tag{24}$$

$E^*(j\omega)$ is the conjugate of $E(j\omega)$.

H follows immediately as soon as we have the cross-power-density spectrum $\Phi_{\varepsilon r}(j\omega)$ and the power-density spectrum $\Phi_{\varepsilon\varepsilon}(j\omega)$. It is simply the ratio of the first to the second. The reason for this is easy to see in the expression

$$\frac{\Phi_{\varepsilon r}(j\omega)}{\Phi_{\varepsilon\varepsilon}(j\omega)} = \frac{E^*(j\omega)R(j\omega)}{E^*(j\omega)E(j\omega)} = \frac{R(j\omega)}{E(j\omega)} = H(j\omega). \tag{25}$$

The thing that remains to be explained about this procedure is how using the cross-power-density spectrum avoids the problem caused, in the approach based on input and output power-density spectra, by noise in the response.

Probably the simplest way to see why the cross-spectrum is insensitive to response noise is to examine the situation over in the time domain. Consider two responses, $r'(t)$ and $r(t) = r'(t) + n(t)$.

$$r'(t) = \mathcal{J}^{-1}[H(j\omega)E(j\omega)] . \tag{26a}$$

$$r(t) = \mathcal{J}^{-1}[H(j\omega)E(j\omega) + N(j\omega)]. \tag{26b}$$

It is well-known that the cross-correlation function (the inverse Fourier transform of the cross-power-density spectrum) between $e(t)$ and $r'(t)$ is the same as the cross-correlation function between $e(t)$ and $r(t)$. This is true in the limit, as the time average in the cross-correlation is extended over all time, but it is a good approximation in the application to the tracking problem. The reason for the equality of the two cross-correlation functions is of course that the cross-correlation between $\epsilon(t)$ and $n(t)$ is zero. The noise was assumed to be linearly uncorrelated with everything else in the situation.

Since the two cross-correlation functions are equal, the two cross-power-density spectra that correspond to them must be equal too:

$$\Phi_{\varepsilon r'}(j\omega) = \mathcal{J}[\varphi_{\varepsilon r'}(\tau)] \tag{26c}$$

and

$$\Phi_{\varepsilon r}(j\omega) = \mathcal{J}[\varphi_{\varepsilon r}(\tau)] . \tag{26d}$$

This leads directly to

$$H(j\omega) = \frac{\Phi_{\varepsilon r'}(j\omega)}{\Phi_{\varepsilon\varepsilon}(j\omega)} = \frac{\Phi_{\varepsilon r}(j\omega)}{\Phi_{\varepsilon\varepsilon}(j\omega)} . \tag{26e}$$

and establishes that the same insensitivity to noise in the response is a property of the cross-power-density spectrum.

Krendel actually used more variables than E and R because he wanted to make dynamic measurements of the performance of the simulator as well as of the human operator. In principle, however, the situation was as described in the foregoing, and things are already complicated enough that it may be better to leave the discussion of procedure in this "simplified" stage and to turn, now, to the results.

The results published thus far suffer from two defects that are due directly to the difficulty we mentioned in the introduction to this section. First, equipment failures rather spoiled the factorial design of the tests. The data are therefore somewhat fragmentary. Second, the plan of the measurements yielded rather few datum points per curve. There are not enough to give one the feeling of confidence that is given by numerous points that fall closely along a smooth function. Nevertheless, Krendel has made the first direct empirical determinations of the quasi-linear frequency-response characteristic of an aircraft pilot, and that is a considerable accomplishment.

Krendel's principal results were obtained with two pilots who had had much experience flying the simulator. They tracked in two dimensions, operating the joystick in the ordinary way and thereby controlling both the ailerons and the elevator. In both dimensions, the input signal was essentially a random noise with a root-mean-square (rms) fluctuation of 0.6 inch and a pass band from 0 to 2 radians per second.

Average open-loop transfer characteristics for the two operators are shown in Fig. 12. The characteristics are represented in the form in which amplitude and phase are shown as separate functions of frequency.

The first striking feature of the frequency-response characteristics is the fact that, on the whole, the amplitude curves rise with increasing frequency. Krendel qualified this result with the statement that the confidence limits are very broad for the higher frequencies. He stated, without further explanation, that "as the frequency goes far enough beyond the upper limit of the input bandwidth, the linear model breaks down." It may be that he was referring to the high-frequency noise often found in the response, especially in compensatory tracking. But the immediate difficulty appears to be that one can determine cross-power-density spectra only for frequencies in which there is measurable energy both in the input and in the output. Inasmuch as the input signal was passed through a low-pass filter with cut-off frequency of 2 radians per second, there was not much energy in the input signal at 4 or 5 radians per second.

The second striking feature is the difference between the phase characteristics for aileron control and the phase characteristics for elevator control. Inasmuch as the dynamics of the aircraft involve one more integration in the aileron circuit than in the elevator circuit, the human operator introduces an additional differentiation, as it were, in controlling the ailerons. This adjustment is reflected, also, in the reaction times which can be derived from the average slopes of the phase plots. The situation here is somewhat paradoxical, however. The reaction times for aileron control are longer (0.62 and 0.80 second) than are the reaction times for elevator control (0.27 and 0.29 second). Krendel reported that, "phenomenally, elevator control

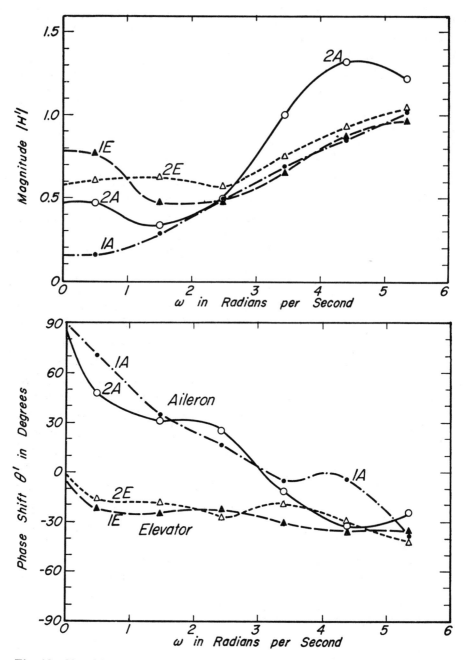

Fig. 12. Closed-loop magnitude and phase shift versus frequency for two of Krendel's operators (1 and 2) in compensatory tracking. *A* (Aileron) is the horizontal mode of display and the lateral mode of control, *E* (Elevator) is vertical and fore-and-aft. [After Krendel (1954)]

[236]

has relatively little lag, whereas aileron control is sluggish. The pilot may use part of the greater reaction time in aileron [control] to engage in short-term prediction of the target position."

The same kind of adjustment to the external dynamics is reflected in a comparison of a pilot's performance in the simulator with his performance in a simpler tracking set-up with no external dynamics. The frequency-response characteristics of the operator under the two conditions were quite different. However, the curves were brought together when the one derived from the simulator data was corrected on the assumption that the simulator introduced a time integration and that the pilot compensated for it by introducing a time differentiation.

Another result of the tests, not shown in Fig. 12, is that the tracking performance was essentially stationary — invariant over time — during the interval of a 6-minute run. Moreover, there was no statistically significant difference between runs on two different days. These results have to be interpreted cautiously, however, because the differences would have had to be rather great to be statistically significant.

Krendel made tests also with signals of greater and lesser amplitude (1.2-inch and 0.3-inch rms) and of greater and lesser bandwidth (1 radian per second and 4 radians per second). The variability of the results of these tests suggests that they be considered only preliminary. Evidently, individual differences grow greater as the bandwidth is increased and the conditions of test become more severe. When the bandwidth is made narrower, and the task thereby made easier, on the other hand, the experiment rather defeats itself because the cross-spectra are determinable only at one of the six frequencies at which measurements were made.

In drawing conclusions from Krendel's work, we cannot do better than to paraphrase some of his own discussion ([1954], pp. 38—39): We are searching for the expected value of a linearized transfer function to describe pilot responses, together with a measure of the variance about this expected function. Furthermore, we are interested also in lawful trends. The results thus far are fragmentary. The following conclusions may nevertheless be drawn:

1. There are obvious differences among human transfer functions for different tracking tasks.

2. The day-to-day and trial-to-trial variations are small.

3. Phase characteristics for bandwidths 2 and 4 radians per second are similar. The time delay or reaction time was about 0.6 second for aileron control and 0.3 second for elevator control.

4. In tests with a simple tracking set-up (no external dynamics) the operator's gain drops off rapidly and his phase lags considerably with increasing frequency. In the simulator, which attenuates the high-frequency components of the human operator's response and retards the phase, the operator introduces more gain and less lag at high frequencies.

Krendel's experiments thus far constitute a bare start but an important start on the analysis of the operator characteristics of pilots.

Walston and Warren's Tests with Noise. In their report to which we have referred, Walston and Warren [1954] described tests, with one operator in a pursuit and another operator in a compensatory tracking situation, in which a filtered random noise was used as the target signal. The filter through which the noise was passed was a band-pass filter, rather than a lowpass filter. Its center frequency was at 0.5 cps and its bandwidth between half-power points was also 0.5 cps.

The parameters of the operators are given in Table 4. Because the operators and the tasks were confounded, we should probably make nothing more of the differences between the parameters for pursuit and those for compensatory than to note that they are in the expected direction. In pursuit, the reaction time is shorter, more use is made of derivative control, and the noise is less pronounced. The "break frequency," at which the amplitude-*vs*-frequency curve flattens out and at which the phase shift exclusive of reaction time is $\pi/4$, is a little above 1 radian per second in the case of pursuit and only about 1/3 radian per second in the case of compensatory tracking.

Table 4.

Parameters of operators in Walston and Warren's tests with random target signals

Op.	Task	L sec	c_1 rad/in	c_2 rad/in sec	N^2 (volt)^2/rad
G	Pursuit	0.2	0.018	0.104	0.018
H	Compen.	0.25	0.006	0.102	0.464

Elkind's First Experiment. Elkind's initial approach to the study of tracking was influenced by the work of Wiener [1949] and Lee [1950] and other developments in communication theory that related to random functions. In particular, it was inspired by Huggins' [1949] memorandum, outlining a technique for determining linear operator characteristics from measurements with random signals, and by the availability of an electronic computer that Huggins had obtained to facilitate applications of the technique.

Another element influencing Elkind's approach was the idea that more might be learned about the human operator, *per se*, in an idealized test situation than in a realistic situation. He noted that, in any tracking set-up, parameters of the display and the control would affect the operator's performance, and that a particular laboratory situation is no more general than a particular situation in the field. The idea was, rather, that it is easiest to analyze the situation in which the most parameters have the value zero or infinity. Accordingly, Elkind began his work with an idealized display and control: a low-pass gaussian target signal moving the beam of a cathode-ray tube, and a pencil-like stylus which the operator tried to keep in contact with the target dot. The tracking problem was, in fact, made as nearly as possible like writing at a desk on a sheet of paper, except that the target moved in only one dimension.

In the first experiment, Elkind [1953] studied only pursuit tracking. The target spectum was shaped by a filter with the characteristic $1/(1 + Tp)^4$. The half-power bandwidth, one of the variables of the study, was set at 2, 4, and 6 radians per second. The root-mean-square amplitude of the target fluctuations, the other variable, was adjusted to 1.0, 0.5, 0.25, and 0.1 inch. Three subjects participated in the experiment.

The input-output cross-correlation functions obtained with the aid of the correlator were of interest in and of themselves. They rose to a maximum at a value of $\tau = 0.2$ second, which may be interpreted as an approximation to the operator's reaction time to the low-pass random inputs. However, the problem of deconvolving stood in the way of finding true impulse-response functions. Elkind therefore transformed his cross-correlation and autocorrelation functions into the frequency domain and proceeded in the way discussed in earlier parts of this chapter.

The frequency-response functions thus determined were closed-loop characteristics. Curiously, since Elkind's was a pursuit task and the interpretation is therefore quite different, they resembled rather closely those of Krendel's model, $|G|e^{-Lp}$, in which $|G|$ is a gradually declining function of frequency. The amplitude-*vs*-frequency curves were almost flat, out to frequencies well beyond the half-power points of the target signal, and the phase-*vs*-frequency curves showed phase retardations roughly proportional to frequency and consistent with the assumption of a reaction time of 0.2 second.

Since the length of a run must be long compared with the reciprocal of the lowest frequency of the analysis, it is difficult to determine the frequency response down to very low frequencies. The amplitude curves were determined only down to about 0.5 radian per second. It is therefore not possible to make a certain check of Russell's idea that the zero-frequency closed-loop gain should fall short of unity. If we make what seem to be natural extrapolations toward zero frequency, however, we find no suggestion that the operator acts in pursuit tracking as though he contained an integrator.

When the magnitude $|H(j\omega)|$ is plotted on a linear scale against linear frequency, the area under the curve is approximately 6.5 second^{-1}. This is true (for subject A, the subject for whom curves are shown in the report) for each of the three bandwidths. It would be interesting if further tests confirmed that the human operator has a "gain-bandwidth constant."

Elkind's first experiment provided, for the first time, an analysis of signal-to-noise ratio as a function of frequency. The plot, against frequency, of the ratio of signal power (i.e., power of output linearly related to input) to noise power (i.e., power of output not so related) for the tests with the 4-radian-per-second bandwidth falls from approximately seven at 2 radians per second to six at 4 radians per second and then declines almost linearly to zero at 10 radians per second. Therefore the quasi-linear model cannot be far wrong within the band of a reasonably wide signal spectrum. All but about 15 per cent of the response variance below 4 radians per second is accounted for by linear relation to the target signal.

Elkind's Second Experiment. The near necessity of eventually getting into the frequency domain led Elkind to question the desirability of making the first step of the analysis in the time domain. It appeared, in fact, that the transformation of correlation functions into power spectra was the source of much trouble, because truncation of correlation functions introduces spurious ripples into power spectra. It is neither feasible nor efficient to determine correlation functions out to very large values of the time-shift τ.

Elkind therefore designed and constructed a computer to carry out the entire operation in the frequency domain. The computer works with signals that have been speeded up with the aid of a tape recorder and playback, and it shifts the signals up the frequency scale for convenience in processing. We need concern ourselves, however, only with the basic principle of its operation.

Given $x(t)$ and $y(t)$, the object is to determine their cross-power-density spectrum $\Phi_{xy}(j\omega) = X^*(j\omega)Y(j\omega)$. Alternatively, given $x(t)$ twice, it is to determine the ordinary power-density spectrum $\Phi_{xx}(j\omega) = X^*(j\omega)X(j\omega)$. Except for the selection of input signals, the operations are the same. They are, in principle:

(1) With a filter, isolate a narrow band of frequency components of $x(t)$ and, with an identical filter, isolate the corresponding band of frequency components of $y(t)$. Let us call the two filtered signals $X(j\omega_c,t)$ and $Y(j\omega_c,t)$, ω_c being the center-frequency of the filters.

(2) With a phase shifter, retard the components of $X(j\omega_c,t)$ 90 degrees. We then have both $X(j\omega_c,t)$ and the shifted signal $\bar{X}(j\omega_c,t)$ for further use.

(3) In separate channels, form the products $X(j\omega_c,t)Y(j\omega_c,t)$ and $\bar{X}(j\omega_c,t)Y(j\omega_c,t)$.

(4) With separate integrators, integrate the products over the span of a tracking test.

The voltage in the first integrator at the end of the run, divided by the duration of the run, is the in-phase or real part of the cross-power-density coefficient $\Phi_{xy}(j\omega_c)$. The voltage in the second integrator, divided by the duration, is the quadrature or imaginary part of the cross-power-density coefficient at ω_c.

(5) In order to determine the coefficients at the other frequencies that are to be sampled, repeat operations (1) through (4) for the other values of ω.

Plotting the coefficients against frequency displays the cross-power-density spectrum in complex form. With the aid of some desk machine computations, amplitude-*vs*-frequency and phase-*vs*-frequency curves may be obtained.

Elkind displayed his results principally in the form of graphs showing the amplitude- and phase-*vs*-frequency characteristics of the closed-loop operator $H'(j\omega)$. To permit analytical examination of the error and output signals, he found other characteristic functions, also. For example, he determined the part of the output that is linearly related to the input by forming the product $\Phi_{xx}(j\omega)|H(j\omega)|^2 = X^* X H^* H(j\omega)$. The part of the output *not* linearly related to the input was then $\Phi_{nn}(j\omega) = \Phi_{yy}(j\omega) - \Phi_{xx}(j\omega)|H(j\omega)|^2$. This provided the basis for calculating signal-to-noise ratios as functions of frequency, etc.

With the frequency-domain analyzing equipment, Elkind set out to obtain data that would let him trace the changes in the human operator's characteristics that are produced by changes in the target power-density spectrum. He made three main changes in the test set-up.

First, he added compensatory tracking as a second task.

Second, in order to adapt his set-up for compensatory tracking, he separated the display and control surfaces, orienting the display oscilloscope in a vertical plane above the cathode-ray tube on the surface of which the operator responded by moving the stylus. In pursuit tracking, both the target dot and a follower dot, slaved to the stylus, appeared on the display oscilloscope. In compensatory tracking, there was a reference dot in the center of the screen and an error dot, displaced by $-\epsilon(t) = y(t) - x(t)$.

Third, he changed the method of generating the target signals. He took this step because it appeared that even the four-stage filtering $[1/(1 + Tp)^4]$ did not produce a sufficiently close approximation to a rectangular pass band. In the second experiment, therefore, the target signals were synthesized by superposing sinusoids. Instead of using three or four frequencies, however, Elkind used 30 to 80, depending upon the bandwidth. This provided essentially continuous spectra, since the stability of the oscillators and tape recorders used in the synthesis was hardly great enough to keep neighboring frequencies clearly separate. It turned out, incidentally, that if signals made in the old way and the new were equated in half-power bandwidth, the new ones were markedly easier to track.

Elkind's second experiment was divided into four parts. The same three practiced subjects participated in each part. The main variables were characteristics of the power-density spectrum of the target displacement. They were:

(1) Bandwidth of low-pass, sharp cut-off spectrum: 1.0, 1.5, 2.5, 4.0, 6.0, 10, 15, and 25 radians per second.

(2) Center frequency of rectangular spectrum: 2.0, 6.0, and 10.0 radians per second. (Bandwidth, 4.0 radians per second.)

(3) Root-mean-square displacement of target: 1.0, 0.3, 0.1 inch. (Pass band 0—4.0 radians per second.)

(4) Shape of spectrum governed by $\Phi_{xx}(j\omega) = 1/(3 + 2p)^{2n}$, with $n = 1$, 2, 3. This produces spectra that fall off 6, 12, and 18 decibels per octave, respectively, at high frequency.

At the time of this writing, Elkind has not entirely completed the analysis of the data. He has completed enough of it, however, to have far more frequency-response characteristics, signal-to-noise ratio curves, etc., than resulted from all previous tracking studies combined. Some of these he has made available, through personal communication [1955], for use here.

Probably the most basic of the conclusions to be drawn is one that is supported also by observations made in other experiments not directly concerned with quasi-linear models. It is that the characteristics of the linear part of the human operator are approximately invariant over a range of input amplitudes or display scale factors, and that — within that range — the magnitude of the noise introduced by the human operator is roughly proportional to the magnitude of response. More simply said, within limits it does not matter much whether one amplifies the stimulus and attenuates the response or attenuates the stimulus and amplifies the response. In the part (3) of the experiment concerned with amplitude as a variable, the results for 1-inch and 0.3-inch rms displacements were quite similar. Probably, performance would have been about the same with rms displacements somewhat greater than 1.0 inch. When the rms displacement was only 0.1 inch, however, the response was noticeably noisier. The conclusion that the quasi-linear operator is invariant over a range of scale factors therefore holds only approximately and only over a modest range. There is much other evidence on this point. We shall discuss later the other face of the coin — the advantage provided by magnification when the signal amplitude falls outside the range of invariance.

The data bear on the question: in compensatory tracking, does the operator behave as though he contained an integrator? Elkind's results for wide-band target signals support Russell's observation that the operator does not. In Fig. 13, which shows frequency-response characteristics for one subject, the magnitude curves for 2.5-, 4.0-, 6.0-, and 10-radian-per-second cut-offs are far enough below unity to warrant extrapolation. One of them may appear to be heading for $|H'| = +1$ at $\omega = 0$, but the others do not.

The phase characteristics are perhaps more sensitive indications than the magnitude characteristics. If the operator included an integrator, the open-loop phase curve would start out at $-\pi/2$ radians or -90 degrees. Closing the loop around the operator has the effect (as we saw in an example) of making the integrator appear to be leaky, i.e., of changing $1/p$ to $1/(p+a)$. But this does not change the phase curve for $\omega \ll a$. The high-frequency part of the phase curve might be advanced also by other parts of the operator's transfer function. However, only a pure differentiation could neutralize the phase lag all the way to $\omega = 0$. Returning to Fig. 13, we see that there is not even a suggestion that the phase curves start at $-90°$. Evidently, therefore, the human operator does not introduce integration when he has himself adjusted for compensatory tracking of low-pass random

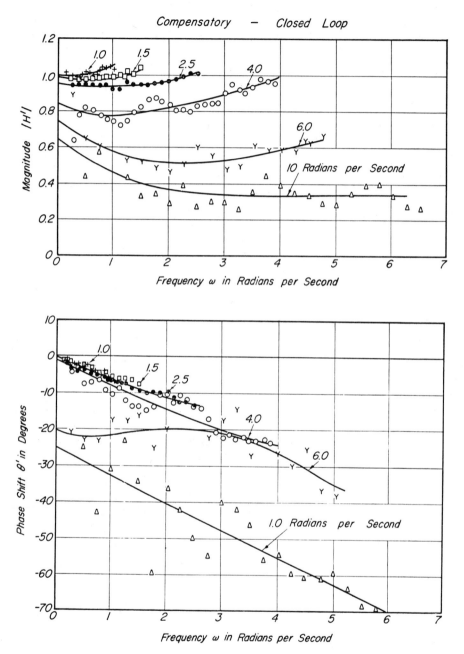

Fig. 13. Closed-loop magnitude and phase shift versus frequency for one of El-kind's operators in compensatory tracking. The parameter is upper cut-off frequency of the target spectrum. The lower cut-off frequency was in each case the same, essentially zero. [After Elkind (1956)]

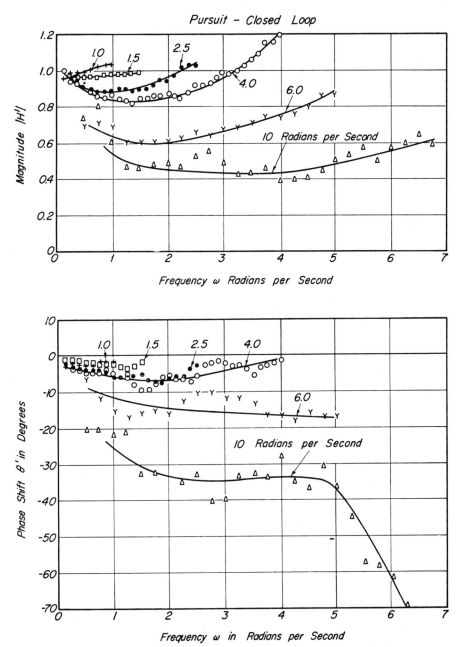

Fig. 14. Closed-loop magnitude and phase shift versus frequency for (the same) one of Elkind's operators in pursuit tracking. The target waveforms and spectra were the same as in the compensatory tests (Fig. 13). The parameter is target bandwidth. [After Elkind (1956)]

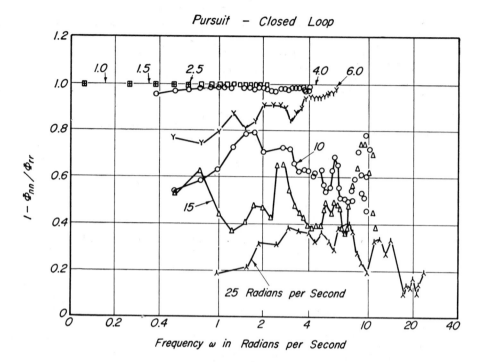

Fig. 15. The fraction of the output signal that is linearly related to the input signal, plotted as a function of frequency. $\Phi_{nn}\,(j\omega)$ is the power-density spectrum of the operator's output noise (i. e., output not linearly related to input). Φ_{rr} $(j\omega)$ is the power-density spectrum of the operator's entire response or output. One minus the ratio of Φ_{nn} to Φ_{rr} is therefore the normalized power-density spectrum of the part of the output that is linearly coherent with the input. Since the normalization is with respect to the output, $1 - \Phi_{nn}/\Phi_{rr}$ is in a sense the linearly coherent fraction of the output variance, displayed as a function of frequency. [After Elkind (1956)]

noise of moderate bandwidth. In respect of very-narrow-band target signals, however, we cannot tell very much from the open-loop characteristics.

We see in Figs. 13 and 14 that, as long as the target components lie below 1.5 radians per second, the magnitude of the closed-loop characteristic is close to unity. In pursuit tracking, moreover, there is essentially no phase shift and therefore no overt reaction time. If it is not too noisy, it appears that a pursuit tracking loop may be a fairly good engineering component.

We turn, therefore, to Fig. 15, which shows what fraction of the response signal power is linearly related to the input. We see that 98 or 99 per cent of the output is "signal" and only 1 or 2 per cent "noise." In terms of displacement, therefore, the pursuit (closed-loop) operator is linear within — to be conservative — 5 per cent. (This is better than Elkind found in his first experiment, but in the earlier tests the target signal had greater bandwidth and less sharp cut-off.) When it is working with narrow-band, low-pass signals ($\omega \leq 1.5$ radians per second), a pursuit loop containing a human operator appears to be a simple amplifier with approximately unity gain, little or no phase shift, and noise about 20 decibels below signal level.

In compensatory tasks, the closed-loop operator is approximately as good insofar as magnitude and noise are concerned, but it appears (from the roughly constant slope of the phase curves) to have a reaction time. The reaction time is a little less than 0.1 second. This brings to mind again the question of "stuttering" that we discussed in connection with Krendel's model.

The foregoing characteristics refer, of course, to target movements 1.5 radians per second or below in bandwidth and to the idealized tracking situation. It is probably important that the control was a light (35-gram) stylus held by the fingers normally used in writing and moved across an almost frictionless surface. Performance would probably not be as good with a handwheel or joystick or spade grip or pistol grip.

Shifting attention from the narrow-band to the wider-band target spectra, we see in Figs. 13 and 14 that the amplitude characteristics of the closed loop fall away from unity in the neighborhood of 1 and 2 radians per second and then tend to slope upward. This is rather marked in the case of compensatory tracking. When the target bandwidth reaches 6 or 10 radians per second, the amplitude characteristics are level again, but they are quite irregular. The peaks and valleys do not show up in the same places in successive tests, but the general level and tendency toward flatness are repeating characteristics.

The shortness of the reaction time in pursuit tracking warrants investigation. Even 0.02 second seems to be an overestimate of the reaction time indicated by the data. Because the target signal follows closely the model of a filtered gaussian process, there is no possibility of learning the target course. Evidently, the operator neutralizes his normal delay of reaction by predicting where the target is going. He bases the prediction, of course, on the constraint imposed by the filter.

Elkind examined the possibility that, in pursuit tracking, the operator might act as an optimal linear predictor. As Russell had noted in connection with one of his tests, the optimal predictor is simply an attenuator if the target signal is shaped by a simple low-pass filter of form $1/(1 + \tau p)$. It is more complicated, but calculable, for target signals shaped by several such filters in cascade. Elkind therefore worked with the data of part (4) of his experiment, in which the target signals were of that nature.

The first question, of course, was to find the time delay over which the predictor had to operate. That, to adopt a simple model of the process, would be the reaction time, which should show up as a constant slope in a linear plot of phase against frequency. Replotting the phase curve shown in Fig. 16 for the tests with the one-stage-filtered target signal yielded the straight-line graph of Fig. 17. The line slopes at 0.22 radians per radian per second, and the reaction time is therefore 0.22 second. Reaction times only a little different from that were found from the other phase curves.

The curves of Fig. 16 are the magnitude- and phase-*vs*-frequency curves for one subject, together with corresponding curves for ideal linear predictors. The nature of the predictor changes with the power-density spectrum of the target signal. When the latter is shaped by two cascaded filters, the predictor works on the time derivative $dx(t)/dt$ as well as on the value $x(t)$ of the target function. When the signal is shaped by three filters, acceleration becomes important. An ideal predictor would predict an ideally rectangular spectrum perfectly, for in that case the signal would be mathematically analytic. However, the predictor would have to be infinitely complicated, and it seems that the human operator must fall short of the ideal predictor somewhere along the line. Actually, as the phase curves show, he falls behind as soon as velocity becomes important. He does the right thing insofar as magnitude is concerned, but he does not adjust his phase response properly.

In the case of compensatory tracking, one can argue rather directly from the behavior of the closed loop to the behavior of the operator within it. The results obtained by Tustin and by Russell were presented in terms of the operator's open-loop response. Taking that step involves making the

---

Fig. 16. Closed-loop magnitude and phase shift versus frequency for (the same) one of Elkind's operators in pursuit tracking. In this case, the power-density spectra of the targets were uniform out to a break frequency of 1.5 radians per second, beyond which they declined as frequency increased. The spectrum determined by the one-stage filter fell off 20 decibels per decade of frequency at high frequencies; two-stage filter, 40 decibels per decade; and three-stage filter, 60 decibels per decade. The rectangular spectrum stopped abruptly at 1.5 radians per second. The solid lines show the magnitude and phase shift of ideal linear predictors for the three filtered targets. [After Elkind (1956)]

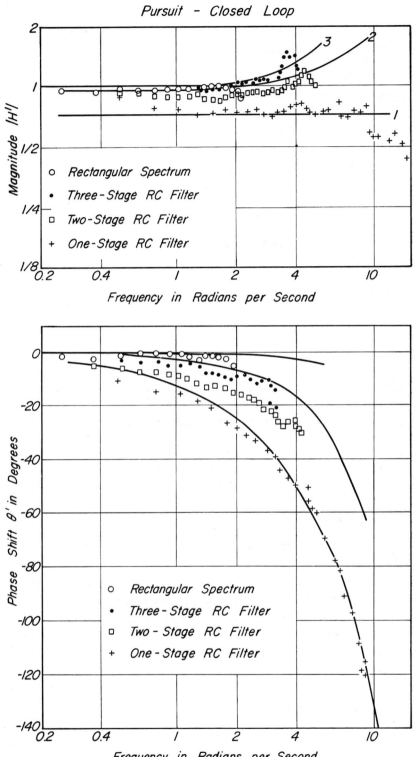

Pursuit — Closed Loop

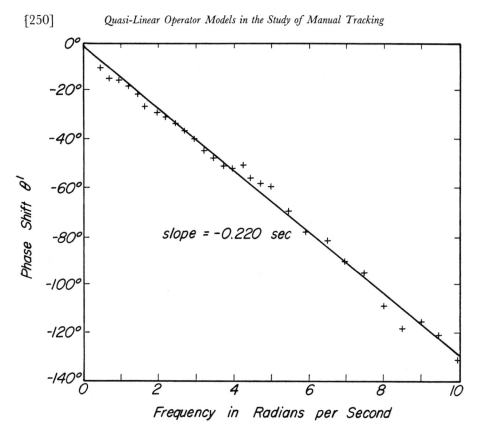

Fig. 17. One of the phase-shift functions of Fig. 16, replotted against a linear frequency scale. This function describes the phase shift in the closed-loop response to the one-stage-filtered target. Negative phase shift that increases linearly with frequency corresponds to pure time delay, the slope of the phase function being the amount of delay. [After Elkind (1956)]

assumption, which is perhaps a bit dangerous (and which certainly cannot be made in the case of pursuit tracking), that the operator does not manage at all to separate the target signal from his response. If he did that, some undetermined part of the operation might proceed without being directly influenced by feedback, just as much of it surely does in pursuit tracking.

Nevertheless, it is helpful to keep the open-loop characteristics in mind. When changes in the conditions of test alter the operator's characteristics, the open-loop curves change much more markedly than the closed-loop curves. This fact is of course a reflection of the stabilizing property of negative feedback. Perhaps even more important, the open-loop characteristics provide a direct view of the properties of the system that determine its stability, and they indicate the features that underly the closed-loop charac-

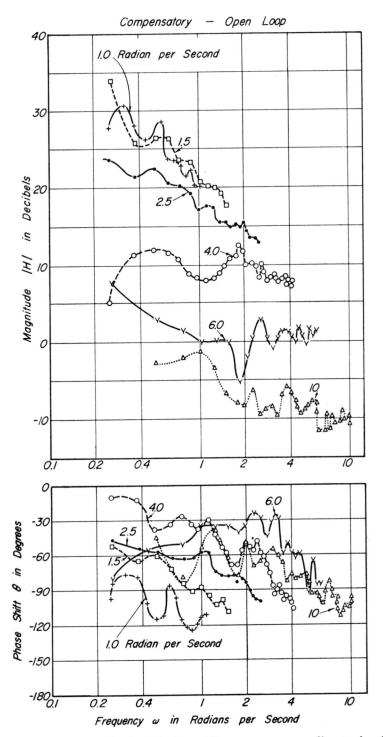

Fig. 18. Open-loop magnitude and phase-shift curves corresponding to the closed-loop magnitude and phase-shift curves of Fig. 13. The parameter is target bandwidth. [After Elkind (1956)]

teristics. They reveal, for example, whether variations in the gain of the over-all system are due to variations in the gain of, or to phase shifts caused by, the components of the system.

Open-loop magnitude and phase characteristics are shown in Fig. 18. They correspond to the closed-loop characteristics of Fig. 13. Because the closed-loop characteristics change so greatly when the bandwidth is varied, the magnitude scale has been made logarithmic. The quantity that is plotted, magnitude $|H|$ in decibels, is $20 \log_{10} |H(j\omega)|$ or $10 \log_{10} |H(j\omega)|^2$. The frequency scale is also distorted logarithmically, but it is labeled as before in radians per second.

It is evident from inspection of Fig. 18 that the outstanding effect is an effect upon gain. As the bandwidth is increased from 1.0 radian per second to 10 radians per second, the operator's gain falls about 25 decibels. Also, the curves of gain versus frequency flatten out as the bandwidth increases. On the whole, the phase shift appears to decrease as the bandwidth increases. The phase curves are rather irregular, but that may be only a reflection of the fact that variations in open-loop phase response are rather unimportant as long as the gain is high and the phase shift is not too great.

The open-loop plots take us back to the question of the presence of integration. We may now examine the behavior in the narrow-band tests, which was not well displayed by the closed-loop plots. The magnitude curves for 1.0 and 1.5 radians per second slope approximately 20 decibels per decade. The phase shift, in the first instance, extends even beyond $-\pi/2$ and, in the second, it is not very much less. It appears, therefore, that we should conclude as follows: The human operator can adjust himself to perform something analogous to pure integration when integration is desirable. When he has to track a fluctuating target, however, it is more important for him to minimize some such quantity as mean-squared error than it is to have the property of ultimately errorless response to a step displacement. He therefore introduces the attenuation (and other adjustments of parameters, insofar as possible) required to optimize prediction over an interval corresponding to his inherent time delay. Little attenuation is required if the target moves very slowly, and in that case he approximates integration closely. More attenuation is required if the target moves rapidly, and in that case he does not approximate integration.

It is possible to study the stability of a servomechanism with the aid of graphs of magnitude and phase versus frequency. One must consider the behavior of the curves in the neighborhood of $|H(j\omega)| = 1$ and $\theta(j\omega) = 180°$. But it is more convenient, and the more generally accepted practice, to have the data displayed in a Nyquist diagram. If the range of magnitudes is too great for that, a Nichols diagram [a plot of log |H| versus θ with ω as the parameter] is used instead. We examined Russell's results in Nyquist-diagram form. Here we shall have to use a Nichols plot.

The data of Fig. 18 are replotted in Fig. 19, and one additional curve, for the test with target bandwidth 15 radians per second, is added. We see again the progressive reduction of gain with increasing bandwidth. We see,

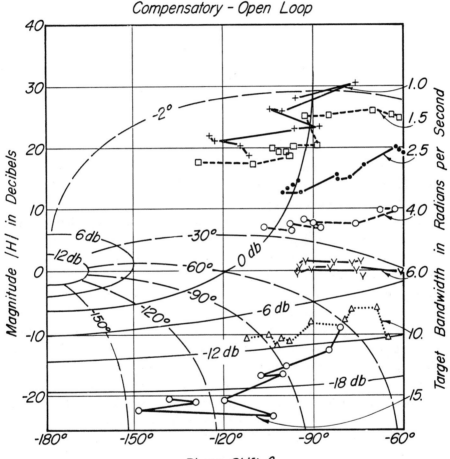

Fig. 19. The open-loop characteristics of Figs. 13 and 18 replotted in the form of a modified Nichols plot. Magnitude is plotted against phase shift with frequency the parameter. Frequency increases along each curve from near zero at the right-hand end to the cut-off frequency at the left-hand end. The distorted grid is the co-ordinate frame against which the closed-loop response can be read. [After Elkind (1956)]

also, that all the curves stay far away from the point (0 db, —180°). The significance of that point stems from the facts (1) that, with a phase shift of —180°, negative feedback becomes in-phase positive feedback, and (2) that feeding back the output at the same level (cf. 0-db gain) and in the same phase as the input is precisely the condition for sustained oscillation.

As we have seen, the open-loop transfer function $H(p)$ of a simple servo is related to the closed-loop transfer function $H'(p)$ by

$$H'(p) = \frac{H(p)}{1 + H(p)} \tag{27a}$$

and

$$H(p) = \frac{H'(p)}{1 - H'(p)} \tag{27b}$$

Those relations are represented by the relations between the rectangular open-loop grid and the distorted closed-loop grid in Fig. 19. We see that the high gain of the narrow-band open-loop characteristics was spent almost entirely for low closed-loop phase shift. The wide-band open-loop characteristics had no gain to spend. The wide-band closed-loop characteristics therefore have marked phase shift. Stability was never a problem. In the narrow-band tests, there was plenty of room to get the gain curve down from its high value inside the target band to a low value at the frequency corresponding to —180° phase shift. And in the wide-band tests there was not enough gain at any frequency to cause oscillation.

The problem presented to the operator was more difficult in the tests with target spectra shaped by filters. In those tests, the bulk of the signal power was at low frequency, but there were significant components of the signal in the higher frequency bands, also. In order to track the signal well, the operator needed to construct phase-advance networks within himself. But phase-advance networks tend to increase the gain at high frequency. The operator had the task, therefore, of guaging his nearness to oscillation and of adjusting his parameters to avoid it.

Curves for the same one subject in the tests with filtered target signals are shown in Fig. 20. This, also, is a modified Nichols diagram. In it, we see that the characteristic (1) for the tests with single-filter roll-off follows approximately along the closed-loop grid-line for —6 db. We recall that good prediction corresponded to attenuation in that case. In the tests (2) with double roll-off, the operator adjusted himself to provide more gain and less phase shift. And in the test (3) with triple roll-off, he almost adjusted himself to the point of oscillation. If he had slipped 40 or 45 degrees in phase, he would have oscillated at 5 or 6 radians per second.

Evidently, the wisdom of the human operator (to paraphrase Cannon's title) includes a fair mastery of loop-compensation techniques.

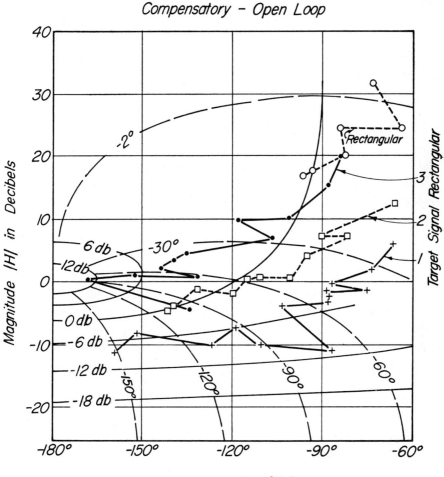

Fig. 20. Modified Nichols plot (similar to Fig. 19) of the transfer functions in Elkind's tests with filtered target spectra. The parameter is the number of simple low-pass filters used in shaping the target spectrum. [After Elkind (1956)]

9. THE ROLE OF VISION IN TRACKING

Linearization of Visual Space. Typically, the target signal is presented as the displacement of a dot or a spot of light, or perhaps of an object, in the visual field. Some use of non-spatial dimensions was made in "Flybar" (Forbes, [1946]), but there appears to have been little study of tracking of light intensity or wavelength or of sound intensity or frequency. (A quantitative study of the tracking of a melody by a singer might be quite interesting.)

There is doubtless good reason behind the choice of visual displacement. We can make at least as many and as fine discriminations in visual space as we can in any other field (Miller, [1955]; Quastler [1955]; Licklider, Stevens, and Hayes [1954]). Even handicapping visual space by using only one dimension of it does not put it below hearing, except perhaps for persons with unusual pitch perception. For our purposes, however, the main advantage of vision is its nearly linear metric. Through life-long experience, a nearly one-to-one correspondence has been developed between pointing and reaching reactions and points in a plane normal to the line of sight. Because the arms and hands move relative to the head and eyes, this correspondence has had to be made linear. Linear correspondence is the only type that is invariant under translation and magnification. It is natural, at the outset, therefore to adopt a model of the operator that is linear insofar as spatial displacement is concerned.

We should of course not expect the approximation to linearity to be of high order. Our experience has made us only as linear as we have needed to be. We are therefore probably not linear over as great a range as we would be if each of us were both a watchmaker and a *jai alai* player. Nor are the tolerances as tight as they would be if there were a mouse trap beside every door handle. Probably our reactions betray some trace of the anatomical metric of our neural mechanism. There may, for example, be some distortion due to the marked departure from linear isomorphism in the geometry of the projection of the retina upon area 17 of the cerebral cortex — some residual not evened out by such a process as statistical satiation (Köhler and Wallach [1944]). Or there may be some nonlinearity attributable to the distortions inherent in illusions. But these are small. And, if they are constant, they may be neutralized by complementary nonlinearity in the display or control. Insofar as the metric of visual space is concerned, therefore, we may say that we are working with a system that is reasonably linear in the gross.

Noise in Visual Perception. The situation becomes more complicated as we proceed. We come at once to the question of noise. Why does the precision of tracking depend as it does upon the scales of display and control? Why is there not a wide zone of invariance? There appear to be two supplementary answers.

First, wherever Weber's Law applies (even approximately) over a wide range of stimulus magnitudes, the psychophysical relation is highly non-linear, and the range of the magnitudes of the subjective attribute or of the objective response is not remarkably wide. The range of Weber's Law therefore does not remain impressive when the stimulus magnitude is plotted on a scale that linearizes the psychophysical relation. In space perception, there is no need for such a transformation, for the relation is already linearized. The stimulus range is simply deprived of the exponential magnification we are used to giving it, and it seems small in spurious contrast.

The other answer is that, in making our everyday reactions to signals from the visual field, we are free to adjust our point of view until the display is of reasonable size, and to adjust our mechanical leverage (to some extent independently of point of view) until the scale of the reaction is proper. Very fine work may need a magnifying glass, and a very distant operation may require a telescope, but the very small and the very far distant probably have minor influence on the organization of our visual-motor reaction patterns. We have only a moderate dynamic range in visual space, this is to say, because it is ordinarily easy to bring things into that range.

This line of reasoning has a bearing on the practical problem of selecting the proper magnification for use in a tracking system. In some situations, magnification has been shown to aid tracking (Helson [1949]). One cannot conclude that magnification is helpful in general, however, because the optimal degree of magnification depends upon the amplitude (linear or angular) of the target motion, just as much as it does upon the optimal scale of display (Edson [1948]).

In pursuit tracking, the main thing is to adjust the display scale factor until the target motion makes an appropriate excursion on the display surface. In compensatory tracking, the amplitude of the error depends upon the accuracy of the operator, and the accuracy of the operator depends upon the amplitude of the error excursion on the display. The problem of finding the optimal target magnification is therefore less simple, but again it is essentially a matter of getting the error excursion into the operator's dynamic range.

If the dynamic range of visual space perception is the fundamental determiner of the amount of magnification to use in any specific situation, we should examine the operator's normal mode of extending that dynamic range. He moves his eyes, his head, and even his body in such a way as to keep the stimulus, to which he is adjusting, in the most sensitive part of his field. If the target in a pursuit task moves slowly enough, he can follow it through wide excursions by moving along with it, and thereby achieve very great relative accuracy. In a compensatory task, he is spared the necessity of moving as long as he operates accurately, since accurate operation keeps the error small.

Intermittency in the Visual Process. Head and body movements connected with visual adjustment sometimes occur, but in most tracking situations they are infrequent and largely incidental. Even during tracking of wide-band signals, however, there are eye movements. They are usually sudden jumps of fixation. What happens within the human operator when he shifts fixation? Does intermittent shifting introduce a fundamental intermittency into the operator characteristic? We have to make room for that possibility in our thinking. The alternative appears to be that the nervous system pieces together the data from the retina and the data from the centers that control the eye movements, and uses the pieced-together picture as a basis for control of the tracking response. The piecing together would appear to require considerable computation and therefore probably to introduce a time delay.

Another potential source of intermittency in the visual process is scansion. A number of theorists (e.g., Pitts and McCulloch [1947]) have suggested that the process underlying visual perception involves a scanning of the primary sensory data at a rate corresponding approximately to that of the alpha rhythm of the electro-encephalogram. There is accumulating evidence (Rosenblith [1955]) that the brain may have a regular time base, and it seems not entirely unlikely that there is a fundamental quantization of the time variable in perception. If there is, then tracking may be best understood in terms of a model based on quantized time.

Visual Time Lag and Delay. Inasmuch as time lags and delays appear to be the main shortcomings of the human tracker, we should inquire into other temporal features of the visual process than intermittency. We do not ordinarily perceive the intermittency of the perceptual process, if the process is indeed intermittent, and one might therefore postulate that a smoothing follows the postulated scanning. There is also other evidence, freer of semantic difficulty.

The apparently continuous motion produced in moving pictures and television by intermittent stimulation must almost certainly result from the action of something analogous to smoothing filters. Even at 16 frames per second, movies are fairly free of flicker. A rather undemanding specification for a flicker-rejection filter might require 20 decibels of attenuation at 16 cps. This could be provided by a very simple filter, for example our familiar $1/(1 + Tp)$ with break frequency $a = 1/T$ at about 10 radians per second, but such a filter would not meet another visual requirement: faithful response up to 6 or 7 cps. The joint requirements, faithful response to discrete frequencies up as near as possible to the transition point, and flickerless apparent motion as shortly as possible beyond the transition point, require a more elaborate filter. A cascade of two second-order filters with low damping would provide the required performance. But such a network would have another exceedingly interesting property.

A second-order low-pass filter with low damping has a resonant peak. Its amplitude response is greater at the break frequency (or slightly below the frequency) than it is at lower frequencies where its response is uniform. The break between 7 and 16 cps has to be near 10 or 12 cps, which is the frequency interval in which the alpha rhythm is found, in which the occipital cortex has heightened sensitivity, etc. Evidently, the peculiarity of the behavior of the brain in the neighborhood of 10 or 12 cps is closely related to the reasonableness of its behavior above and below that frequency.

For tracking, the implications of the idea are two-fold. First, if we encounter anomalous behavior in the neighborhood of 10 cps, we should not jump immediately to an intermittent or nonlinear theory to explain it. One should not support the linear hypothesis with overly great vigor, either, of course, but it is worthwhile to hold onto it as a possibility until the data require its rejection. Second, one has good basis for assuming that the linear operators of a quasi-linear model have several low-pass factors that break in the vicinity of 10 cycles per second. In most tracking situations, these have little effect because other factors at lower frequencies send the magnitude-*vs*-frequency curve down first. When every effort is made to introduce phase advance, however, their influence may make itself felt. At any rate, they set an upper limit to the human operator's frequency response.

In addition to the separation of intermittency at 7 cps from continuity at 16 cps, there are other lags, leads, and delays in the visual process. The retina introduces a delay of perhaps 25 milliseconds, and about 10 more are required to get the signal to the occipital cortex. Transit time (distance-velocity lag or transportation lag) is essentially pure time delay. It must appear in the L of e^{-Lp} in the over-all open-loop transfer function. There is no sure basis for estimating the delays and lags of the rest of the visual process. All we can do is recognize that (1) factors of unknown order but with high break frequencies and/or (2) computation time delays are seen to be involved in visual anticipation and smoothing.

10. THE ROLE OF THE MOTOR SYSTEM IN TRACKING

THE MOTOR SYSTEM is evidently well-matched to the perceptual system. One can tap periodically only a very little faster than he can count. The masses and elasticities and dampings of small movements appear to be carefully calculated just not to filter out the most rapid outputs of the perceptual mechanism.

Evidently, muscular adjustments are controlled by an arrangement that follows a servo model quite closely. This arrangement is a feedback system within the motor system. Only its closed-loop behavior is included in the descriptions of the operator models we have discussed.

Among the muscle fibers that do work are others, specialized for the purpose of reporting back to the control centers. They are in direct connection with afferent neurons. Other afferent neurons arise at specialized receptors associated with the tendons and joints. The afferent neurons return to the spinal-cord or brain-stem motor centers and deliver to those centers signals that reflect the current state of the reaction. The feedback is given a certain amount of phase advance by an intrinsic feature of the kinesthetic receptors: they are responsive to the time derivative of tension as well as to tension itself.

The servo-mechanism of muscular response has been investigated and discussed in considerable detail (see Gibbs [1954]). For our purpose, it is sufficient to note that, within the operator, there is a closed-loop system with rather clearly definable dynamic properties. As good engineering design would have it, the dynamic characteristics of this system are not directly the limiting factors in small movements but they nevertheless have effects. When the motor loop is made very tight — given high gain — tremor results, and it does affect tracking performance. The motor characteristics must contribute, also, to high-frequency attenuation and phase shift. In fact, it seems entirely possible that the dynamic characteristics of the perceptual and motor mechanisms set the requirements for a central low-pass factor with a much lower break frequency.

11. THE CENTRAL PROCESS IN TRACKING

IF THE DYNAMIC factors of the perceptual and motor systems are of the forms we have suggested — second- or higher-order with break frequencies near 10 per second — it is necessary to do something more than connect the perceptual output to the motor input if the over-all system is to function inside a feedback loop. Closing the loop through the environment, from response to stimulus, would set a directly connected perceptual-motor system into oscillation. One of the problems presented to the intermediate parts of the central nervous system, therefore, is to establish stability. The central nervous system faces that general problem not only in tracking, of course, but at all levels of behavior from social adjustment to respiration and circulation. Perhaps the most thorough studies have been made in connection with regulation of the internal environment and maintenance of posture. Tracking borders directly on the latter field. It may be that the neural mechanism involved in tracking may be understood better as studies of postural adjustment continue. At present, however, we do not get as much guidance from neurophysiology in selecting a model of the operator as we do from servo engineering.

The simplest and most widely-used technique for avoiding oscillations due to high-frequency resonances in complex systems is to introduce a "spoiling factor." The spoiling factor has a gain-*vs*-frequency curve that falls off fast enough to make the over-all open-loop gain less than unity at the frequencies at which oscillations threaten to occur. The question is, does the nervous system of the tracker do anything analogous?

If the open-loop transfer function is $H(p) = (k/p)(1 + Tp)e^{-Lp}$, as Tustin and Phillips and Walston and Warren assumed, he does not. He does not, that is, unless T is very small, and the main part of the job is performed by the integration $1/p$. But that would unnecessarily depress the gain in the upper part of the tracking band. And, in any event, we have seen evidence in Tustin's and Russell's and Elkind's results that, except possibly when tracking very slow signals, the human operator does not integrate.

A more likely spoiling factor is the factor $1/(1 + Tp)$ of Elkind's model.

If we think of the human operator as having a preferred or neutral open-loop form, therefore, we may well choose such a form as

$$H(p) = \frac{k[(1 + T_1 p)^{n_1} (1 + 2\zeta T_2 p + T_2^2 p^2)^{n_2}]}{(1 + Tp)[(1 + T_3 p)^{n_3} (1 + 2\zeta T_4 p + T_4^2 p^2)^{n_4}]} e^{-Lp}. \qquad (28)$$

The first factor in the denominator is the spoiling factor. T and k are variable. With L, they provide a rough description of the operator's behavior. The other factors between brackets in the numerator and denominator are high-frequency factors associated with perception and with motor response. T_1, T_2, T_3, and T_4 constitute a cluster of values near 0.02 second, corresponding to the break frequency of 10 cps. The bracketed numerator factors are phase-advance factors, related to the anticipatory aspects of sensation and motor response. The bracketed denominator factors are smoothing factors related to the continuity of subjective and objective response.(*) The bracketed factors ordinarily do not show up markedly in tracking behavior, but if they were not in the network the operator would perform in a quite different way.

If we select (28) as the neutral form of the model, we have to make a place for the possibility that additional low-frequency factors may be introduced to neutralize corresponding factors in the external dynamics of the tracking system. It appears from some of Russell's and Krendel's results that the human operator can introduce such factors. Taylor and Birmingham [1954] have developed an approach to the optimization of man-machine systems based on the assumption of a very simple description (essentially, transfer function equals unity) of the neutral form. We do not yet, however, have data that will support a quantitative analysis.

From Elkind's results, it is clear that the operator adjusts T to optimize response to the particular target spectrum. He does introduce phase-advance factors, but not entirely optimal ones. The same rules may turn out to govern both the adjustments to external dynamics and the adjustments to target spectra. A large part of the phase retardation in the over-all operator is associated with these dynamic factors we have been discussing. Another part, approximately a constant 0.1 second, is due to true reaction time L and appears in the e^{-Lp} of the model.

Our quasi-linear model for compensatory tracking, then, has a linear part of the form

(*) Some of the denominator factors may be directly associated with numerator factors in lead compensation "dipoles."

$$H(p) = \frac{k}{(1 + Tp)} \frac{(A)}{(B)} \frac{(A')}{(B')} e^{-Lp}. \tag{29}$$

(A) and (B) are relatively simple factors with break frequencies in the tracking range. The operator has some, but not complete, control over them. He introduces them as compensations, and they are usually nearer to unity than they should be for optimal compensation. (A') and (B') are relatively complicated factors with break frequencies near 10 cps. The operator has little or no control over them. T and k are variable. L is roughly constant at 0.1 second.

The quasi-linear model includes noise sources. Elkind's results indicate that the output noise spectrum is of more nearly constant shape — it is rather uniform out to 6 radians per second, then falls off gradually — than we might suppose. No general conclusion can yet be made about the sources of the noise. The most that can be said is that noise doubtless arises in several parts of the over-all process, and that its level appears to increase as (A) and (B) depart from unity.

12. DISCONTINUOUS AND NONLINEAR FUNCTIONING OF THE HUMAN OPERATOR

OUR DISCUSSION thus far has been made from a point of view favourable to quasi-linear models. We have permitted switching from one set of linear operator parameters to another. We have not rejected slow drifting. We have even tolerated intermittency at a rate high enough (e.g., 10 per second) to permit effective filtering. The quasi-linear formulation stands up, in fact, under test by any of the data we have mentioned — and by other data, also, that are usually interpreted as evidence of nonlinearity or discontinuity.

The pro-linear viewpoint was adopted because this chapter is about quasi-linear models, models in which a basic linearity of action is assumed. We did not want to reject the topic before discussing it. It is time now, however, to examine the possible advantages of intermittent and nonlinear models.

Intermittency. If perception and response are organized on a quantized time base, we should expect to see only indirect reflection of the quantization in open-loop response characteristics. We should not expect to see a strong output component at the basic 10-per-second rate. (Let us assume that value to make the discussion concrete.) It would almost certainly be filtered out by dynamics introduced for that purpose.

Let us assume with Stroud [1954] that the perceptual output at any time depends upon the sensory input in a preceding block of time. Blocks are of somewhat flexible duration, but on the average they are about 0.1 second long. The central data-processing system works with the perceptual output, and gets a new signal every 0.1 second. If the whole mechanism is well engineered, the computations are probably made on the same time base, and we may therefore expect that something will be ready for the motor system no sooner than the beginning of the third tenth-second interval. The motor system starts responding at once, and the movement begins after a signal transit time of say 20 milliseconds. But the response is smoothed, and it is not completed until 0.2 second later. The operator has to wait to see where his response has taken him before he can make an appropriate correction.(*) It takes perhaps 40 milliseconds for the information to get through the sensory channel (transit time, again), and then the whole cycle repeats. If the operator over-responded each time, successive adjustments would be in opposite directions, and the period of oscillation would be the time·required to make two trips through the operator, or about 0.9 second.

The picture just outlined was described in roughly that way shortly after the war by Craik [1947, 1948] and by Hick [1948]. They did not mention the separation of the perceptual from the computational operation. That is an idea mentioned by Stroud [1950]. Perhaps we should keep separate the two notions, (1) intermittency due basically to the operator's need for information about effects of the last response before making the next one, and (2) intermittency due basically to time quantization in the neural process.

In any event, the general notion of intermittent action is quite popular in the field of tracking. The "waviness" of the compensatory tracker's response, and the fact that it appears to contain corrective adjustments at intervals of roughly 0.5 second, have been accepted as support for the intermittency hypothesis. We have discussed the evidence from experiments with step-displacement signals.(†) We have discussed, also, the use of the hy-

(*) This is a crucial part of the refractory-phase argument. If it did not have to wait for completion of the response, the perceptual system would be working on the next input block.

(†) The discrepancy between Vince's [1948, 1950] results and those of Ellson and his co-workers [1948, 1949] may be related to the two notions discussed in the preceding paragraph. If the operator did not always wait for visual check before making the next adjustment, he would respond in the way Ellson observed. If he did wait for a visual check, he would respond in the way the operators usually did in Vince's tests.

pothesis in the calculation of the time constants for "aiding" controls: the constants based on 0.5-second sampling turned out best. However, before accepting these items of evidence as critical, we should note that a noisy but otherwise linear system with phase advance and high gain would produce a wavy output, just as an intermittent system would. Moreover, under some circumstances the "adjustments" would appear to come at 0.5-second intervals. We should note, also, that the same aiding time constants might well be derived from a quasi-linear model. In short, the objective evidence of intermittent reaction in tracking tests with continuous signals is not critical.

There are, however, other much stronger reasons for assuming intermittent action. First, time delays are less likely to cause instability in sampled-data servos than in continuous servos (Truxal [1955]). The intermittent action of the periodic sampler has a stabilizing effect that is difficult to duplicate with linear networks. Second, problems of computation and storage are much more simply solved in time-sampling systems than in continuous ones. The second reason seems to be almost compellingly strong. One need only consider the problem raised in connection with eye movements — the problem of shifting the excitation pattern by an amount proportional to the shift of the eyes — to see how difficult it is to perform continuous computations upon a manifold of continuous time functions.

North's Approach through Finite-Difference Equations. The natural tools for use in work with sampled-data systems include linear finite-difference equations. North [1952, 1954, 1955] adopted an approach based on difference equations, justifying it through references to Craik and Hick and to reaction time and the psychological refractory phase. He showed that, if the interval between samples is made smaller and smaller, the result of the analysis based on linear finite-difference equations approaches the result obtained with differential equations with constant coefficients or with linear transform methods. In principle, therefore, there is close connection between an intermittent linear model and a time-invariant linear model. However, if the interval of intermittency is 0.5 second, there appear to be rather great differences between their behaviors.

The intermittent model is difficult to handle, and no one but North has carried it all the way through tracking problems. Intuitively, one would not expect it to stand up (with 0.5 second interval) under test against Elkind's results with 6.0-radian-per-second (i.e., almost 1.0-cps) targets. The autocorrelation has almost died out, and the target is in quite a different place, before the next sample is ready.

As applied to the other conception of intermittency — the one based on 0.1-second time quantization — however, the intermittent model seems very interesting. On gross features of the response, it should agree well with a linear model. And it may handle some subtle features of the response better. For example, it may better explain why the tracker gets farther behind when the signal reverses direction and catches up during intervals between reversals.

North [1954, 1955] is developing a rather comprehensive mathematical theory of the human operator, or, to use his more accurate phrase, of "mechanically extended man." He considers man in a situation in which his relations with the external environment are delimited by a machine. The machine both restricts and extends his sensory channels and responses. This makes "tracking" the central problem.

But North considers a wider class of environments than we have discussed. The target may sometimes be indifferent to the operator's response ("neutral"). On other occasions, it may be "cooperative" or "competitive." The operator may have a preview of the target course ("precognitive"). He may be able to judge its future from its past ("regenerative"), as evidently he does in pursuit tracking. If neither of those alternatives applies, the tracking is "compensatory." This is a bit different from our use of the term. The operator appears to be able to predict something about the future course of the target in what we have called a compensatory set-up.

North's analysis takes him into information theory and game theory, and beyond the scope of this chapter. His work is of considerable interest in connection with more complex models than those with which we are dealing here. The main problems are that it is difficult to follow and that the theory has rather outstripped available relevant data.

13. CONDITIONAL SERVO MODELS

IN THE FOREGOING SECTIONS, we have suppressed two considerations that we must now bring into the discussion. The first is the dual input to the operator in pursuit tracking. The second is the larger role of proprioceptive feedback — feedback not confined to the motor centers but extending to the perceptual centers as well. These are closely related, because the proprioceptive feedback gives the compensatory tracker to some extent the same information that the pursuit tracker derives from his display.

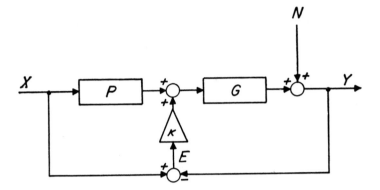

Fig. 21. Schema of a conditional servo. If P is the inverse of G (i. e., if $PG = 1$), and if $N = 0$, $Y = X$ and there is no feedback. If G becomes different from P, or if there is a disturbance $N \neq 0$ at the output, $X - Y = E$, and E is fed back with gain k. Since the feedback is negative, it stabilizes the output against variations in G and against disturbance N, without affecting the desired response.

A concept useful in thinking about these problems is the "conditional servo." It is a feedback arrangement discussed by Ham [1954] and suggested as a model for tracking by Elkind [1955]. It has the feature of functioning as an open-loop system as long as the output agrees with an "intention," but of subjecting any discrepancy between output and intention to negative feedback.

A simple conditional servo is represented schematically in Fig. 21. G is a network to be stablized. P is its inverse: $PG = 1$. For the sake of simplicity, we assume that P is correctly designed and stable. If G is correctly designed and stable, also, and if $N = 0$, then $Y = X$, and there is no error E and therefore no feedback. However, if the parameters of G change, or if there is a disturbance N at the output, the deviation of Y from X is subjected to negative feedback through the amplifier k, and the discrepancy is reduced to the fraction $1/(1 + kG)$ of the value it would otherwise have had.

This concept is useful for us because in some (particularly pursuit) situations the human operator tends to run freely in more or less open-loop fashion as long as all is going well, but to operate as a servomechanism when his responses cease to be appropriate. The simple schema has to be adapted, of course, but it makes a useful component for models of the human operator.

A second useful concept might be called feedback control of parameters. It appears that the adjustments of the parameters of the human operator are made in part on a trial-and-error basis, and that the optimization and

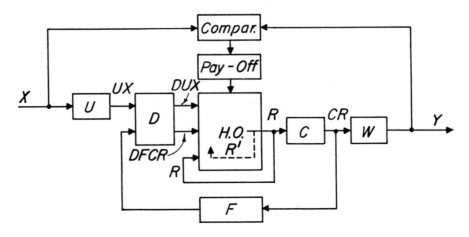

Fig. 22. Schematic diagram showing various feedbacks that operate in a pursuit tracking situation. The output of the control is fed back through F and displayed to the operator as $DFCR$. The operator sees his hand move the control. This gives him R, and therefore a chance to learn something about DFC. Internally, he has proprioceptive feedback from the movement. Putting this together with the visual information about R, he can in principle discover the input impedance of C. In simple cases, that may determine also the transfer function of C. The feedback path for "knowledge of results" involves comparing Y with X and selecting pay-off or reinforcing stimuli on tne basis of the comparison. The shaping of the human operator is governed by the pay-off and by information, derived from the other feedbacks, about the external situation. There is usually also an "instruction" channel into the operator.

stabilization of behavior depend largely upon the preserving or discarding of trial adjustments under the influence of feedback. Ashby [1952] has developed this idea in detail.

Conditional Model for Pursuit Tracking. With the aid of those concepts, we may consider building a fairly literal model of the human operator in a visual-manual pursuit tracking situation.

First, we should distinguish among the several feedbacks represented in Fig. 22. (1) A feedback signal $DFCR$ is presented to the operator via the display. (2) The manual response R usually is seen directly by the operator. (3) There is kinesthetic and somesthetic return R' from various parts of the hand, arm, and body. There often is, or often should be, feedback concerning the effectiveness of the performance of the over-all system or the section of it within which the operator is working.

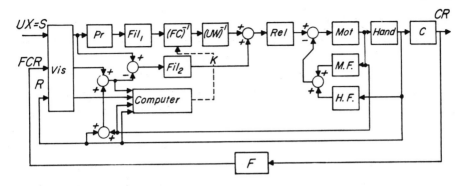

Fig. 23. Semi-detailed schema showing some of the signal paths in pursuit tracking. The target signal UX and two feedback signals are delivered to the visual system. The perceptual system operates in part on the target signal and in part on its relation to the fed-back signals, trying to predict (Pr) ahead enough to neutralize the processing time delay. $(FC)^{-1}$ and $(UX)^{-1}$ are envisaged as networks developed insofar as possible to be inverse to FC and UW. The "computer" shares in guiding the development of $(FC)^{-1}$, since there is some basis in the feedback signals for discovering the nature of the control-feedback dynamics. $(UW)^{-1}$ can be developed, however, only on the basis of pay-off (see Fig. 22). The relay Rel passes the perceptual output on to the motor system, which is envisaged as a servo loop, with feedback $M.F.$ from the contractions of the muscles and $H.F.$ from the resulting displacements of the hand. The two filters (Fil_1) and (Fil_2)] are developed in part to represent inversely the dynamics of the motor system and in part to suppress tendencies toward oscillation that may result from the predictor's failure to neutralize the time delay. Fil_2 has high gain at low frequencies and acts as a conditional feedback path.

Next, referring to Fig. 23,(*) we should note that the target signal UX, the system feedback signal FCR, and the incidental visual signal R from arm, hand, etc., are delivered in parallel to the multi-channel visual system. They are kept separate and at the same time inter-related in the process of visual perception.

For convenience, we may divide the over-all processing into (perhaps largely arbitrary) stages. First, we have the visual sensory process (Vis) culminating in a display of data to the perceptual mechanism. The perceptual mechanism predicts, from the display data, where the target is going. (It probably also predicts where the follower and the hand are going, but the schema will be complex enough without that.) In a separate operation, the perceptual mechanism measures the difference between the dis-

(*) To simplify the discussion, we shall assume that the display D may be represented by unity.

played target and displayed error. This difference is filtered and used as a conditional feedback and also as a "knowledge-of-results" signal K to supplement the reinforcement P provided by the pay-off system.

Following the predictor is a cascade of filters. The first filter, Fil_1, adjusts itself to be the inverse of the relay and motor dynamics of the operator. Presumably he comes to the task with this network partly formed, since it is the component that translates the sensory signal into motor terms. The adjustment is refined by K and P. The second filter, $(FC)^{-1}$, adjusts itself insofar as possible to be the inverse of the cascaded control C and feedback network F. The required dynamics are computed from FCR and R, and the adjustment is refined by K and P. The third filter, $(UW)^{-1}$ adjusts itself insofar as possible to be the inverse of U and W, which are external to the loop. The only aid to that adjustment is P, and there appears to be little hope of accomplishment unless U and W are simple. However, if the system were set up with $U = 1$ and $W = -1$, for example, the operator should in due course learn to reverse his reaction.

The order of Fil_1, $(FC)^{-1}$, and $(UW)^{-1}$ as linear operators is of course immaterial. In the human operator, there doubtless is either a preferred sequence or a combining into one network.

Insofar as the networks we have discussed are perfectly adjusted, there is no need for feedback and, since the feedback is conditional, there is none. The adjustments will not be perfect, however. For one thing, there is no perfect, physically-realizable inverse to a time delay. The error signal K is therefore continually in action, feeding back into Rel, the relay to the motor system, in such a way as to bring the response into line with the target.

The motor system is represented in Fig. 23 as a follow-up system, paced by control signals from the relay. The two feedback paths represent the relatively unimportant distinction between the kinesthetic and other purely internal receptors, on the one hand, and tactile receptors, etc., that gain information from the surface of the control, on the other.

The complexity of the arrangement just described almost precludes experimental analysis. In principle, however, analysis is possible, and work in the general area continues at such a pace that it may eventually be made for a few tracking situations. The basic problem, stated in terms of quasi-linear models, is to find transfer functions for $(Pr)(Fil_1)(FC)^{-1}(UW)^{-1}$ and for Fil_2 that, taken together with high-frequency factors appropriate for Vis, Rel, and the motor feedback loop, will check with experimental results. There is of course no need to analyze the cascades into separate blocks. It would be of considerable theoretical interest to trace the adjustment of

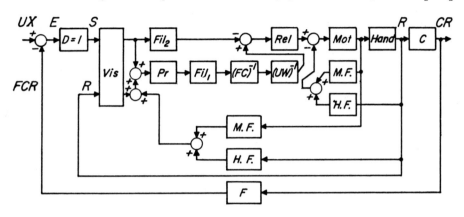

Fig. 24. Semi-detailed schema for compensatory tracking, corresponding to Fig. 23 for pursuit tracking. Here the visual system does not see the target motion *UX*. The predictor and the several "inverse" networks can function effectively, therefore, only to the extent that *UX* can be recaptured through joint analysis of *R* and *S*. If $D = 1$, $S = E$ and $UX = E + CR$. The main hope is for the "computer" (not shown here in the interest of relative simplicity; see Fig. 23) to solve the dynamics of *C* and to form *CR* from *R*. Then the chain Pr, Fil_1, ... can operate on $UX = E + CR$ and the system can function, as in Fig. 23, as a conditional servo. In practice, of course, the human operator does the necessary computing and circuit-arranging imperfectly. Evidently the task of reconstructing *UX* from *E* and *R* is particularly difficult for him.

parameters during learning. Tracking appears to offer an excellent setting for such study.

Conditional Model for Compensatory Tracking. A variation of the model just described lets us bring compensatory tracking into the same general paradigm. In compensatory tracking, only the error is displayed to the operator, but he has his hand on the control and therefore has direct visual and/or proprioceptive access to *R*. In Fig. 24, the feedback signals from *R*, and from within the motor system, are added to the sensed error signal, with the aim of re-creating *X*, the target motion. If the control, feedback, and other external dynamics are unity, this is operationally a very simple matter. And experience in compensatory tracking suggests that one can and does to some extent figure out what the target is doing in more or less the way suggested. With that information, the operator can in principle proceed just as he does in pursuit tracking.

It is clear, however, that even the simple task of adding the error and feedback signals together is in practice very difficult, particularly if the feedback is mainly proprioceptive and the error visual. Even when the operator sees his response directly, he does not make very effective use of the possibility that lies open to him. The conditional servo is therefore usually in operation as a feedback system.

In most practical tracking situations, the control and other elements in the external dynamics involve integrations. This further complicates the problem by requiring the operator to match the integrations by adjusting his own feedback paths. This requires very much time and practice. Probably the development of the appropriate networks accounts for a large part of the experienced operator's skill.

There is one idealized situation, however, in which the operator might rather easily take full advantage of the possibility of reconstructing the target motion. Let all the external dynamics be unity, and let the control be located directly on the display. Then, if the control is truly compensatory — if an error to the right is corrected by a control motion to the left, and vice versa — the target position is given directly by the geometry. All the operator has to do is to examine as a function of time the distance between his control and the error dot. That is the target signal.

Even if the control is not immediately adjacent to the display, the operator may be able to use this geometrical aid to some extent. The thought suggests itself, therefore, that this notion may have a bearing on the question of display-control compatibility (e.g., Grether, 1947; Clutton-Baker, 1951; Mitchell and Vince, 1951). It is very much easier for an operator to learn to operate a compensatory control that has to be moved away from the error dot than one that has to follow the dot. The widely accepted theory that explains this sometimes quite dramatic difference is sometimes called the "principle of the moving part." As applied to simple situations with only one moving element, the principle states that the element in the display that moves with respect to the display's co-ordinate system should correspond to, and move in the same direction as, the element in the real situation that moves with respect to the earth's co-ordinate system. The principle leads, however, to a paradox: according to the theory, a pilot's view through his windscreen is a poor display, for, relative to the frame of the windscreen, the earth moves and the aircraft stands still. It seems possible that the distinction between pursuit and compensatory control may be basic to the whole problem, and that display-control compatibility in the case of compensatory control may be in large part a matter of approaching pursuit control as closely as possible.

14. POSSIBILITIES

LOOKING BACK over the chapter, we see a disproportion between the mathematical apparatus(*) ready to be brought to bear upon the results of tracking experiments and the results upon which the apparatus can be set. The reason for the existence of this disproportion is two-fold: First, the problem of processing data for use in testing models has proven difficult. Only very recently has there been more than a trickle of experimentally determined transfer functions. Second, many of the experiments on tracking have not been formulated in relation to models at all. There are many bits and pieces, and few real sets of modelable data.

The main need, therefore, is for reliable and practical data processing equipment. The whole field could be revolutionized by a few comprehensive experiments, but at the present rate they would take years and hundreds of thousands of dollars.

Several interesting possibilities are nevertheless open for research. These include:

(a) Study of effects of set and instructions. Elkind [1956] found in an informal test, for example, that in response to verbal instruction one of his subjects altered his transfer characteristic from one involving far too much phase advance to a much more effective one approximating an attenuator. The instruction was merely "stop trying so hard to follow and concentrate on minimizing the mean-squared error."

(b) Analysis through controlled load disturbances. Experimenters always control the input signals. The other terminal of the human operator is relatively neglected. Much can be learned about the motor system by using load-disturbance techniques suggested by the theory of regulators.

(c) Tracking experiments are usually made with analogue variables as signals. It would be interesting to introduce symbols and coding into the picture. This might permit experimental manipulation of what we have vaguely called "computation time."

(d) Use of sampled-data servo models. The notion that sampled-data servos have stability properties that are desirable in interaction with time delays seems to be potentially very important.

(e) It is possible that highly nonlinear systems with fixed parameters may be able to duplicate the behavior of linear systems with time-varying parameters. This idea, suggested by Booton [1956], emphasizes the desirability of bringing nonlinear models into the field of tracking, and also such

(*) We examined only a fraction of the techniques that are available.

nonlinear analytic techniques as those developed by Wiener [1949] and Singleton [1950]. Some work formulated in relation to nonlinear servo theory is already under way (Platzer 1955; Senders 1955).

15. SUMMARY

IN THE HIGHLY DELIMITED situation studied under the heading, manual tracking, the human being and the environment interact through channels we can monitor and by means of signals we can record and analyze in great detail. The number of variables is small. We can obtain a mile of records in an hour. The situation seems ideal for a flourishing of models.

However, there have been problems — mainly, problems of data analysis — and the field is actually not very far advanced. There are at best only one or two fully formulated and carefully tested models of the human operator in a tracking situation. Nevertheless, the field affords an opportunity for the examination of models at work. And the context within which they work has interesting features.

In particular, there is a need for models that will be compatible with those used in the engineering of systems within which human beings function as trackers. To meet that requirement, time-invariant linear models would be ideal. But the behavior of human beings is by no means time invariant, and it is noisy enough that a rigorous concept of linearity is hardly applicable. The solution has been, therefore, to drop as many as possible of the restrictions associated with the assumption of constant linearity while still retaining the basic notion of linear superposition of components within a segment of time. The result is called quasi-linearity.

In the section on time-domain and frequency-domain characteristics, some of the tools used in analysis and synthesis of linear models are introduced. They are considered in relation to quasi-linearity, and the advantages of methods involving cross-correlation functions and cross-power spectra are described.

A number of experimental investigations of tracking are examined. Their results are related to quasi-linear models. One model, proposed independently by several workers, figures strongly in the discussion, but has to be rejected because experimental results indicate that the human operator usually does not introduce true time integration. Another model, in which the main components are an amplifier, a low-pass filter, and a time delay, is found to fit the data of compensatory tracking better. In pursuit tracking, prediction of the target course plays an important role, but the human operator is by no means an optimal predictor.

An effort is made to relate some of the properties of the model to a conception of the visual and motor processes. This, however, is largely speculative and rather far from contact with data. Quasi-linear models are compared briefly with intermittent models, and mention is made of North's approach involving finite-difference equations.

Finally, compensatory and pursuit tracking are brought together in one paradigm based on the notion, suggested by Elkind's recent work, that the human operator functions as a "conditional" servomechanism.

ACKNOWLEDGEMENT

Many of the ideas and many of the results described in this chapter stem from J. I. Elkind, with whom I have had many discussions on the subject of tracking during the last four years. I am most appreciatively indebted to Elkind for them, and to W. H. Huggins, who facilitated my introduction to linear network analysis and synthesis, and to many colleagues in the Electrical Engineering and Mathematics Departments and in the Research Laboratory of Electronics, the Acoustics Laboratory, and the Servomechanisms Laboratory at M.I.T., who have given me some small insight into quantitative approaches to psychological problems. I am afraid, however, that I have done poor justice to their inspiration and to their techniques. Lest I create a total misrepresentation, I wish in this last sentence (1) to relieve them of the responsibility for the particular interpretation of quasi-linearity given in this chapter, for it is not yet sufficiently precise, and (2) to report that they are at present developing nonlinear models that will doubtless be of greater interest in the behavioral sciences than quasi-linear models can ever hope to be.

BIBLIOGRAPHY

Ashby, W. R. (1952) *Design for a brain.* New York, John Wiley and Sons, Inc.
Bates, J. A. V. (1947) *Design and performance of the human servo.* Paper presented at a meeting of the Institution of Electrical Engineers. [Mentioned by Hick (1948)].
Booton, R. C. (1956) *Personal communication.*

Chestnut, H., and Mayer, R. W. (1951) *Servomechanisms and regulating system design,* vol. 1. New York, John Wiley and Sons, Inc.

Clutton-Baker, J. (1951) *Some alternative control lever arrangements in a compensatory tracking task.* Report RNP 51/655, Royal Naval Personnel Research Committee, Great Britain.

Craig, D. R. (1949) *Effect of amplitude range on duration of response to step function displacements.* Tech. Report No. 5913, Air Materiel Command, Wright-Patterson Air Force Base, Dayton, Ohio.

Craik, K. J. W. (1947) Theory of the human operator. I. The operator as an engineering system. *Brit. J. Psychol.,* *38,* Part 2, 56—61.

—, (1948) Theory of the human operator. II. Man as an element in a control system. *Brit. J. Psychol.,* *38,* Part 3, 142—148.

Edson, J. B. (1948) *Tracking telescope fundamentals.* Report No. 672, Ballistics Research Laboratory, Aberdeen Proving Ground, Maryland.

Ellson, D. G., and Gray, F. (1948) *Frequency responses of human operators following a sine wave input.* Memo. Report MCREXD-694-2N, Engineering Division, Air Materiel Command, Wright Field, Dayton, Ohio.

—, and Hill, H. (1948) *The interaction of responses to step function stimuli:* I. *Opposed steps of constant amplitude.* Memo. Report No. MCREXD-694-2P, Engineering Division, Air Materiel Command, Wright Field, Dayton, Ohio.

—, Hill, H., and Craig, D. R. (1949) *The interaction of responses to step function stimuli:* II. *Equal opposed steps of varying amplitude.* Tech. Report No. 5911, Air Materiel Command, Wright-Patterson Air Force Base, Dayton, Ohio.

Elkind, J. I. (1953) *Tracking response characteristics of the human operator.* Memo. No. 40, Human Factors Operations Research Laboratories, Air Research and Development Command, Washington, D. C.

—, (1955) *Personal communication.*

—, (1956) *Personal communication.*

Fitts, P. M. (1951) Engineering psychology and equipment design. Chap. 35 in Stevens, S. S., ed., *Handbook of experimental psychology.* New York, John Wiley and Sons, Inc.

Forbes, T. W. (1946) Auditory signals for instrument flying. *J. Aeronaut. Sci., 13,* 255—258.

Gardner, M. F., and Barnes, J. L. (1942) *Transients in linear systems,* vol. 1. New York, John Wiley and Sons, Inc.

Gibbs, C. B. (1954) *Servo principles in sensory organization and the transfer of skill.* Report 218/54, Medical Research Council Applied Psychology Unit, Cambridge, England.

Grether, W. F. (1947) *Direction of control in relation to indicator movement in one-dimensional tracking.* Memo. Report No. TSEAA-694-4G, Engineering Division, Air Materiel Command, Wright Field, Dayton, Ohio.

Guillemin, E. A. (1953) *Introductory circuit theory.* New York, John Wiley and Sons, Inc.

Ham, J. M., and Lang, G. (1955) Conditional feedback systems: a new approach to feedback control. *Trans. Amer. Instit. Elec. Engrs., 74,* Part II, 152—161.

Helson, H. (1949) Design of equipment and optimal human operation. *Amer. J. Psychol., 62,* 473—499.

Hick, W. E. (1948) The discontinuous functioning of the human operator in pursuit tasks. *Quart. J. Exper. Psychol.*, *1*, 36—51.

—,   Hick, W. E. (1951) Man as an element in a control system. *Research*, *4*, 112—118.

—,   (1952) On the rate of gain of information. *Quart. J. Exper. Psychol.*, *4*, 11—26.

Huggins, W. H. (1949) *Memo on the experimental determination of transfer functions of human operators and machines.* Memo. E-4070, Cambridge Field Station, Air Materiel Command, Cambridge, Mass.

James, H. M., Nichols, N. B., and Phillips, R. S., ed. (1947) *Theory of servomechanisms.* New York, McGraw-Hill Book Co., Inc.

Köhler, W., and Wallach, H. (1944) Figural after-effects. An investigation of the visual process. *Proc. Amer. Philos. Soc.*, *88*, 269—357.

Krendel, E.S. (1951) *A preliminary study of the power-spectrum approach to the analysis of perceptual-motor performance.* Tech. Report No. 6723, Wright Air Development Center, Wright-Patterson Air Force Base, Dayton, Ohio.

—,   (1952) *The spectral density study of tracking performance. Part 1. The effect of instructions. Part 2. The effects of input amplitude and practice.* Tech. Report 52—11, Wright Air Development Center, Wright-Patterson Air Force Base, Dayton, Ohio.

—,   (1954) *Interim report on human frequency response studies.* Tech. Report 54—370, Wright Air Development Center, Wright-Patterson Air Force Base, Dayton, Ohio.

Lee, Y. W. (1950) *Application of statistical methods to communication problems.* Tech. Report No. 181, Research Laboratory of Electronics, Massachusetts Institute of Technology, Cambridge, Mass.

Licklider, J. C. R., Stevens, K. N., and Hayes, J. R. M. (1954) *Studies in speech, hearing, and communication.* Final report under Contract No. W19 122 ac-14, Acoustics Laboratory, Massachusetts Institute of Technology, Cambridge, Mass.

Marill, T. M. (1953) The psychological refractory phase. (Abstr.) In *Final report of psychological research program for the Human Factors Operations Research Laboratories.* Research Laboratory of Electronics, Massachusetts Institute of Technology, Cambridge, Mass.

Mayne, R. (1951) Some engineering aspects of the mechanism of body control. *Elec. Engr.*, *70*, 207—212.

Miller, G. A. (1955) *The magic number seven, plus-or-minus two, or some limits on our capacity for processing information.* Report PNR-174, Psycho-Acoustic Laboratory, Harvard University, Cambridge, Mass.

Mitchell, M. J. H., and Vince, M. A. (1951) The direction of movement of machine controls. *Quart. J. Exper. Psychol.*, *3*, 24—35.

Noble, M., Fitts, P. M., and Warren, C. E. (1955) Response of skilled subjects in a pursuit tracking task. *J. Exper. Psychol.*, *49*, 249—256.

North, J. D. (1952) The human transfer function in servo-systems. In Tustin, A., ed., (1952) *Automatic and manual control.* London, Butterworth's Scientific Publications.

—,   (1954) *The rational behavior of mechanically extended man.* Boulton Paul Aircraft, Ltd., England.

North, J. D. (1955) *Application of communication theory to the human operator.* Paper presented at the third Symposium on Information Theory, Imperial College, University of London, London, England.

Phillips, R. S. (1947) Manual tracking. In James, H. M., Nichols, N. B., and Phillips, R. S., ed., (1947) *Theory of servomechanisms,* New York, McGraw-Hill Book Co., Inc., 360—368.

Pitts, W., and McCulloch, W. S. (1947) How we know universals. The perception of auditory and visual forms. *Bull. Math. Biophys., 9,* 124—147.

Platzer, H. L. (1955) *The phase plane as a tool for the study of human behavior in tracking problems.* Forthcoming Tech. Report, Wright Air Development Center, Wright-Patterson Air Force Base, Dayton, Ohio.

Quastler, H. (1955) *Human performance in information transmission.* Report No. R-62, Control Systems Laboratory, University of Illinois, Urbana, Illinois.

Raggazini, J. R. (1948) *Engineering aspects of the human being as a servomechanism.* Paper presented at a meeting of the American Psychological Association.

Rosenblith, W. A. (1955) Correlation studies of brain potentials. In *Progress Report,* 15 April 1955, Research Laboratory of Electronics, Massachusetts Institute of Technology, Cambridge, Mass.

Russell, L. (1951) *Characteristics of the human as a linear servo element.* Master's Dissertation, Massachusetts Institute of Technology, Cambridge, Mass.

Searle, L. V. (1951) *Psychological studies of tracking behavior: IV. The intermittency hypothesis as a basis for predicting optimum aided-tracking time constants.* Report 3872, Naval Research Laboratory, Washington, D. C.

—, and Taylor, F. V. (1948) Studies of tracking behavior: I. Rate and time characteristics of simple corrective movements. *J. Exper. Psychol., 38,* 615—631.

Senders, J. W. (1955) *Personal communication.*

Singleton, H. E. (1950) *Properties of nonlinear transducers.* Tech. Report 160, Research Laboratory of Electronics, Massachusetts Institute of Technology, Cambrigde, Mass.

Sobczyk, A. (1943) *Aided tracking.* Report No. 430, Radiation Laboratory, Massachusetts Institute of Technology, Cambridge, Mass.

Stroud, J. M. (1950) *Personal communication.*

—, (1954) *Notes on the fine structure of psychological time.* Tech. Memo. No. TM-49, Navy Electronics Laboratory, San Diego, Calif.

Taylor, F. V. (1949) *Nonlinearity in human response.* Report N-ONR-NRL-PSRD-11/49, Naval Research Laboratory, Washington, D. C.

—, and Birmingham, H. P. (1948) Studies of tracking behavior: II. A study of the acceleration pattern of quick manual corrective responses. *J. Exper. Psychol., 38,* 783—795.

—, and Birmingham, H. P. (1954) *A human engineering approach to the design of man-operated continuous control systems.* Report 4333, Naval Research Laboratory, Washington, D. C.

Telford, C. W. (1931) The refractory phase of voluntary and associative responses. *J. Exper. Psychol., 14,* 1—36.

Truxal, J. G. (1955) *Automatic feedback control system synthesis.* New York, McGraw-Hill Book Company, Inc.

Tustin, A. (1947) The nature of the operator's response in manual control, and its implications for controller design. *J. Instit. Elec. Engres.*, *94*, IIA, 190—203.

—,   (1952) *Discussion*, following the paper by North (1952).

Vince, M. A. (1948) Corrective movements in a pursuit task. *Quart. J. Exper. Psychol.*, *1*, 85—103.

—,   (1950) *Some exceptions to the psychological refractory period in unskilled manual responses*. Report 124/50 of the Medical Research Council Applied Psychology Unit, Cambridge University, Cambridge, England.

Walston, C. E., and Warren, C. E. (1954) A mathematical analysis of the human operator in a closed-loop control system. *Research Bulletin, AFPTRC-TR-54-96*, Air Force Personnel and Training Research Center, Lackland Air Force Base, San Antonio, Texas.

Wiener, N. (1948) *Cybernetics*. New York, John Wiley and Sons, Inc.

—,   (1949) *Extrapolation, interpolation, and smoothing of stationary time series*. New York, John Wiley and Sons, Inc.

—,   (1949) *Informal lectures on nonlinear network analysis*.

Index of Authors

Index of Subjects

[289]